A N A T O M Y   and

P H Y S I O L O G Y

Volume 1: Cells, Tissues, Integument,
Skeletal, Muscular, and
Digestive Systems, Blood,
Lymph, Circulatory System

About the Authors

Edwin B. Steen completed graduate courses at the University of Chicago, at Columbia University where he received the A.M. degree, at the University of Cincinnati, and at Purdue University where he received the Ph.D. degree. He has taught the biological sciences at Wabash College, New York University, the University of Cincinnati, and Purdue University; since 1941 he has taught anatomy and physiology at Western Michigan University where he is Professor of Biology. He has contributed to standard text-books on anatomy and bacteriology and to medical reference works and has served as editorial consultant to leading publishers in these fields.

Ashley Montagu studied at the universities of London and Florence and also at Columbia University where he received his Ph.D. degree. He has taught anatomy and physical anthropology for many years to undergraduate and graduate students at medical and dental schools, including New York University, the Hahnemann Medical College and Hospital, Philadelphia, and Rutgers University. Professor Ashley Montagu is the author of many notable works on anatomy, physical anthropology, and other biological sciences.

ANATOMY and PHYSIOLOGY

Volume 1: Cells, Tissues, Integument, Skeletal, Muscular, and Digestive Systems, Blood, Lymph, Circulatory System

Edwin B. Steen, Ph.D.

Ashley Montagu, Ph.D.

BARNES & NOBLE, INC.
NEW YORK
Publishers · Booksellers · Since 1873

Printed in the United States of America

PREFACE

This book is designed to meet the needs of students and others who wish to learn or review the essentials of human anatomy and physiology. It provides a comprehensive summary for students of the biological sciences, nursing, occupational therapy, and physical education. It should be most helpful to medical and dental students at all stages of their education—undergraduate, graduate, and post-graduate.

Since the authors have for many years taught all the groups of students mentioned above, they are acutely aware of the fact that in this field of study there is no satisfactory substitute for work in the laboratory. No one can acquire a thorough, functional knowledge of anatomy and physiology by merely reading a book. Consequently, this volume is not intended as a substitute for laboratory research but rather as a supplement to it, as a remembrancer following laboratory work, and, finally, as a refresher of the memory long after introductory studies of the subject have been concluded.

The Outline constitutes a completely integrated textbook of anatomy and physiology, covering the fundamentals of these inextricably intertwined subjects. The reader is asked to bear in mind always that anatomic structure and physiological function are but different aspects of the same thing, just as physics and chemistry are but two different ways of looking at matter. Anatomy and physiology are the names we give to two ways in which we look at organic matter, structure being a function of function, and function being a function of structure. There is rarely a structure without function and no function without structure, the two being inseparably associated.

For additional study aids, the reader is referred to the following companion volumes published by Barnes and Noble, Inc.:

Frohse, Brödel, and Schlossberg: *Atlas of Human Anatomy*
Tokay: *Fundamentals of Physiology*
Alexander: *General Biology*
Bryan and Bryan: *Bacteriology*

In a work of this kind, accuracy is an indispensable requirement. The authors have done everything in their power to make the text as accurate and as reliable as possible. The work has been critically read as a whole or in part by Dr. A. C. Boyer, of West Virginia University; Dr. E. S. Nasset, of the Rochester University School of Medicine; and Dr. Thane Robinson, of Western Michigan University. We are grateful to these colleagues for their comments and suggestions. Dr. Samuel Smith, editor of Barnes and Noble, Inc., has at every stage been our most kindly and helpful mentor. We are deeply grateful to him. To Miss Harriet Meiss, editorial assistant of Barnes and Noble, Inc., and to Mr. George Cantzlaar, their consulting editor, we are indebted for constant assistance in the preparation of the manuscript. To Mr. Albert W. Janson and Mrs. G. H. Lahr for preparation of numerous illustrations, we express our appreciation. Finally, it remains to be said that seldom can two authors have enjoyed working together as have the present collaborators.

EDWIN B. STEEN
ASHLEY MONTAGU

TABLE OF CONTENTS

NOTE TO THE READER

The Tabulated Bibliography and Quick Reference Table on the following pages are valuable study aids. They make it possible to compare the discussion of any major topic in anatomy and physiology with the treatment of the same topic in widely used standard textbooks. The reader can thus obtain a summary or preview of a topic in this volume and then study the same information presented somewhat differently in a selected textbook. He can also study a topic in any of the listed textbooks and then review the same topic in this volume. Systematic use of this cross-reference system may thus contribute to a clear understanding of the subject.

TABULATED BIBLIOGRAPHY
OF STANDARD TEXTBOOKS

This *College Outline* is keyed to standard textbooks in two ways.

1. If you are studying one of the following textbooks, consult the cross references here listed to find which pages of the *Outline* summarize the appropriate chapter of your text. (Roman numerals refer to textbook chapters, Arabic figures in parentheses to the corresponding *Outline* pages.)

2. If you are using the *Outline* as your basis for study and need further explanation of a topic, consult the pages of any of the standard textbooks as indicated in the Quick Reference Table on pages xiv–xv.

Anthony, C. P. *Textbook of Anatomy and Physiology*, 4th ed., 1955, Mosby.
   I (1–12); II (13–43); III (44–87, 90–91); IV (88–140); VI (211–301); VIII (141–210).

Best, C. H. and Taylor, N. B. *The Human Body*, 3rd ed., 1956, Holt.
   1 (19–24); II (13–20, 25–34); III (44–87); IV (88–103); V (103–140); VI–IX (211–229); X (187–189, 262–273); XII (230–236); XIII (238–261); XIV–XVII (230–237, 274–302); XXIV (166–181, 192); XXV (141–165); XXVI, XXVII (182–192); XXVIII (193–201); XXIX (201–210); XXX (193–201); XXXI, pp. 424 ff. (35–43).

De Coursey, R. M. *The Human Organism*, 1955, McGraw-Hill.
   II (13–34); III (44–81); IV (88–103); V (103–140); XI (211–229); XII (230–262); XIII (274–301); XV (141–165); XVI (166–182, 193–201).

Edwards, L. F. *Concise Anatomy*, 2nd ed., 1956, Blakiston.
   Introd. (1–12); I (13–34); II (44–52); III (82–87); IV (88–102); VI (211–237); VII (35–43); VIII (68–74); IX (119–129); X (82–87); XI, pp. 150–175 (238–273); XII (74–81); XIII (130–139); XIV (82–87); XV, pp. 222–230 (246–273); XVI (52–62); XVII (109–115); XIX (238–273); XX (62–68); XXI (115–124); XXII (82–87); XXIII, pp. 358–366 (238–273); XXV (141–165); XXVIII, pp. 459–469 (238–273).

Francis, C. C. and Farrell, G. L. *Integrated Anatomy and Physiology*, 3rd ed., 1957, Mosby.
I (1–12); II, III (13–34); V (44–81); VI (82–87); VII (88–102); VIII (103–140); XV (211–229); XVI (230–262); XVII (274–301); XVIII (262–273); XX (141–192); XXI (193–201); XXIII (35–43); XXIV (201–210).

Greisheimer, E. M. *Physiology and Anatomy*, 7th ed., 1955, Lippincott.
I (1–12, 24–43); II (13–24); III (44–87); IV (25–34, 88–92, 103–140); V (92–103); IX (211–229); X (230–273); XI (274–301); XIV (141–165); XV (166–201); XVII (201–210).

Jung, F. T. and Earl, E. C. *Anatomy and Physiology*, 3rd ed., 1956, Davis.
II (1–12); IV (13–24); V, VI (25–34); VIII–XI (44–81); XII (82–87); XIII–XVIII (88–91, 103–140); XVIII (92–102); XXVII (211–229); XXVIII (230–237); XXIX–XXXI (383–494); XXXV–XXXVII (141–166); XXXVIII (166–181); XXXIX (182–191); XL (192–200); XLIV (35–43).

Kimber, D. C. and Gray, C. E. et al. *Textbook of Anatomy and Physiology*, 13th ed., 1955, Macmillan.
I (1–12); II, III (13–24); IV (25–34); V (44–81); VI (82–87); VII (88–92); X (211–229); XI (230–235); XII (236–262); XIII (274–301); XIV (262–273); XVII (141–165); XVIII (166–192); XIX (193–201); XXII (35–43).

Millard, N. D., King, B. G., and Showers, M. J. *Human Anatomy and Physiology*, 4th ed. 1956, Saunders.
I (1–12); II (13–24); III (25–43); IV (34); X (44–81); XI (82–87); XII (34, 88–92); XIII (92–103); XIV (102–140); XV (211–229); XVI (230–235); XVII (236–262); XVIII (274–301); XX (262–273); XXIII (141–165); XXIV (166–192); XXV (193–201); XXVII (201–204).

Chapter in This Outline	TOPIC	Anthony	Best & Taylor	DeCoursey
I	Introduction to Anatomy and Physiology	17–39		
II	Cell and Protoplasm	40–46	13–18 23–24	1–9
III	Tissues	46–59	18–22	10–30 58, 111
IV	Integument (The Skin and Its Derivatives)	60–70	424–428	479–482
V	Skeleton System	71–136	27–66	31–57
	Articulations	87	66–69	
VI	Muscular System	137–166	70–74	58
	Muscular Tissue	47–50	20–22 70–72	58–64
	Physiology of Muscle	166–205	75–89	64–77
	Skeletal Muscles	139–166	90–135	78–110
VII	Digestive System	470–490	322–338	316–353
VIII	Physiology of Digestion Foods	490–492	307–311 311–321	316–347 355–378
	Digestion Absorption	492–502 503–504	339–371 317, 365	347–354
	Metabolism of Foods	504–520	373–379 388–399	379–398
	Body Temperature	520–532	380–387	
IX	The Body Fluids Blood	328–344	137 137–169	220–245
X	Circulatory System	326–328	190–199	246
	Heart	344–359	190–194 223–229	246–254
	Systemic Arteries	363–366	200–217	254–264
	Systemic Veins	365–384	217–225 257	264–272
	Lymphatic System	405–417	172–177	284–293
XI	Physiology of Circulation	384–405	230–260	273–284

See pages xii–xiii

TO STANDARD TEXTBOOKS

refer to pages.

Edwards	Francis & Farrell	Greisheimer	Jung & Earle	Kimber, Gray et al.	Millard, King & Showers
1–2	17–20	7–19	30–40	3–17	2–16
11–16	21–22 34–41	19–23	51–69	18–51	17–36
25–28, 34–36, 46–49 59	22–23	23–39 145–149	70–99	52–84	37–53 218
95–103	527–539	39–46 685–686	655–661	670–679	53–56
107–115, 169–182 241–252, 311–324	57–122	75–125 129–142	115–164	72–127	162–209
140–149, 204–221 248, 347–357	123–149	126–129	165–176	128–135	210–217
46–53	150 161–162	151–154	177–186	136–142	239–240
46–48	150	145–150	177	137–142	219–222
53–58	151–160	154–158 217–240	237–250	142–153	223–238
116–139, 183–204 253–262, 325–346	161–209	158–215	187–236	153–216	239–296
396–430	444–489	580–617	543–593	521–558	417–443
	444–489	618–639 619–626	543–607 594–600	559–632 559–575	444–460 444–445 463
	444–489 444, 479 481, 487	626–639 639–641	543–593 601–607 608–613	575–606 607–611	445–460 461
	490–505	642–655	613–616	612–625	461–476
	540–543	699–716	661–664	145, 679– 694	489–494
79		387, 401	383	43–51	
79–81	327–336	387–401	383–406	315–340	298–311
81–91	338–340	416–418 424–433	383–494	18, 341 358–361	312, 328
86–88, 459	338, 341	418–424	407–427	341–350	312–327
150–154, 222–227 295–300, 358–362 460–465	347–361	433–449	428–447	358–382	333–359
154–157, 227–229 300–302, 362–364 465–469	361–370	449–465	447–458	383–403	344–359
91–93, 154–157 229–230, 364–366 469–470	336 380–401	465–475	477–488	437–452	381–388
	371–379	475–525	459–476	404–436	360–380

for complete titles.

A N A T O M Y and

P H Y S I O L O G Y

Volume 1: Cells, Tissues, Integument, Skeletal, Muscular, and Digestive Systems, Blood, Lymph, Circulatory System

1 : INTRODUCTION TO ANATOMY AND PHYSIOLOGY

Anatomy is the science of the structure of organisms. It is concerned with the discovery and the systematic statement of facts about the structure of the organs and organ systems which make up the machinery of the complete living organism. (A fact is a "verifiable datum of experience.") Originally restricted to the gathering and classification of facts by means of dissection, anatomy (from the Greek, *ana*, apart, and *temnein*, to cut) now comprises many branches.

BRANCHES OF ANATOMY

The branches of anatomy are known by terms which indicate either the nature of their procedures, their objectives, or the parts or regions of the body under investigation.

Gross anatomy is the macroscopic study of structure through dissection, in which inspection is achieved with the naked eye. In it the regions and parts of the body are studied with regard to their general form, external features, and main divisions. The study of form is known as *morphology*. The study of the regions of the body by dissection and by means of sections taken through the body at different planes, and resulting in a sort of descriptive geography of the body, is called *regional* or *topographic anatomy*.

Microscopic anatomy, also termed *histology*, is the study of the minute structure of organs and tissues, accomplished by means of the microscope. The study of individual tissues with reference to their cellular structure, function, and mode of development is known as *cytology*.

Developmental anatomy is the study of growth and development during the entire life of the organism. Treating a more restricted area, *embryology* is concerned with the origin and development of the organism from the egg to birth.

Comparative anatomy is the study of the organ systems of various classes of organisms with emphasis on their structural relationships to each other and to man.

Genetics is the study of heredity. It deals with the transmission of traits from one generation to the next and with the nature and causes of variations.

Systematic anatomy is the study of the various organ systems as

1

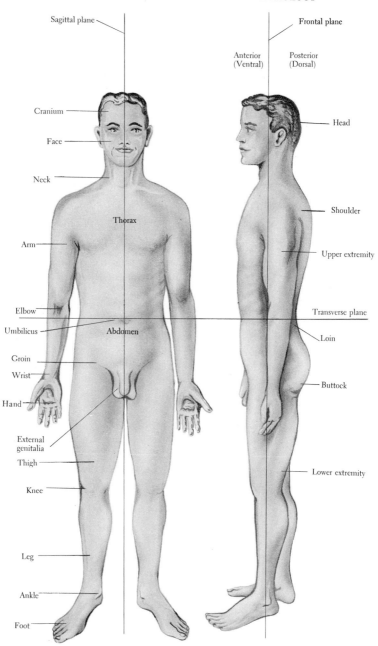

Fig. 1-1. Outline of body in anatomic position.

structural and functional units. The study of the skeletal system is called *osteology;* of joints, *arthrology;* of the muscular system, *myology;* the integumentary system, *dermatology;* the nervous system, *neurology;* the circulatory system, *angiology;* the endocrine system, *endocrinology;* the internal organs collectively comprising the digestive, respiratory, urinary, and reproductive systems, *splanchnology.*

Some special fields are: *applied anatomy, pathologic anatomy, radiographic anatomy,* and *surgical anatomy.*

ANATOMIC TERMINOLOGY

The need for accurate reference and economy of expression demands a special and uniform terminology for communication of anatomic data. Such a terminology serves at least two specific purposes: (1) to give names to structures so that they may be readily identified and distinguished from all others, and (2) through terms that refer to location, position, direction, and plane, to describe unambiguously the relationships between structures.

Terms Referring to Location or Position. The following terms assume the body to be in the "anatomic position," in which the individual is standing erect, with face forward, arms at the sides, and palms forward.

Anterior   toward the front of the body
Posterior   toward the back of the body
    (In quadrupeds: *anterior* means "toward the head end"; *posterior,* "toward the caudal or tail end"; *ventral,* toward the underneath or the belly side; *dorsal,* toward the back or the uppermost side.)

Ventral   toward the anterior side
Dorsal   toward the posterior side

Superior   above, upper
Inferior   below, lower

Superficial   on or near the surface
Deep   remote from the surface

Internal   within, inside
External   without, outside
    (*Inside* or *interior* and *outside* or *exterior* are reserved for reference to body cavities and hollow organs.)

Proximal   nearest to the body or to some other point regarded as the center of a system; nearest to the point of attachment
Distal   farthest from the body or from some other central point; farthest from the point of attachment

Medial   toward the medial plane of the body
Lateral   away from the medial plane of the body

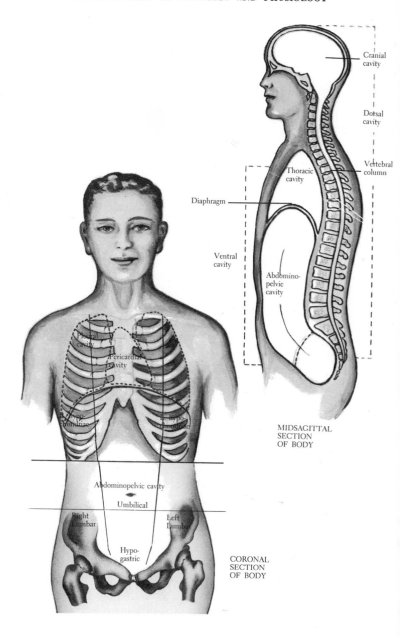

Fig. 1-2. Diagram of body to show planes and sections.

Terms Referring to Direction. Anatomic terms specifying direction are:

Craniad	toward the cranium
Cephalad	toward the head end
Mesiad	toward the midline
Caudad	toward the tail end; away from the head
Laterad	toward the side; away from the midline

Terms Referring to Sections of the Body. For purposes of study or description, a body or an organ may be cut into "sections" that lie in various "planes." These sections are:

Sagittal	a vertical cut that divides the body into right and left portions
Midsagittal	a sagittal section that divides the body into right and left halves
Transverse or Cross	a cut made at right angles to the long axis of the body, dividing the body into upper and lower portions
Coronal	a vertical cut made at right angles to the sagittal plane, dividing the body into anterior and posterior portions

The foregoing terms can also be applied to individual organs or structures. In this sense, the axis of the organ (not the axis of the whole body) is the basis of description. Frequently, therefore, in discussions of the body as a whole, "longitudinal" is substituted for "sagittal," and "median longitudinal" for "midsagittal."

A cut made in any plane other than the foregoing is called an oblique section, but such a section is not commonly used.

GENERAL PLAN OF BODY STRUCTURE

Body structure may be studied in terms of specific regions, or divisions, with definite boundaries.

Regions of the Body. The regions of the body and the organs or structures they contain are are follows:

Region	*Organs or Structures It Contains*
Head	Brain and sense organs, and some of the food-getting and respiratory structures
Neck	Larynx, trachea, esophagus, thyroid and parathyroid glands
Thorax *	Heart and large blood vessels, lungs, trachea, bronchi, esophagus, thymus, thoracic duct
Abdomen *	Digestive, urinary, and reproductive organs; spleen and adrenal glands
Extremities	Arms, forearms, hands, thighs, legs, feet

* The thorax and the abdomen together constitute the *trunk*.

A general impression of the structure of the body can be obtained from a study of midsagittal, cross, and coronal sections.

Midsagittal Section. The body contains two *cavities* (the dorsal cavity and the ventral cavity) which, with their divisions and the organs contained within them, are shown in the following schema:

Dorsal cavity
{ Cranial cavity (brain)
{ Vertebral canal (spinal cord)

Ventral cavity
{ Thoracic cavity
    { Pleural cavity (lungs)
    { Pericardial cavity (heart)
{ Abdominopelvic cavity
    { Abdominal cavity (stomach, intestines, liver, pancreas, spleen)
    { Pelvic cavity (bladder, sigmoid colon, rectum, reproductive organs)

Cross Section. A cross-section diagram shows that the body is essentially a "tube within a tube." The body wall comprises the *outer* tube; the digestive tract (with its derivatives) constitutes the *inner* tube. The two are separated by a space, the *coelom* or body cavity.

The body wall consists of the following layers: (1) the outer covering or *integument*, the skin; (2) the underlying subcutaneous tissue, or *fascia*; (3) the *muscular layer*, consisting of the muscles lying on (4) the *skeletal layer*, composed of the sternum, vertebrae, ribs, intercostal muscles and their fascia; (5) the *pleura*, the innermost, serous membrane, layer of the thoracic wall; (6) the *peritoneum*, a serous membrane, the innermost layer of the abdomino-pelvic cavity.

Observe how the peritoneum of one side meets that of the other side in the dorsal midline, to form a double-layered membrane, the *mesentery*, which supports the intestine and encloses the blood vessels, the lymphatic vessels, and the nerves supplying it.

The dorsal and ventral cavities are also seen in this section. Note that the kidneys are not actually within the body cavity, but lie dorsal to the peritoneum (they are said to be "extraperitoneal").

The vertebral column is clearly shown as the main supporting axis of the body.

Coronal (or Frontal) Section. This view of the trunk shows the subdivisions of the ventral cavity and the organs contained within them. The diaphragm is a muscular wall that separates the thoracic and abdominal cavities.

PHYSIOLOGY

Physiology, the *study of function*, encompasses all the activities of an organism—not only the activities of the organism as a whole but also those of individual organs or tissues. It is concerned with all phys-

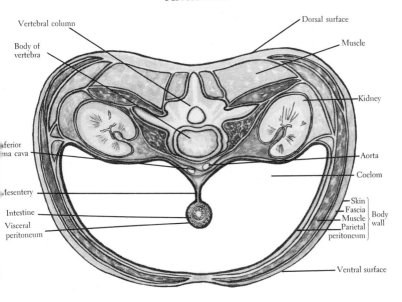

Fig. 1-3. Cross section showing plan of body.

ical and chemical changes that take place within the organism. Physiologists study man as a physicochemical machine. They seek to explain life processes in the body on the basis of physical and chemical changes that occur within it and among its parts. It should be borne in mind, however, that *function is an aspect of structure* and that *all functions imply structure.*

The following methods are employed by anatomists and physiologists in the study of the body:

Observation—examination of body functioning, to note changes that occur under various environmental conditions.

Chemical analysis—investigation of substances used and products given off by the body or its organs (e.g., food, air, urine, blood, gastric juice).

Microscopic examination—study of structures in various stages of activity by means of the microscope (e.g., noting differences in muscle tissue during contraction and relaxation, or in gland cells before, during, and after secretion).

Tissue culture—growth of body cells and substances in culture media outside the body.

Perfusion methods—procedures for removing organs from the body and studying them while supplying them artificially with blood or nutrient fluids.

Injection methods—introduction of specific substances (such as dyes, radioactive tracer elements, and hormones) into the body so that their course may be traced or their effects noted.

Grafting—transference of tissue from one part of the body to another or from one organism to another.

Graphic methods—techniques for obtaining written or photographic records of activities of the body or specific organs. Instruments used to obtain such records include the kymograph, calorimeter, electrocardiograph, electroencephalograph, and others.

Using these methods and techniques, physiologists have accumulated a vast store of information about the activities of the body and have come to understand many of the factors responsible for abnormal functioning of organs. Progress in physiology has enabled the physician to adopt reliable procedures for diagnosis and to devise and make effective use of therapeutic measures that have done much to alleviate pain and to prolong life.

BASIC LIFE PROCESSES

The basic life processes can be better understood if they are first studied in a very simple organism, such as the ameba. The ameba is a one-celled animal consisting of protoplasm, a jelly-like substance of which every plant and animal cell is composed. The form of an ameba, though roughly the same for each species, is variable among individuals. As a living entity, however, the ameba exhibits characteristics which are generally attributable to all animal life: irritability, conductivity, contractility, metabolism, reproduction, and adaptation.

Irritability and Conductivity. *Irritability* is the power of an organism to respond to a stimulus (i.e., an environmental change). If an ameba is disturbed, as by a weak electric shock or by being touched, it will respond with movement accomplished by a flow of its protoplasm and the formation of blunt, root-like processes called pseudopodia. The ability to respond to a point remote from the stimulus is the result of *conductivity*, a property possessed by nerve cells in a high degree.

Contractility. Contractility is the ability of an organism to change its form by shortening. Such a reaction may be due either to an external stimulus or to factors within the animal. In the human body certain cells (the white blood cells, or leucocytes) have this ability, a reaction termed *ameboid movement*. All muscle activity depends on the ability of protoplasm to shorten.

Metabolic Activities. The foregoing processes require the expenditure of energy, and for the supply of energy the ameba, like all other living organisms, depends on food. While the term *metabolism* in its broadest sense includes all physical and chemical processes involved in life activities, it is commonly applied only to the processes by which food substances are converted into energy or protoplasm. Metabolism has two aspects: (1) *anabolism*, the building-up processes involving synthesis of complex molecules from simple ones, and (2) *catabolism*, the breaking-down processes, in particular the breakdown of food, and the resultant liberation of energy.

The detailed processes of *food-getting and utilization* are: (1) ingestion; (2) digestion; (3) utilization; (4) respiration; (5) excretion; and (6) egestion.

INGESTION. The ameba extends its pseudopodia and engulfs a food particle, which consists of organic material. The particle becomes enclosed in a cavity, the *food vacuole*.

DIGESTION. Within the vacuole, the food, which is composed of complex chemical compounds, is broken down, by the action of catalytic agents (enzymes), into simple, diffusible substances. The enzymes, produced by the ameba's protoplasm through *secretion*, pass from the protoplasm into the vacuole by means of *diffusion*. The products of digestion diffuse from the vacuole into the surrounding protoplasm, a process called *absorption*.

UTILIZATION. Within the protoplasm the food is utilized in the following ways: (1) to *increase the amount* of protoplasm (growth by assimilation); (2) for *repair* (rebuilding of protoplasm broken down through cellular activities or injury); (3) for *regulation* of cellular activities; (4) as a *source of energy*.

RESPIRATION. The energy in a food molecule is released as a result of *oxidation*. Oxygen is taken in from the surrounding water (the ameba's life milieu) by diffusion through the cell membrane. It reacts with the food molecules, which are broken down principally into carbon dioxide (CO_2), and water (H_2O) and energy is released. This exchange of gases between the organism and its environment is called *respiration*, or, more specifically, *external respiration*; the oxidative processes within the cell constitute *internal respiration*.

EXCRETION. As a result of metabolic activities, waste products such as water, urea, uric acid, and carbon dioxide are produced. Excretion is the process of eliminating these substances through the surface of the cell.

EGESTION. Ingested food usually contains some indigestible or unusable material which has taken no part in metabolism. In the ameba the food vacuole eventually ruptures and discharges this material from the cell. A normal activity for the ameba, this process is known as *egestion*.

Reproduction. While metabolic processes continue, the ameba is a living and growing cell. Eventually, however. growth would cease and degenerative changes occur, and the ameba would die, but for reproduction. The process of reproduction or reduplication averts the end result of death by continuing the species. It is accomplished by cell division, in which the nucleus and cytoplasm are divided equally between each of two daughter amebae. In this process, the protoplasm is rejuvenated so that, in the new-born cells, degenerative changes do not occur, and growth proceeds.

Adaptation. The ameba lives in a special environment, fresh water, which contains many types of chemicals, some favorable to life processes and others unfavorable. Furthermore, the environment is constantly changing; to survive, the ameba must adapt itself to these changes. Life processes, then, are those activities resulting from interaction of the life substance (protoplasm) with the environment. Indeed, life has been defined as *the continuous adjustment of an organism to its environment.*

UNICELLULAR AND MULTICELLULAR ORGANISMS

The continuity between the unicellular and the multicellular organisms stretches in a long, unbroken chain from the beginnings of life on earth. The differences which have come into being between such organisms are the result of the process of *evolution.* In this process, progressively adaptive variations have occurred, leading to the development of the highly complex specialized forms which inhabit the earth today.

Life Processes in a Multicellular Organism. A complex organism such as a human being is composed of trillions of cells, each consisting of protoplasm, the same type of substance as that found in, the ameba. The same fundamental processes described for the ameba take place in each cell of the organism: food and oxygen are taken in, energy transformations occur, protoplasm is built up and broken down, waste products are formed and eliminated, and cell division occurs or cells may die. As compared with unicellular organisms, however, the more complex living forms have certain *additional qualities:* specialization of activities, interdependence of cells, and phenomena of sexual reproduction.

SPECIALIZATION. In a multicellular organism, division of labor prevails. Cells are structurally differentiated into diverse types each adapted for the performance of specific functions. A fundamental specialization and division of labor is that between cells reserved and later specialized for reproduction, and all the remaining cells of the body. The former constitute the *reproductive* or *germ cells* and the latter, the *soma.* The soma includes collectively all the cells which share in the structure of the body and the maintenance of its activities, such as muscle, gland, nerve, blood, and connective tissue cells; the reproductive cells include only the egg and the sperm. Their sole function is the production of a succeeding generation.

INTERDEPENDENCE. While the ameba is an independent cell carry
ing on all the necessary life activities, in a complex organism each cell
is dependent on other cells. Whereas the ameba (a cell) is free to
move about more or less at will, the cells of a complex organism are
generally *fixed in position*. For this reason special mechanisms are required for the circulation of substances to and from cells that are
remote from the surface of the organism. In addition, highly developed *correlating and integrating* mechanisms are required for the
coordination of activities in various parts of the body.

PHENOMENA OF SEXUAL REPRODUCTION. The simplest organisms reproduce by asexual means. Most of the single-celled organisms, such
as the ameba, and single cells of the body reproduce by means of
binary fission (asexual cell division); in this way the parent cell divides itself and becomes a pair of daughter cells. In a majority of multicellular animals, including man, reproduction is sexual: two parent
organisms produce sex cells which unite to form a third individual.
From a single cell (the zygote) resulting from the union of two sex
cells (the egg and the sperm) all the succeeding cells of the new organism develop by repeated cell division. The two original sex cells
contain the hereditary "packets" (chromosomes containing the genes)
which influence the expression of the responses of the tissues to the
environment and transmit these potentialities from one generation
to the next.

The Body as a Machine. A machine is capable of releasing energy
and performing work. By this definition, all organisms may be regarded
as "living machines." If an organism is compared with a nonliving
machine, certain similarities and differences are noted.

SIMILARITIES. Nonliving machines and organisms have the following similarities: (1) Each requires fuel as a source of energy. (2) The
nature of the fuel is the same for each; i.e., it consists of combustible
organic substances. (3) Oxidation or combustion occurs within each,
resulting in the release of energy. (4) The released energy is used for
the performance of mechanical work or in the production of heat.
(5) Waste products are formed which must be eliminated. (6) Various
parts have specialized functions, and the failure of one part may cause
stoppage of the entire machine (death, to the organism).

DIFFERENCES. Organisms differ from nonliving machines in the following respects: (1) They are automatic, or self-operating. (2) They
are self-repairing. (3) They have the capacity for growth. (4) They
are capable of reproducing their kind. (5) They are adaptable and,
within limits, have the power to alter their structure. (6) They exhibit
an awareness of their environment. (7) They exhibit purpose and fore-
sight. (8) They cannot be set in motion again after stoppage (death)
has occurred.

THEORIES OF THE NATURE OF LIFE

In striving to understand the nature of life, the physiologist makes use of the *mechanistic theory*. This theory holds that all life processes are the result of the chemical and physical activities within the protoplasm, and that death is the cessation of these processes in the protoplasm of an organism. Notwithstanding the foregoing, another theory, the *vitalistic theory*, holds that life is something more than merely an organization of chemical compounds and the physical and chemical reactions taking place in protoplasm. It maintains that life is a "vital something," the nature of which is not yet known, and that this life does not stop at death. The vitalistic theory embodies essentially the spiritual viewpoint on the nature of life.

The cornerstone of our modern knowledge of life processes, and of the mechanistic theory, is the work of Lavoisier (1743–1794), who discovered the nature of burning (oxidation) and applied this to the study of living things. When it was learned that the oxidative processes within the cells of living organisms are basically the same as those occurring outside such cells, the foundation was laid for interpreting living phenomena in physicochemical terms.

Although a vast body of facts has been amassed about fundamental processes involved in bodily functions, there is still much to be learned. Physiology is an experimental science; with each new generation of students and researchers, new contributions are made and a better understanding of life is obtained.

2: THE CELL AND PROTOPLASM

The *cell*, also called "protoplast," is the basic structural unit of all living organisms. A mass of protoplasm, it contains a *nucleus*, or nuclear material, and usually is surrounded by a *cell membrane*. In some instances the cell membrane that separates the nuclei may be lacking, resulting in a multinucleated cell called a *syncytium* or *coenocyte*.

THE PROTOPLASMIC DOCTRINE

The cell was first seen in plants and so named by Robert Hooke (1635–1703), and described in his *Micrographia*, 1665. Observing a thin slice of cork under a microscope, he saw what reminded him of the "hexangular cells" of honeycomb; hence, the name by which *cells* have since been known. With great prescience Hooke wrote of the possible "passages," or interactions, between the cells: ". . . me thinks, it seems very probable, that Nature has in these passages, as well as in those of Animal bodies, very many appropriated Instruments and contrivances, whereby to bring her designs and end to pass, which 'tis not improbable, but that some diligent Observer, if help'd with better Microscopes, may in time detect." This appears to have been the first guess that the materials, the "Instruments and contrivances," of development are contained in the cell.

It was not until much additional work had been done by "diligent Observers" that the cell theory was finally formulated on firmer foundations than were available to Hooke. In 1839 Theodor Schwann (1810–1882) stated the view that "all organisms are composed of essentially like parts, namely, of cells," and in 1859 Rudolf Virchow (1821–1902), with the statement that "Every cell arises from a pre-existing cell," clinched the argument for the cell theory. The theory greatly stimulated investigation into the nature of cells and led to Max Schultze's formulation of the *protoplasmic doctrine* in 1861. This doctrine regarded the jelly-like substance (protoplasm) within the cell membrane as the living substance of all animals and plants.

CELL STRUCTURE

Animal cells range in *size* from 2 micra * (protozoan blood parasites) to 2 inches or more (ostrich egg yolks) in diameter. Red blood cells of the body have a diameter of 7 micra; egg cells in the ovary

* A *micron* (pl., micra) = .001 millimeter.

13

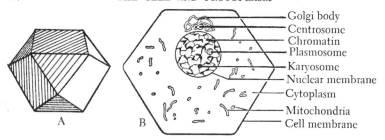

Fig. 2-1. A typical animal cell. (A) Diagram of surface view. (B) A section through the same cell, in the plane of this page, enlarged. (From Alexander, *Biology*, College Outline Series, copyright, 1954, by Barnes & Noble, Inc.)

have a diameter of 115 micra. Some multinucleated cells, such as those of striated muscle, may attain a length of 6 centimeters (2.4 inches). When free and suspended in a fluid, cells tend to assume a spherical shape. In the body, however, they may have almost any shape, depending on their function and their relationship to other cells.

A generalized cell, when killed, fixed, and stained, usually shows a nucleus and cytoplasm.

Nucleus. The nucleus, a specialized mass of protoplasm, is essential to the life of the cell. Ordinarily, it is a spherical body located near the center of the cell.

PARTS OF THE NUCLEUS. A typical nucleus contains the following parts: the *nuclear membrane*, which encloses the nuclear substance and regulates the exchange of materials between cytoplasm and nucleus; *chromonemata*, fine particles or filaments containing *chromatin*, a substance which stains deeply with basic dyes; the *linin net*, a network of fine filaments which support the chromonemata; and the *nucleolus (plasmosome)*, a darkly staining body which disappears during cell division. One or more *nucleoli* may be present; their function is unknown, although it is thought that they play a role in the synthesis of cytoplasmic proteins.

During cell division the chromonemata become concentrated into *chromosomes*, which are believed to hold the hereditary particles, the *genes*. The number of chromosomes in the cell is constant for a given species (46 in the somatic cells of man).

FUNCTIONS OF THE NUCLEUS. The nucleus performs the following functions: (1) It regulates or controls metabolic activities. (2) It is involved in growth and repair. (3) It is essential for reproduction.

Cytoplasm. The cytoplasm is that portion of the cell's protoplasm lying outside the nucleus. It is especially concerned with the functional activities of a cell, such as secretion, absorption, conduction, and contraction. Specialized *parts* of the cytoplasm are: (1) the *cell mem-*

brane, the outermost portion which forms the limiting membrane of the cell; (2) *cell organoids*, the living components of a cell; and (3) *inclusions*, the lifeless, temporary constituents of a cell (fats, proteins, carbohydrates, crystals, secretory granules, pigment granules, and chromophil substance).

Included among the cell organoids are: *mitochondria*, small bodies which are usually rod-shaped; the *Golgi apparatus* (*Golgi-body*), a specialized structure in the form of granules, rods, or reticulum; a *cell center* or *central body* containing one or two small granules, the *centrioles*, surrounded by the *centrosome* and *astrosphere* (the former a clear area immediately surrounding the centriole; the latter located more peripherally and consisting of radiating fibrilla-like structures).

CELL DIVISION

Cells originate by means of cell division, a process in which a parent cell divides and gives rise to two daughter cells. The methods by which cell division is accomplished are *amitosis* and *mitosis*.

Amitosis. Amitosis is a simple, direct method of division in which the nucleus and the cytoplasm both constrict, the two resulting masses forming two new cells. Amitosis rarely occurs in the human body.

Mitosis. Mitosis is a complex, indirect method of cell division. This process rearranges the chromatin filaments of the nucleus into chromosomes each of which divides into duplicate parts; these identical parts (*chromatids*) then line up opposite each other, each set to become the content of a distinct and separate daughter cell. Thus the chromosomes, which contain the genes, are divided equally, half of the split parts being passed on to each daughter cell. Since all cells in the human body are derived through successive cell divisions from the original fertilized egg cell, it follows that by mitosis the nuclear material possessed by all cells of the body is identical in chromatin content.

Mitosis is a continuous process, but for convenience it is usually described as occurring in four stages, or *phases*. (A cell that is not in process of division is said to be in a *resting stage*, or *interphase*. In such a cell the chromatin particles are scattered throughout the nucleus.) The four phases are: prophase, metaphase, anaphase, and telophase.

PROPHASE. The *centrioles* separate and, with the surrounding attraction spheres, move to opposite poles of the cell. *Astral lines* (*rays*) develop, those between the centrioles forming the *spindle*. Chromatin granules condense and form linear units, the *chromosomes*, which divide longitudinally and become arranged in an *equatorial plate*. The nuclear membrane and the nucleolus disappear.

METAPHASE. The chromosomes, which have split longitudinally into halves, lie suspended in the spindle midway between the centrioles.

ANAPHASE. The halves of each chromosome separate and move, or are drawn, along the spindle fibers toward the two centrioles. In this phase each centriole may divide in preparation for the next division.

TELOPHASE. Each set of daughter chromosomes reconstructs itself into a nucleus. The chromosomes begin to break up into irregular chromatin granules. Nucleoli reappear and the nuclear membrane re-forms. The cytoplasm constricts and the two daughter cells become distinct from each other and enter the *interphase*.

There is a modified form of mitosis, known as *meiosis*, occurring only in the development of reproductive cells. In this process the chromosomes line up as pairs (*synaptic mates*). In the division of the cell, one chromosome of each pair goes to each daughter cell. The re-

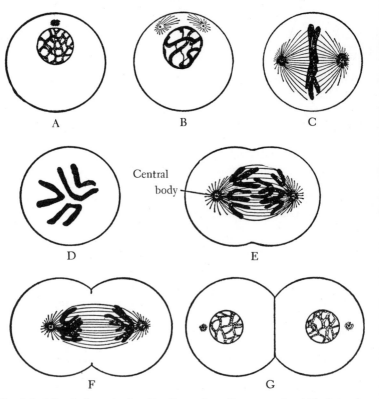

Fig. 2-2. Mitosis in animal cells. Somewhat diagrammatic. (A) Interphase (resting cell). (B) Prophase. (C) End of prophase, beginning of metaphase—chromosomes at equator of spindle. (D) Polar view of chromosomes at equator of spindle. (E) Anaphase. (F) Early telophase. (G) Two daughter cells in interphase. (From Alexander, *Biology*, College Outline Series, copyright, 1954, by Barnes & Noble, Inc.)

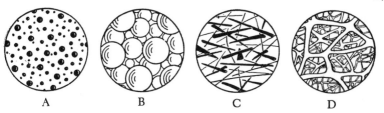

Fig. 2-3. Diagram showing physical nature of protoplasm. (A) granular, (B) alveolar, (C) fibrillar, (D) reticular. (From Alexander, *Biology*, College Outline Series, copyright, 1954, by Barnes & Noble, Inc.)

sult is that the daughter cells possess half the normal number of chromosomes.

Through meiosis the number of chromosomes in the functional egg and sperm is reduced to one-half, which is then termed the *haploid number* (23 in man). At fertilization the normal, *diploid number* (46) is restored.

PROTOPLASM

Protoplasm is the *living substance*, constituting, as T. H. Huxley put it, the *physical basis of life*. All living things are composed of protoplasm or of its products. Nonliving things do not contain any protoplasm.

Physical Nature of Protoplasm. *Consistency:* viscid, jelly-like; a colloidal mixture which may have at one time a fluid consistency (*sol* state) and at another a semisolid glue-like consistency (*gel* state). *Color:* usually semiopaque, grayish in appearance. *Structure:* as seen under the microscope, the protoplasmic substance may be (1) *granular*, containing granules of various sizes; (2) *alveolar*, having the appearance of soapsuds or bubbles; (3) *fibrillar*, consisting of fine fiber-like structures; or (4) *reticular*, consisting of an interlacing net of thread-like structures.

Chemical Nature of Protoplasm. Protoplasm, as such, cannot be analyzed chemically; when an analysis is attempted, the organization of the cell or of a tissue is disrupted and life processes stop. The substance is thereupon nonliving, and whether it is of the same nature as it was in the living cell cannot be readily determined. This suggests that "life" depends on a specific chemical and physical organization of protoplasm.

It is possible, however, to determine which elements and compounds are present in a cell or an organism at the time of its death or shortly afterward. The table which follows shows the results of such an analysis of man, but the percentile distribution applies generally to most living organisms.

ELEMENTS COMPRISING THE HUMAN BODY

Element	Per Cent	Element	Per Cent
Oxygen (O)........	65	Potassium (K)......	0.35
Carbon (C)........	18	Sulfur (S)..........	0.25
Hydrogen (H).....	10	Chlorine (Cl).......	0.15
Nitrogen (N)......	3	Sodium (Na).......	0.15
Calcium (Ca)......	2	Magnesium (Mg)....	0.05
Phosphorus (P)....	1	Iron (Fe)..........	0.004
		Other elements *....	0.046
	99		1.000

* Among the "other elements" are: Iodine (I), Copper (Cu), Manganese (Mn), Rubidium (Rb), Cobalt (Co), and Nickel (Ni).

Compounds in Protoplasm. Only the gases (oxygen and nitrogen) are found in the body in their elemental state. All the other elements are present in the form of compounds, which are either *inorganic* (lacking carbon) or *organic* (containing carbon):

Inorganic Compounds	Organic Compounds
Water	Proteins
Inorganic salts	Carbohydrates
	Fats (Lipids)

The foregoing compounds are common to all protoplasm. Other compounds, both inorganic and organic, may occur in the protoplasm of specific types of cells.

The percentile distribution of the common compounds in different kinds of living tissue is variable, as shown in the following table:

Compound	Striated Muscle	White Matter of Brain	Entire Body
Water	75.0	70.7	66.0
Proteins	20.00	10.00	16.0
Fats	2.0	18.5	13.0
Carbohydrates and extractives	2.0	.....	0.61
Inorganic salts	1.0	0.8	5.0

WATER. Water is the principal chemical constituent of protoplasm. It is indispensable in metabolic processes because enzymatic activity can take place only in the presence of water. In the body, water exists as *free water*, in which form it acts as the chief solvent and a medium for metabolic processes, and *bound water*, in which form it is tied to proteins by hydrogen bonds. Water plays the following role in protoplasm:

1. It serves as a *solvent*. More substances are soluble in water than in any other solvent. Substances in solution are free to move about within the cell or from one cell to another. Most chemical reactions take place only in solutions, and enzymes act only in a fluid medium.

2. In water, substances such as acids, bases, and salts readily *ionize;* that is, their molecules separate into atoms bearing electrical charges. For example, sodium chloride (NaCl) separates into a positive sodium ion and a negative chlorine ion $(NaCl \rightarrow Na^+ + Cl^-)$. Such a solution is called an *electrolyte* and is a ready conductor of electric current.

3. The properties of water make it important in the *regulation of body temperature*. These properties are its *high specific heat* (i.e., its capacity to take up and give off large amounts of heat with little change in its own temperature) and its *high latent heat of vaporization*.

4. Water has a *high chemical stability*. This makes it possible for chemical reactions to occur in water without involving the water itself.

5. Water has a *high surface tension*, which is of significance in the production of protoplasmic membranes.

6. Water serves as a reacting agent; it is essential in all hydrolytic reactions.

INORGANIC SALTS (MINERAL SUBSTANCES). These are substances which, upon burning, leave an ash. The common salts are compounds of the following elements:

Sodium		Chlorine		Chlorides
Potassium	which	Carbon dioxide		Carbonates
Calcium	combine	Sulfur	to form	Sulfates
Magnesium	with	Phosphorus		Phosphates
Iron				

Salts are essential in the body for:

1. Proper osmotic conditions, to secure proper concentration of water in cells;
2. Proper acid-base balance (buffer salts in blood);
3. Development of bone and teeth (calcium and phosphorus);
4. Normal coagulation of the blood (calcium);
5. Formation of red blood cells (iron for hemoglobin);
6. Proper state of irritability (sodium and potassium ions);
7. Formation of certain endocrine secretions (iodine for thyroxine).

PROTEINS. Proteins are compounds of carbon, hydrogen, oxygen, and nitrogen (and sometimes sulfur and phosphorus). They are built up from *amino acids*, compounds consisting of a carboxyl (COOH) group and an amino (NH_2) group. Examples are albumin and hemoglobin. Proteins are essential in the body for:

1. Forming the framework of the protoplasm of cells;
2. Maintenance of proper consistency and osmotic pressure of blood;
3. Provision of energy;
4. Maintenance of the physical consistency of protoplasm. (Proteins, which are colloids, change readily from *sol* to *gel* state and vice versa).

FATS (LIPIDS). Fats are compounds of carbon, hydrogen, and oxygen. An example is olein ($C_{57}H_{104}O_6$). In the body, fats:

1. Are sources of energy;
2. Serve as a reserve supply of food;
3. Serve to support and protect body organs;
4. Influence the permeability of cell membranes (in cells, fats are concentrated in the membranes);
5. Serve for body insulation.

CARBOHYDRATES. Carbohydrates are compounds of carbon, hydrogen, and oxygen, with the latter two nearly always in the ratio of 2:1. An example is glucose ($C_6H_{12}O_6$). Carbohydrates in the body serve primarily as a source of energy for body activity and heat production.

CELL PERMEABILITY

For the maintenance of life processes which are going on unceasingly in cells, substances are moving more or less continuously from outside into the cell and from the cell into the surrounding environment. Food, oxygen, salts, hormones, and other substances must enter the cell, and carbon dioxide, water, products of secretion, and waste materials must be discharged from the cell. These substances pass through the cell membrane, some readily, others with difficulty.

Factors Influencing Cell Permeability. The degree of permeability of a cell membrane is determined by: the size of the openings, the nature of the substance that is to pass through, the electrical charge borne by the ions, the action of salts, and certain as yet unknown factors which result in selective permeability.

SIZE OF OPENINGS. In the cell membrane the size of the opening in relation to the size and structure of the particles (atoms or molecules) influences permeability. Water and glucose will pass readily through most cell membranes, but larger and more complex molecules, such as starches and proteins, will not.

NATURE OF SUBSTANCE. This refers specifically to whether or not the substance is fat-soluble. Fats or lipids form an integral part of the protoplasm which constitutes the cell membrane. Fat-soluble substances usually pass through the membrane with little difficulty; non-fat-soluble substances may not. Cell functioning may be altered by substances in the blood which dissolve the fat of cells; this is perhaps the basis for the anesthetic action of ether and chloroform.

ELECTRICAL CHARGE BORNE BY IONS. Many substances (acids, bases, salts) exist in ionic form in the body fluids surrounding cells and in the surface membranes of cells. It will be recalled that ions with like charges tend to repel each other, and those with unlike charges tend to attract each other. If the charges of the ions in or on the cell membrane are negative, positive ions will be attracted to and enter the cell while negative ions will be repelled.

ACTION OF SALTS ON THE MEMBRANE. Calcium salts have a gelatinizing effect on a cell membrane. Sodium salts have a liquefying effect. Cell permeability is altered by excesses of one or the other of these salts.

SELECTIVE PERMEABILITY. Living cells are able to maintain certain concentrations of their constituents that are different from the concentrations of these same constituents in the surrounding medium. Such substances may be more concentrated within the cell than without, or vice versa. A striking example in which such differences exist even though the substances are readily diffusible is noted in the distribution of sodium (Na) and potassium (K) in red blood cells and in their surrounding medium, the plasma. The potassium content of the corpuscles is high, that of the serum low; the cell membrane is much more permeable to potassium ions than to sodium ions. Such facts can be explained in part by assuming that the cell membrane is not an inert, passive structure acting as a simple sieve but rather an integral part of the living cell with its behavior influenced by the activities going on within the cell. As a result, each cell has, within certain limits, the ability to control passage of certain substances through its membrane. This regulatory capacity is known as *selective permeability*.

Physicochemical Processes of Cell Permeability. The processes important to bodily activities which are involved in the passage of substances through cell membranes are: *diffusion, filtration,* and *osmosis.*

DIFFUSION. Any kind of chemical activity involves the movement of atoms, ions, molecules, or groups of molecules. Where particles are free to move, there is a general tendency for them to move from a region of high concentration to one of lower concentration. This process is called *diffusion.*

The consequence of diffusion is a uniform distribution of the particles of the diffused substance. Thus, if two gases are admitted to a container, the molecules of each gas will diffuse among those of the other until they are uniformly distributed. Two liquids will behave in the same way, but their diffusion takes place at a slower rate. Solids diffuse only with extreme slowness, if at all.

The Membrane as a Factor. Diffusion is modified by the presence of a membrane. If the membrane is permeable to the substance that is diffusing, the particles will pass through the membrane as though it does not exist. If the particles are larger than the pores of the membrane, they will not pass through at all; that is, diffusion will not take place.

Selective Diffusion (*Dialysis*). The passage of a substance *in solution* through a membrane is referred to as *dialysis*. Colloids do not dialyze; they do not pass through animal membranes or parchment paper. Crystalloid substances will pass through such membranes. Indeed, this property makes it possible to differentiate colloids from crystalloids and to separate them one from the other.

Examples of Diffusion in the Body. Examples of diffusion are the passage of oxygen from the alveoli of the lungs into the blood and from the blood to the tissue cells; the passage of carbon dioxide from tissue cells into the blood and from the blood into the lungs; and the passage of molecules of digested food from the digestive tract into the blood and from the blood into the tissue cells. In addition, within each cell, diffusion is constantly occurring as particles move about within the protoplasm of the cell.

FILTRATION. This process involves the passage of a substance through a barrier or filter as a result of the difference in mechanical pressure on the two sides of the filter. The principle can be illustrated by filtering a mixture of salt, sand, and water through filter paper. The water and the salt will pass through; the sand will not.

Examples of Filtration in the Body. The action in the glomerulus of the kidney and that in the blood capillaries provide excellent examples of filtration in the body.

In the *glomerulus of the kidney* the mechanical force is supplied by the blood pressure; the wall of the glomerulus (a capillary net) and Bowman's capsule constitute the filter. Water and crystalloid solutes (sugar, salts, urea) pass through. Blood proteins do not pass through, because they are colloids and do not dialyze.

In the *blood capillaries* the mechanical force, again, is the blood pressure. Blood plasma is forced through the capillary wall into the tissue spaces. Blood proteins may get through by passing between the cells rather than through the cell membranes. Red blood cells do not pass through the capillary wall.

OSMOSIS. Osmosis is the movement of water molecules through a semipermeable membrane as a result of differences in the concentration of dissolved substances on the two sides of the membrane. The force which causes this movement is called *osmotic pressure*.

Demonstration of Osmosis. A thistle tube is set up with its large end covered by a semipermeable membrane such as an animal bladder. If the tube is filled with water and the large end is placed in a beaker of water so that the levels in the tube and the beaker are the same, it will be noted after a period of time that the level in the tube does not change but remains the same as that in the beaker. *But* if the thistle tube is filled with a sugar solution and then placed in a beaker of water with the levels the same, after a short period of time the fluid in the tube will begin to rise and may go upward for a considerable distance, sometimes as much as several feet. From this action it becomes obvious that water molecules are moving through the membrane from the beaker into the tube. By the force of osmotic pressure the movement of the water molecules is tending to equalize the concentration of the two solutions.

In the first of the foregoing demonstrations, the levels remain constant because as many water molecules are passing through the membrane out of the tube as into it. In the second instance, however, both water molecules and sugar molecules are striking against the upper surface of the membrane, but the membrane is permeable only to the water molecules, so that these pass out into the beaker while the sugar molecules are retained in the tube. At the same time that the water molecules in the sugar solution are striking against the membrane the molecules of the dissolved substance (sugar) are also striking the surface area of the membrane. It is apparent that in a given unit of time fewer water molecules will strike a given area of this surface on the inside (that is, on the side of the tube) than will strike on the outside (the side of the beaker). Consequently, more water molecules enter the tube than leave, and the level rises.

Application of the Principle of Osmosis to Living Tissues. In essence all cells in the body are small "sacs" of water containing dissolved substances, such as sugars and salts. The surface layer of protoplasm is a semipermeable membrane. Water tends to move through this membrane as the concentration of the fluids on either side of the membrane changes. This process can be illustrated with body cells as follows:

1. If red blood cells are placed in a salt solution with a concentration of .85 per cent, no change in size is observed. The salt solution exerts an osmotic pressure which is exactly equal to that exerted within the cell. Such a solution is referred to as *isotonic*.

2. If red blood cells are placed in a very dilute salt solution or in distilled water (water containing no salt at all), water molecules will move into the cell, which will increase in size. This condition is called "turgor." The membrane of the blood cell may become distended, even to the point of bursting (cytolysis). Such a solution is said to be *hypotonic*.

3. If red blood cells are placed in a highly concentrated salt solution, say 2 per cent, water will leave the cells and the cells will shrink. This phenomenon is known as "plasmolysis." Ultimately they present

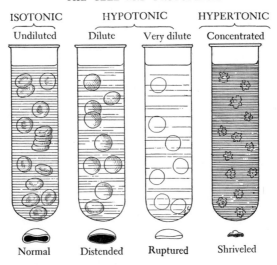

Fig. 2-4. Diagram to illustrate effect of solutions on cells, (Reprinted with permission of W. B. Saunders Company from Millard, King, and Showers, *Human Anatomy and Physiology*, 4th ed., 1956.)

a shriveled appearance ("crenated" cells). Such a solution is said to be *hypertonic*.

From the foregoing paragraphs 2 and 3, it can be seen that it is important, in the transfusion of a fluid such as blood plasma or a saline solution, that the fluid transfused exert the same osmotic pressure as that of the fluids the cells live in (in this case, the blood plasma).

PHYSIOLOGICAL SALINE SOLUTION. When living cells are studied or examined outside the body, they will retain their normal form and carry on their usual activities only if they are kept in an isotonic solution. For man, such a solution is a .85 per cent saline solution. In this solution there are 8.5 grams of salt (sodium chloride) to 1,000 milliliters of distilled water. This is a *physiological saline solution*. Another form of physiological saline solution is known as *Ringer-Locke solution*. For the study of human cells, each 1,000 ml. of such a solution would contain: 8.5 gm. of sodium chloride, 0.42 gm. potassium chloride, 0.24 gm. calcium chloride, 0.2 gm. of sodium bicarbonate and 2.0 gm. of glucose. The salts provide Na^+, K^+, and Ca^{++} ions in the same proportion as they exist in the blood plasma. Glucose is added to provide energy and sodium bicarbonate is added to maintain constant hydrogen-ion concentration (a buffering action).

3: TISSUES

There are four primary types of tissues in the body: (1) *epithelial,* which covers surfaces, lines cavities, and forms tubes; (2) *connective,* which forms supporting and binding structures; (3) *muscular,* which comprises the contractile elements; and (4) *nervous,* which makes up the regulating and conducting structures. The principal differences among the various types of tissues arise from the types of cells of which they are composed, the nature and amount of intercellular material present, and the functions they perform.

EPITHELIAL TISSUE

Epithelial tissue or *epithelium* forms the covering of the outer surfaces of the body and of most internal organs; it lines the digestive and respiratory tracts, the serous cavities, blood vessels, excretory ducts, and reproductive ducts and organs. It comprises the secreting portions and ducts of glands and the sensory portions of sense organs.

Structural Characteristics of Epithelial Tissue. Epithelial cells are arranged in a continuous sheet, usually of one layer. They are packed together closely with little intercellular substance. Blood vessels are absent, but nerve endings are usually abundant. Epithelial cells lie on a *basement membrane,* a thin layer of intercellular substance permeated with reticular fibers.

Types of Epithelium. The types of epithelium are differentiated on the basis of the shape of the cells (squamous, cuboidal, columnar, or transitional) and their arrangement in the epithelial sheet (*simple* or *stratified*).

Squamous epithelium consists of cells which are thin and flat, with regular or irregular outlines. *Simple* squamous epithelium (cells in a single layer) is found lining the body cavities and in Bowman's capsule of the kidney. That lining the serous cavities (pleural, peritoneal, pericardial) is called *mesothelium;* that lining blood and lymph vessels, *endothelium;* that lining cavities in connective tissue (such as the subarachnoid cavity), *mesenchymal epithelium. Stratified* squamous epithelium (cells in several layers) is found in the epidermis, cornea, esophagus, and vagina.

Cuboidal epithelium consists of cube-shaped cells or cells in the form of truncated pyramids. It is found in the thyroid gland, kidney tubules, the ducts of glands, and the smaller bronchi.

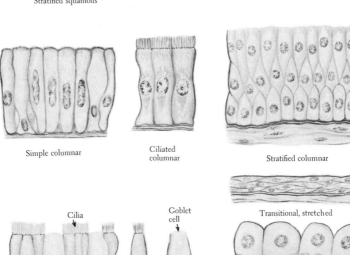

Isolated cells

Simple squamous

Profile view

Cuboidal

Basement membrane

Stratified squamous

Simple columnar

Ciliated columnar

Stratified columnar

Cilia

Goblet cell

Transitional, stretched

Pseudostratified, ciliated

Transitional, contracted

Fig. 3-1. Types of epithelial tissue.

Columnar epithelium consists of cells which are long and cylindrical, sometimes forming tall, irregular prisms. There are six subtypes: *simple*, in the lining of the intestine; *simple ciliated*, in the oviduct, uterus, and nasal sinuses; *stratified*, in the pharynx, on the epiglottis; *stratified ciliated*, in the larynx, on the soft palate; *pseudostratified* (varying in height, with nuclei at different levels, all cells touching basement membrane), in the parotid gland and male urethra; *pseudostratified ciliated*, in the trachea and Eustachian tube.

Transitional epithelium resembles stratified epithelium in that it consists of several layers of cells, but its superficial surface cells are large and rounded instead of being squamous in shape. This enables the membrane to stretch without breaking apart the surface cells. This type is well adapted for lining organs and tubes which are subject to expansion, such as the ureter and urinary bladder. *Transitional epithelium* sometimes consists of cells several layers in thickness, but the number of layers varies with the condition of the organ, as in the urinary bladder.

Free Surface of Epithelial Cells. The free surface of epithelial cells may be modified in various ways. In some cases, the superficial protoplasm is involved; in others, a membrane-like secretion, or cuticle, is formed.

MODIFICATION OF SUPERFICIAL PROTOPLASM. The borders of the epithelial structures may be either striated, ciliated, or of the brush type. The *striated border* is found in cells of columnar intestinal epithelium, usually in areas where absorptive processes take place. It consists of fine striations lying perpendicular to the surface of the cells. The *ciliated border* is representative of respiratory epithelium. Cilia are thin, very numerous, hair-like projections of varied length. At the proximal end of each cilium is a small *basal corpuscle*. Ciliary movement results from the quick bending of the cilia in one direction and a subsequent straightening, or recovery stroke. The action of each cilium follows that of the adjoining one in a wave-like action which is repeated. In this manner mucus or particles in contact with the cilia are moved slowly along the ciliated surface. The *brush border* is found in cells comprising certain portions of kidney tubules. It consists of fine, hair-like processes which are nonmotile. It gives the appearance of a dense brush.

Other specialized borders include: *stereocilia*, nonmotile projections in cells of the epididymis which are thought to aid in eliminating the secretion of the cells; and *nonmotile hairs*, in hair cells of the utricle, saccule, and cochlea of the ear, serving as receptors for vibratory stimuli. Mature spermatozoa possess a flagellum, a single hair-like process which serves for locomotion.

STRUCTURE OF CUTICLES. A cuticle is a layer of more or less solid substance which is secreted by and covers the free surface of an epithelial sheet. It is usually sharply delimited from the cell surface and capable of being separated from it. Examples of cuticles are the enamel of the teeth and the capsule of the lens of the eye.

Binding Together of Epithelial Cells. The cells of an epithelial sheet are so closely bound to one another that it usually requires considerable mechanical force to separate them. The factors operating to bind them together are: (1) *interstitial substance,* usually very small in amount, which acts as an intercellular "cement"; (2) *intercellular bridges,* short protoplasmic processes which run in from one cell to another (conspicuous in the stratified epithelium of epidermis); and (3) *terminal bars,* thin, rod-like structures which outline and cement together the free surfaces of the cells.

Glands. Because they arise from an epithelial surface, glands are included in this discussion of the structure of epithelial tissues. The specialized glands associated with various body systems are described in greater detail in later chapters.

Functionally, a gland is a cell or group of cells that elaborates or manufactures a specific substance which is extruded from the cell onto a surface or into the blood or lymph. The product thus formed does not become a *part* of the body tissues but is either absorbed and used by them or discharged from the body.

Structurally, a gland is a cell or an aggregation of secreting cells. Multicellular glands arise and develop by a process of invagination; the epithelium grows into the adjacent connective tissue, and a simple tube-like or sac-like structure is formed. The cells in the closed portion of the sac assume a *secretory* function while those near the surface narrow to form an *excretory* duct. The more complex multicellular glands arise by repeated invaginations; the result is a complicated, branched organ.

SECRETION. Secretion is the process whereby a cell obtains materials from the blood and lymph and transforms them into products which are passed from the cell.

POLARIZATION. Gland cells (and, for that matter, most epithelial cells) are said to be *polarized;* that is to say, their *proximal* or *basal end* (that nearest to the basement membrane) is different in structure from the *distal* or *free end.* The nucleus lies at the proximal end, whereas, in the active phase of secretion, the secretory products (granules, mucigen, or other substances) fill the distal end, from which they are discharged.

CLASSIFICATION OF GLANDS. Glands may be classified on the basis of (1) the presence or absence of excretory ducts, (2) the nature of the secretion, (3) whether the secretion is a product of the cell or a part of the cell itself, and (4) their structure.

Presence of Excretory Ducts. Exocrine or external-secreting glands possess ducts and empty their products onto a free surface (example: salivary glands). *Endocrine* or internal-secreting glands are ductless; their secretions are absorbed into blood or lymph (example: thyroid gland). Some glands, for example the pancreas, ovary, or testes, are double-functioning, serving as combined exocrine and endocrine glands.

Nature of Secretion. Mucous glands secrete mucus, a viscid substance which principally contains mucin (examples: goblet cells of intestine, tracheal glands). *Serous* glands secrete a clear, watery albuminous fluid (parotid gland). *Mixed* glands contain both mucous- and serous-secreting cells (submaxillary gland).

Secretion a Product of or a Part of the Cell. In *merocrine* glands the secretory product is the only part extruded (salivary gland). In *apocrine* glands the apical end of the cell, containing accumulated products, is broken off and extruded; the remaining portion of the cell is left intact, the cell re-forms, and the process is repeated (mammary gland). In *holocrine* glands the entire cell, along with its contained secretory product, is extruded, and the cell is replaced by a new cell (sebaceous or oil gland).

Classification of Glands by Structure. Glands may be either unicellular or multicellular. *Unicellular* glands are found on free surfaces; they secrete mucous. The *goblet cells* of the intestines are examples. *Multicellular* glands are tubular, alveolar (acinous), or tubuloalveolar (tubuloacinous). The *tubular* type have their secreting portion in the form of a blind, narrow tube. They may be *simple-straight* (in large intestine), *simple-coiled* (sweat glands), or *simple-branched* (gastric glands); or they may be *compound* (in kidney, testis, liver) with a large number of tubes branching repeatedly. The *alveolar* (acinous) type has a flask-shaped secreting portion called an *alveolus,* or *acinus;* they are *simple-branched* (sebaceous glands) or *compound* (mammary gland). The compound *tubuloalveolar* (tubuloacinous) type has a secreting portion that consists of irregularly branched tubules and saccular outgrowths; examples are the majority of exocrine glands (salivary, pancreas).

CONNECTIVE TISSUE

Connective tissue forms the supporting and connecting structures of the body. With one or two exceptions, connective tissues arise from the mesoderm (the middle germ layer of the embryo); more specifically, they arise from the mesenchyme of this layer.

The *mesenchyme* is an embryonic tissue consisting of a network of branching stellate cells. Protoplasmic processes extending from these cells touch and possibly anastomose to form a *syncytium.* The spaces between the cells are filled with a homogeneous fluid. Mesenchymal cells are ameboid and move about quite freely. As development of the embryo proceeds, the nature of this intercellular substance changes. Fibers begin to appear, first the collagenous, then the elastic. Differentiation occurs with the development and from the mesenchyme or embryonal connective tissue the specialized adult types arise.

General Characteristics of Connective Tissue. The cells of connective tissues are relatively few in number, the bulk of the tissue consisting of intercellular material or *matrix*. Connective tissues are highly vascular; that is, they are well supplied with blood vessels. Rarely do they occur on free surfaces.

Classification of Connective Tissues. Connective tissues are classified on the basis of their intercellular substance, as follows: (1) *connective tissue proper*, intercellular substance of a fibrous nature; and (2) *dense connective tissue*, intercellular substance that is rigid or semirigid (cartilage, bone).

CONNECTIVE TISSUE PROPER. There are four types of connective tissue proper: mucous, fibrous, reticular, and adipose.

Mucous Connective Tissue. Also known as *Wharton's jelly*, mucous connective tissue consists of branching cells, irregularly arranged, which sometimes anastomose. This type of tissue has a jelly-like matrix and contains mucin. A few bundles of collagenous fibers may be present. There are no elastic fibers. Wharton's jelly is found only in the umbilical cord of the embryo.

Fibrous Connective Tissue. This type of connective tissue proper is composed of cells embedded in a matrix that is made up of fibers and a semifluid substance. Fibrous connective tissue is further subdivided into: areolar, white fibrous (collagenous), and yellow fibrous (elastic).

Areolar or *loose* connective tissue consists of an interlacing network of fibers in a semifluid matrix throughout which cells are scattered. This kind of tissue forms the interstitial tissue of most organs, surrounds blood vessels and nerves, and constitutes most of the subcutaneous tissue and the deep fascia.

The fibers of areolar tissue are white (collagenous) and yellow (elastic). The *white fibers* occur in bundles and, if not stretched, are usually wavy; the fibers themselves do not branch, but a bundle of them may do so; they are nonelastic yet flexible; they swell in weak acids or alkalies and are digested by acid pepsin but resist alkaline trypsin; the *collagen* they contain yields gelatin upon boiling. The *yellow fibers* are single fibers, usually straight but, containing *elastin*, are highly elastic; they may branch and anastomose; they resist boiling water, acids, and alkalies and are digested slowly by both pepsin and trypsin.

The cells of areolar tissue are: fibroblasts, histiocytes, plasma cells, mast cells, and a number of other miscellaneous cells. *Fibroblasts,*

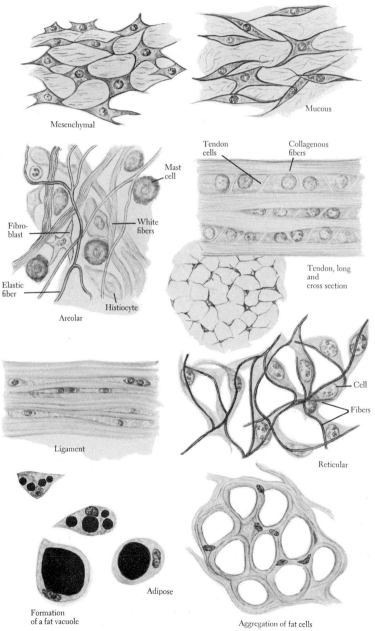

Fig. 3-2. Types of connective tissue proper.

irregularly-shaped cells, are thought to give rise to fibers; they may be phagocytic; they are the most numerous cells in this type of tissue. *Histiocytes* (fixed macrophages), irregularly shaped cells with branching processes and small nuclei, stain deeply and readily take up vital stains such as trypan blue and colloidal carbon; normally they are quiescent but during inflammatory processes become actively ameboid and phagocytic. *Plasma cells* are smaller than histiocytes and fewer in number; their function is unknown. *Mast cells* occurring in varying numbers, are found especially along blood vessels; while their origin and function are not definitely known, they are believed to produce heparin, an anticoagulant. Miscellaneous cells found in areolar tissue are: eosinophils, pigment cells, undifferentiated mesenchymal cells, and lymphoid "wandering" cells.

White fibrous connective tissue consists mainly of white fibers, with few elastic fibers present. It is found in the fibrous capsules of organs, tendons, and aponeuroses. A *tendon* is a flat or cord-like band that serves to attach muscle to bone. Its collagenous fibers are arranged in parallel bundles. Fibroblasts, the only cells present, are arranged in parallel rows between the bundles. An *aponeurosis* is a flat sheet of connective tissue that attaches muscles to bones or other tissue; it is similar in structure to a tendon. A *ligament* also is similar to a tendon in structure except that its fibers are less regularly arranged and some elastic fibers may be present.

Yellow fibrous or *elastic* connective tissue is made up principally of yellow elastic fibers with few collagenous fibers. It is found in some ligaments (especially the ligamentum nuchae) and in the walls of the large blood vessels, especially the aorta and the larger arteries.

Reticular Connective Tissue. Reticular connective tissue consists of a syncytial network of cells with many argyrophilic intercellular fibers running in all directions and forming a *reticulum*. These fibers are so named because of their property of staining intensely with certain silver methods. This type of tissue forms the framework of lymphoid organs such as the spleen, lymph nodes, and bone marrow. It is also found in certain endocrine glands, in the walls of blood vessels, and in digestive and respiratory passages underlying mucous membranes.

Adipose Tissue. Adipose tissue is made up principally of cells that have the capacity for taking in fat and storing it. Mature fat cells contain a large droplet of neutral fat enclosed in a cavity called a *vacuole*. The cytoplasm is reduced to a thin layer surrounding the vacuole. The nucleus is flattened and pushed to one side, giving the fat cell a "signet ring" appearance. Groups of fat cells are separated by areolar tissue. Adipose tissue is found in the superficial fascia under the skin; around organs such as the kidney, bladder, and heart; in mesenteries and the greater omentum; and as individual cells or in small groups in any loose connective tissue, especially that along the blood vessels and nerves. As to its *functions*, adipose tissue (1) serves as a reservoir of reserve food, (2) protects the organs it surrounds against cold (or heat loss), (3) protects against mechanical injury, (4) helps to support and hold organs in place, and (5) fills in the angular areas of the body.

DENSE CONNECTIVE TISSUE. This tissue includes cartilage and bone (osseous tissue).

Cartilage. There are three types of cartilage: hyaline, fibrous, and elastic.

Hyaline cartilage consists of cells lying in cavities (*lacunae*) surrounded by a homogeneous *matrix* of dense, semirigid intercellular sub-

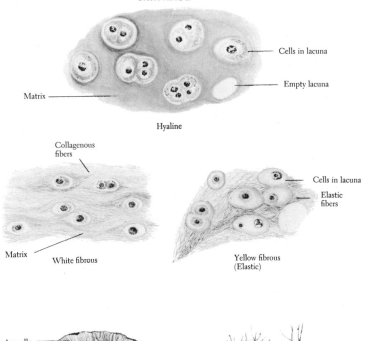

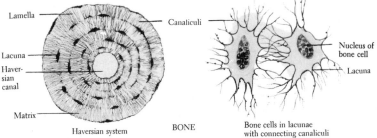

Fig. 3-3. Types of dense connective tissue.

stance. The matrix contains collagenous fibers which, however, cannot be seen in ordinary preparations. The cells, called *chondrocytes*, are usually single although they may occur in pairs or in groups of three or four. Hyaline cartilage is flexible and slightly elastic. It is covered by a membrane, the *perichondrium*, except over articular surfaces of bone. Hyaline cartilage is found in the articular cartilages covering the ends of bones at joints, in costal cartilages between the ribs and the sternum, and in the septum of the nose and cartilages of the larynx and trachea.

Fibrous cartilage consists of a matrix not quite so dense as that of hyaline cartilage and containing many collagenous fibers that are arranged more or less in rows. It possesses great strength and flexibility. The cells, ovoid and enclosed in capsules, are relatively few in number and usually are widely separated. This type of cartilage is found in intervertebral disks between the bodies of vertebrae and in the pubic symphysis.

Elastic cartilage consists of a matrix having many elastic fibers forming an interlacing network. Collagenous fibers are present but not readily seen. The cells, usually single but sometimes in pairs, lie in cavities called *lacunae*. This type of cartilage is flexible and elastic. It is found in the cartilage of the external ear, the wall of the Eustachian tube, the epiglottis, and certain laryngeal cartilages.

Bone (Osseous) Tissue. Bone is a rigid tissue consisting of bone cells imbedded in a matrix that is impregnated with calcium and phosphorous salts. The structural unit is the *Haversian system*, which consists of cylinders of matrix and bone cells surrounding a cavity, the *Haversian canal*. This canal contains blood vessels, lymphatics, and nerves. The matrix is arranged about each Haversian canal in concentric layers called *lamellae*. Between the lamellae are lacunae, within which lie the bone cells (*osteocytes*). Many minute canals called *canaliculi* extend from each lacuna and penetrate the matrix in all directions, connecting the various lacunae.

MUSCULAR TISSUE, NERVOUS TISSUE

Muscular tissue is composed of specialized cells whose function is to contract and thereby exert force, which is utilized for the movement of parts of the body. (See chapter 6.)

Nervous tissue is composed of specialized cells that are involved in the reception of stimuli, and the conduction of nerve impulses and in effecting responses to environmental changes.

4: THE INTEGUMENT
(The Skin and Its Derivatives)

The integumentary system, consisting of the skin and its derivatives, is the largest and one of the most complex systems of the body. The surface area of the skin covers about 1.8 square meters (19.4 sq. ft.) of the body of the average male adult and about 1.6 square meters (17.2 sq. ft.) in the average adult female.

Functions of the Integument. It may be difficult to think of the integument as a system, but it is a complex of organs (sweat glands, oil glands, etc.) and it serves a number of functions, the principal ones being: (1) to protect the underlying tissues from injurious stimuli, which may be physical, chemical, electrical, thermal, or biological; (2) to prevent excessive loss of water or drying of tissues; (3) to act as temperature regulator, preventing loss of heat in a cold environment and facilitating loss of heat in a hot environment; (4) to serve as a reservoir for food and water; (5) to assist in the processes of excretion (through sweating), eliminating water, salts, and, to a limited extent, urea; (6) to serve as a sense organ for the cutaneous senses; (7) to prevent, in large measure, the entrance of foreign bodies; and (8) to serve as the seat of origin of the antirachitic vitamin (vitamin D).

Structure of the Integument. The integument comprises the skin (epidermis and dermis) and the derivatives of the skin. The following table shows the distribution of the various elements:

Skin
- Epidermis
  - Stratum corneum
  - Stratum lucidum
  - Stratum granulosum
  - Stratum germinativum
- Dermis (Corium)
  - Papillary layer
  - Reticular layer

Derivatives of the skin
- Sudoriferous glands
- Sebaceous glands
- Mammary glands
- Hair and hair follicles
- Nails

Epidermis. The epidermis (outermost layer of the skin) is composed of stratified squamous epithelium. It arises from the ectoderm of the

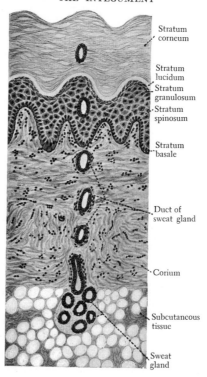

Stratum
corneum

Stratum
lucidum
Stratum
granulosum
Stratum
spinosum

Stratum
basale

Duct of
sweat gland

Corium

Subcutaneous
tissue

Sweat
gland

Fig. 4-1. General view of the skin. (Reprinted with permission of St. Martin's Press and The Macmillan Company, Ltd. from Hamilton, *Textbook of Human Anatomy*, 1956.)

embryo. It varies in thickness from 0.07–0.12 mm. over most of the body to 0.8–1.4 mm. on the palms of the hands and the soles of the feet. The epidermis is devoid of blood vessels. It has four layers:

Stratum corneum—the outermost layer; it consists of nonliving keratinized, flattened cells; the outer surface (*stratum disjunctum*) is shed continuously by the process called *desquamation*.

Stratum lucidum—cells consist of three or four layers packed closely together; appears as a pale or clear layer but is not always apparent.

Stratum granulosum—a very thin layer consisting of two or three layers of flattened cells containing granules of *eleidin*, the precursor of *keratin*. It is in this layer that cornification begins.

Stratum germinativum—known also as the *Malpighian layer*; is several layers of cells in thickness; nuclei are prominent; basal layer stains deeply. Stratum germinativum consists of two regions: the *basal layer*, lying next to the dermis, a single row of cylindrical cells which constantly are dividing and giving rise to cells of the outer layers (in this

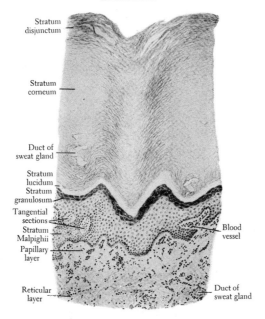

Stratum
disjunctum

Stratum
corneum

Duct of
sweat gland

Stratum
lucidum
Stratum
granulosum
Tangential
sections
Stratum
Malpighii
Papillary
layer

Reticular
layer

Blood
vessel

Duct of
sweat gland

Fig. 4-2. Epidermis. (Reprinted with permission of W. B. Saunders Company from Maximow and Bloom, A *Textbook of Histology*, 6th ed., 1952.)

layer, mitotic figures are common); and the *spiny layer* (stratum spinosum), several layers in thickness, whose cells are polygonal in shape and flattened in the outermost layers. Its cells are connected to each other by tonofibrils which pass through intercellular bridges, to give the cells a spiny appearance when cut tangentially (these are called *prickle cells*).

Dermis or Corium. The dermis is a tough, flexible, and highly elastic layer of connective tissue underlying the epidermis. It varies in thickness, being 2–4 mm. thick in the palms of the hands and soles of the feet and very thin in the eyelids, scrotum, and penis. It has an *outer papillary layer* overlying a *reticular layer*.

The outer papillary layer lies next to the epidermis, into which numerous small processes, the papillae, project. The papillae are highly vascular and contain numerous nerve endings. The layer contains collagenous and elastic fibers closely matted together.

The reticular layer consists principally of bundles of collagenous fibers which interlace, forming a felt-like network. Interspersed among the fibers are numerous elastic fibers. This layer is not sharply delimited from the papillary layer above or the subcutaneous tissue beneath.

The corium is well supplied with blood and lymphatic vessels and with nerves. Cutaneous sense organs are present in this layer. Afferent nerve fibers carry impulses from receptors located here, and efferent fibers carry impulses to blood vessels, smooth muscles, and glands. The corium is the portion of the skin of an animal which, when tanned, yields leather.

In the skin of the scrotum, the dermis contains, in addition to the foregoing structure, scattered bundles of smooth muscle fibers, which are also found in the skin of the prepuce, the perianal region, and the nipples. Contraction of these muscles produces a wrinkled appearance.

Pigmentation of the Skin. The dark color of the skin in certain major ethnic groups of mankind is due principally to a pigment, *melanin*, which is present in the cells of the epidermis. Melanin consists of very small brown or black granules in the cells of the stratum germinativum. In highly pigmented ethnic groups, however, melanin may be present in all the layers of the epidermis. As the cells approach the surface the color becomes less intense.

Absorption through the Skin. Generally speaking there is little absorption through the skin. Water and aqueous solutions of such substances as salts and sugars are not absorbed. Fatty substances such as oils and ointments may be absorbed but only to a limited extent. A few substances such as lead, mercury, and certain aniline dyes are, however, taken up readily. Infectious organisms as a rule cannot pass through the unbroken skin. Organisms such as bacteria can enter the pores (the openings of sweat glands and hair follicles), as can be seen from the large number of infections of these structures.

Derivatives of the Skin. The derivatives of the skin are the sudoriferous glands and sebaceous glands (collectively called the *cutaneous glands*), ceruminous glands, mammary glands, hair and hair follicles, and nails. All these structures are derived from the epidermis, although portions of them may lie in the dermis.

Sudoriferous Glands. These, also known as the *sweat glands,* are found over the entire body surface with the exception of the prepuce, glans penis, margin of the lips, and deeper portion of the auditory meatus. Each gland is a simple coiled, tubular structure consisting of a secretory portion and an excretory duct. Most sweat glands are *merocrine* (secretion leaves the gland cell intact), but some in the axillary region are *apocrine* (in which the secretion-filled end of a gland cell is pinched off).

The *secretory portion* is much coiled. It lies in the dermis, sometimes in the subcutaneous layer. In sections it appears as deeply staining nests of tubes, some cut transversely, diagonally, or longitudinally. The cells are epithelial cells of two types: *myoepithelial*, flattened, spindle-shaped cells with an elongated nucleus which, possibly by contraction, help to discharge the secretion; and *glandular*, cuboidal or truncated cells whose bases pass between myoepithelial cells to rest

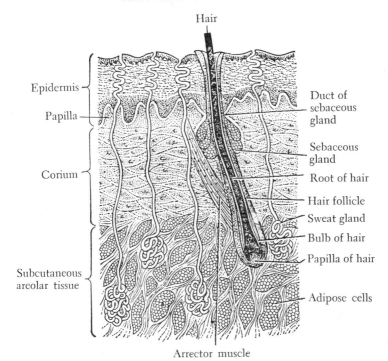

Fig. 4-3. Vertical section of skin, showing sebaceous and sweat glands. (Gerrish.) (Reprinted with permission of The Macmillan Company from Kimber et al., *A Textbook of Anatomy and Physiology*, 13th ed., 1955.)

on basement membrane. These contain fat droplets, pigment, and glycogen.

The *excretory duct* is narrow; its wall consists of two layers of cells enclosing a narrow lumen. Myoepithelial cells are lacking. In the dermis the duct is straight; in the epidermis, where the stratum corneum is thick and cells are lacking in its wall, it is spiral in form.

The *number* of sweat glands varies from 60 to 80 per sq. cm. on the back to 400 per sq. cm. on the palms of the hands. The total number in the body is estimated at about two million. The sweat glands found in the axillary regions, around mammary papillae, on the labia majora, and about the anus are unusually large and produce a much thicker secretion than do those in other regions. The average *quantity* of sweat secreted in 24 hours under average conditions is from 500 to 1,000 cc.

During strenuous exercise, as much as 1,000 or more cc. containing 8 to 10 gm. of sodium may be lost during one hour.

Sweat consists of water (99 per cent), salts, principally sodium chloride (0.2 to 0.5 per cent), and traces of urea (0.08 per cent). The amount of urea lost through sweat is approximately 1 to 2 per cent of the total urea excreted by the body.

Sweating is regulated through the action of the sympathetic nervous system. There is evidence that a sweat center is located in the hypothalamus of the brain which is affected directly by a rise in temperature of the blood and reflexly by stimulation of heat receptors in the skin. Spinal centers are also involved. "Cold sweat," which is most noticeable on the forehead, palms of the hands, and soles of the feet, may result from psychic influences such as fright, embarrassment, or nervousness. Sweating may also accompany nausea, asphyxiation, severe pain, or ingestion of highly spiced foods.

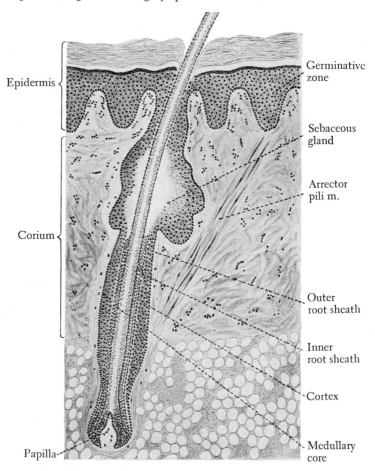

Fig. 4-4. Hair follicle. (Reprinted with permission of St. Martin's Press and The Macmillan Company, Ltd. from Hamilton, *Textbook of Human Anatomy*, 1956.)

SEBACEOUS GLANDS. These are branched alveolar glands which secrete an oil, called *sebum*. They usually open into a hair follicle, but they may open directly to the outside. These are holocrine glands; their secretion results from the disintegration of fat-infiltrated cells which occupy the alveoli of the gland.

The elongated tarsal (Meibomian) glands of the upper and lower eyelids are sebaceous glands which discharge their oily secretion through openings on the posterior edge of the eyelid. Retained secretion and swelling of the gland may result in a cyst or a tumor (chalazion).

CERUMINOUS GLANDS. These are modified sweat glands located in the external auditory meatus. Their ducts open on the surface directly or with the duct of a sebaceous gland into a hair follicle. These glands are apocrine and their secretion plus sebum and desquamated epithelial cells form *cerumen*, or ear wax.

MAMMARY GLANDS. Glands specialized for the production of milk are known as mammary glands. They play an essential role in the functions of the reproductive system.

HAIR AND HAIR FOLLICLES. A hair is an elastic, horny, thread-like structure which develops from the epidermis. It consists of a *shaft*, the part that projects from the epidermis and may extend slightly below the surface of the epidermis; and a *root*, the part that is embedded within the dermis, with its lower portion expanded to form the *hair bulb*. Within the under surface of the hair bulb is a projection of the dermis, the *papilla*. A single hair consists of three layers of cells:

Cuticle, the outermost layer, consisting of a single layer of thin nonnucleated cells; the cells overlay one another, like scales.

Cortex, the main horny portion of a hair, composed of several layers of compact cells; the color of hair is due to the presence of pigment in this layer.

Medulla, the central axis, lacking in fine hairs and consisting of two or three rows of polyhedral cells; it may not extend the entire length of the hair.

Intercellular spaces may contain air, which accounts for the gray or silvery color of hair when pigment is lost.

The *hair follicle* is the structure enclosing the hair root. It consists of an epithelial sheath and a connective tissue sheath. The former has an *inner* root sheath consisting of three layers, the cuticle (a single layer of overlapping horny scales), Huxley's layer (a double layer of flattened nucleated cells), and Henle's layer (a single layer of cuboidal cells); and an *outer* root sheath, a layer which is continuous with the stratum germinativum of the epidermis. The connective tissue sheath (outer or *dermic* coat) is that part of the dermis which encloses the epithelial portion.

The hair follicle usually occupies an oblique position in the skin. Attached to it, also obliquely, is the *arrector pili muscle*, a bundle of smooth muscle fibers, which arises in the superficial portion of the dermis. Contraction causes the hair follicle to assume a more vertical position. Impulses through the autonomic nervous system bring about contraction, as from cold or in fright. When the arrector pili muscle contracts, the epidermis is depressed and the region immediately around the hair is lifted, resulting in a wrinkled appearance, the so-called "goose flesh."

Growth and Replacement of Hair. The bulb of the hair root consists of a mass of growing and multiplying cells. As these increase in number, they move outward and become closely massed together. Chemical changes occur and the cells are transformed into the horny cells of the hair and the inner root sheath. The *dermal papilla* which projects into the bulb contains capillaries through which nourishment is received.

Hairs in each part of the body have definite periods of growth, after which they are shed and then replaced. In some animals, this is a periodic process; in man, growth and loss takes place continuously. The life duration of scalp hairs is two to five years; of eyebrows and eyelashes, three to five months. The replacing hairs of the eyebrows, eyelashes, and scalp of children are progressively larger and coarser than the preceding set. Hormones, especially the sex hormones, influence the growth of hair at puberty in the axillary and pubic regions of both sexes, and on the face and trunk of males. There is no hair on palms and soles.

Hair grows at an average rate of 1.5 to 3.0 mm. per week.

Baldness or *Alopecia.* This condition is due to hereditary factors, or to pathological conditions such as infections, or to irradiation.

Lanugo. This is the layer of fine silk-like hairs which almost completely covers the embryo. It is prominent at about the seventh month of development but is shed before or very shortly after birth.

Nails. A nail is a flat, horny, scale-like modification of the epidermis which corresponds to the hoof or claw of lower animals. It serves to protect the end of the digit. A nail consists of a *body*, the attached, uncovered portion; a *free edge*, the distal unattached portion; and a *nail root*, the portion embedded in a groove of the skin.

The skin which covers the nail root and the lateral edges of the nail is called the *nail wall*, that under the nail the *nail bed*. The *lunula* is the semicircular white portion at the base of the nail.

A nail grows in length and thickness through cellular proliferation at the proximal end of the nail bed, in the region of the root. Nails lost or torn away will regenerate if the *stratum germinativum* is not damaged.

APPEARANCE AND DISORDERS OF THE SKIN

The skin is of importance to the physician in the observation of changes in functioning of the body during health and illness. The appearance of the skin is frequently a reflection of internal disorder. Examples are:

Increased redness (*erythema*), which results from dilation of capillaries. It may indicate hyperemia, hypertension, infection, fever, allergy, or an emotional disturbance.

Pallor, which may be due to constriction of capillaries (as in cases of fright or exposure to cold) or to a reduced amount of red blood cells (as in anemia).

Cyanosis, a bluish appearance which results from incomplete oxygenation of the blood, as in pneumonia, asphyxiation, heart failure, and heart anomalies ("blue baby").

Yellowness, or a "jaundiced" appearance, which results from a liver disorder in which bile pigments are absorbed by blood and circulated throughout the body.

Increased pigmentation, as in Addison's disease.

Extreme dryness, as in vitamin deficiency or heat stroke.

Extreme moisture, a sign of hyperthyroidism.

Examples of common skin ailments are: *abscess* (collection of pus formed by localized disintegration of tissue); *acne* (caused by inflammation of the sebaceous glands, attended by pimples or small pustules, most often on the face); *boils* (localized swellings in the skin caused by infection of hair follicles); *eczema* (inflammatory disease characterized by vesiculation, watery discharge, and the development of scales or crusts); and *urticaria* (characterized by severe itching, skin patches, and rash).

5: THE SKELETAL SYSTEM

The skeletal system lends form to the body. Specifically, its functions are: (1) to provide a framework for all the body systems; (2) to provide attachments for muscles, ligaments, tendons, and fascia; (3) to enclose and protect vital organs, such as the heart, lungs, brain, and sense organs; (4) to serve as the seat of manufacture of blood cells (the "hemopoietic" function); and (5) to serve as a reserve storehouse for calcium.

The components of the skeletal system are: (1) *bones*, which comprise the hard framework of the body; (2) *cartilage*, which forms the connecting and supporting structures; and (3) *ligaments*, which bind the bones together. The microscopic structure of bone and cartilage has been discussed in chapter 3 (Tissues). Ligaments bear an intimate relationship to the functions of the skeletal system; consequently, they are discussed in this chapter.

BONES

A bone consists of organic and inorganic materials. The organic substance includes the living cells and about one-third of the interstitial substance, or *matrix*. The inorganic substance comprises the remaining two-thirds of the matrix and is made up of inorganic salts which are complex compounds of calcium and phosphorus.

If a bone is placed in weak hydrochloric acid, the mineral matter will become separated from it and the organic framework will remain. Such a decalcified bone can be easily bent or even tied into a knot. If a bone is heated, the organic matter will be destroyed and only the mineral matter or ash will remain. Such a bone is extremely brittle, but it retains its external form and, to some extent, its microscopic structure.

Classification of Bones. All bones are classified in three ways:

On the basis of shape, bones are either *long* (most of the bones of the extremities), *short* (bones of the wrist and ankle, and sesamoid bones), or *flat* (bones of the cranium, the scapula, and the ribs). Certain bones, such as the vertebrae, are classified as *irregular*.

On the basis of embryonic origin, bones are either *membranous* (developing directly from connective tissue membrane), or *cartilaginous* (developing from cartilage). In later life, *sesamoid* bones may develop in tendons or in the capsules of joints. A sesamoid bone occurs in the tendon of the short flexor muscle of the thumb as it passes over the head of the metacarpal bone; two sesamoid bones are situated in the tendon of the corresponding muscle of the big toe (the flexor hallucis brevis on the plantar surface of the head of the first metatarsal). The knee cap, or patella, is the largest sesamoid bone (situated in the tendon of the quadriceps femoris muscle).

On the basis of structure, bone tissue is either *compact* (the hard, dense, outside layer of all bones) or *spongy* (also called "cancellous," containing many small cavities which are filled with marrow and are generally enclosed by compact bone).

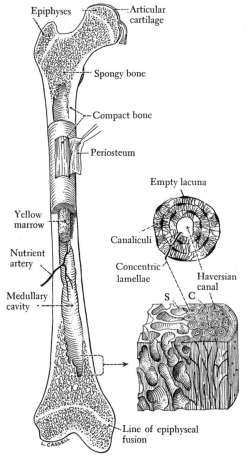

Fig. 5-1. Structure of a long bone. S, on inset, indicates spongy bone; C, compact bone. (Inset adapted from Toldt.) (Reprinted with permission of W. B. Saunders Company from Millard, King, and Showers, *Human Anatomy and Physiology,* 4th ed., 1956.)

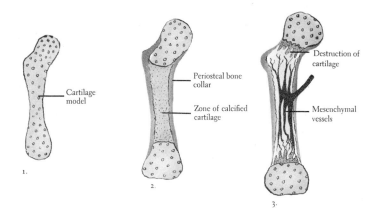

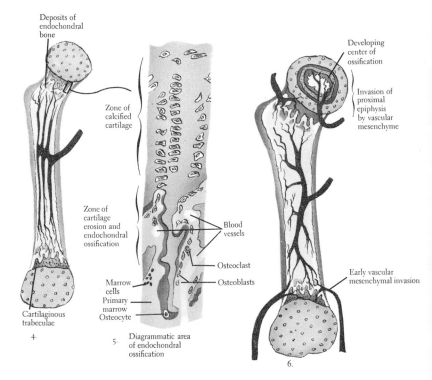

Fig. 5-2. Early stages in growth of a long bone.

Structure of a Typical Long Bone. Using the femur as an example, the following components of a long bone are found: the *diaphysis,* the shaft or main central portion (principally of compact bone); the *epiphysis,* the portion at each end (spongy bone covered with a thin layer of compact bone); the *medullary* or *marrow cavity,* containing yellow bone marrow, within the diaphysis; *periosteum,* the membrane covering the bone (fibrous connective tissue whose fibers extend into the bone as *Sharpey's fibers*); and *endosteum,* fibrous membrane lining the marrow cavity.

There are three kinds of epiphyses: *pressure* epiphyses, at the articular ends of bones; *traction* epiphyses, associated with the insertions of muscles; and *atavistic* epiphyses, which represent bones that were separate in earlier stages of evolution but have lost their function and have disappeared in man.

The periosteum contains blood, lymphatic vessels, and nerves. The blood vessels pass into the bone substance from the periosteum by way of *Volkmann's canals.*

Bone Marrow. Bone marrow is the substance occupying the medullary cavity and the spaces in cancellous bone. *Yellow bone marrow* is found in the marrow cavities of long bones. It consists principally of fat cells. In pathological conditions such as anemia, it may be replaced by red marrow. *Red bone marrow* is found in spongy bone at the ends of most long bones and in the flat bones of the cranium, sternum, ribs, and bodies of vertebrae. It consists of a *stroma* (framework) and free cells within the mesh of the stroma. Red bone marrow is concerned with the formation of blood cells; the process is described in detail in chapter 9 (The Body Fluids).

Formation of Bone (Ossification). Bone develops from the mesoderm and begins to make its appearance about the eighth week of embryonic development. There are two modes of formation: intramembranous and endochondral.

INTRAMEMBRANOUS OSSIFICATION. By this mode, bone is formed within fibrous membranes. The flat bones of the face, those of the cranium, and the scapula develop in this way. They are preceded by a membrane of mesenchymal connective tissue. Within this membrane one or more points of ossification arise, where *osteoblasts* or bone-forming cells appear and begin to deposit a *bone matrix* consisting of calcium salts (carbonates and phosphates) in the form of *spicules.* As the matrix increases in mass, strands called *trabeculae* are formed which extend radially in all directions. The osteoblasts are arranged in a single layer on the surface of the spicules and, as development proceeds, the spicules increase in width and thickness, to produce more matrix. In the process some osteoblasts become entrapped within small cavities of the matrix. Such cells are known as *osteocytes* or *bone cells.* Ultimately, they lose their capacity to form bone, but they are essential to the maintenance of bone that is already formed.

When trabeculae are first formed, they are isolated; as more matrix develops, they meet and coalesce, eventually comprising a lattice-like structure known as *cancellous bone.* Meanwhile, the mesenchymal cells on the outer surface of the membrane give rise to a fibrous membrane, the *periosteum.* At about the same time, on the inner surface the osteoblasts begin to deposit parallel plates of compact bone; this process is known as periosteal ossification. As a result of these two processes, two thin layers of compact bone (the *inner* and *outer* tables) are formed. They are separated by a layer of spongy bone called *diplöe.* In the development of bone, much bone tissue that is formed is resorbed and replaced by new bone. It is thought that resorption is accomplished by the action of large multinucleated cells called *osteoclasts* which are found in hollow cavities (Howship's lacunae) in eroded bone.

ENDOCHONDRAL OSSIFICATION. Endochondral bones are replacements of cartilage. A temporary cartilage model of the bone precedes the formation of the actual bone. In cartilage that is about to be replaced with bone, the following changes take place. Cartilage cells that have been producing cartilage matrix begin to destroy that matrix. Lacunae enlarge and cells begin to be arranged in rows. Some of the matrix begins to calcify, and the cartilage cells disintegrate and disappear. Spaces then appear which are gradually filled with *primary marrow tissue.* The perichondrium over the area becomes active. Cells proliferate and new cells invade the cartilage in bud-like masses, and the perichondrium becomes transformed into periosteum. Now blood vessels invade the honeycombed cartilage and osteoblasts deposit bone matrix until the entire cartilage is replaced with spongy bone. In the last stage of the process, bone marrow develops in the spaces of the bony tissue.

It should be noted that *cartilage is not transformed into bone.* The cartilage is first destroyed, and then bone is formed in the place that was occupied by the cartilage. For this reason, this type of bone is called *replacement* or *substitution* bone.

Growth of a Long Bone. As previously stated, the shape of the cartilage model is in general the shape of the adult long bone. There are usually several ossification centers. The first to appear is that in the diaphysis (shaft), where bone starts to form in a ring-shaped area at the center. As soon as osteoblasts appear and bone formation commences, the membrane covering the cartilage model (perichondrium) becomes the periosteum. Bone formed by this process is called *periosteal bone.* It forms a band or collar about the central region of the diaphysis, called *periosteal band* or *collar.*

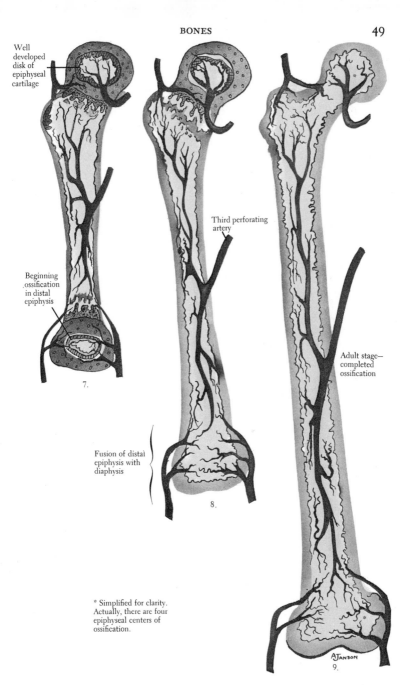

Well developed disk of epiphyseal cartilage

Beginning ossification in distal epiphysis

7.

Third perforating artery

Fusion of distal epiphysis with diaphysis

8.

Adult stage— completed ossification

* Simplified for clarity. Actually, there are four epiphyseal centers of ossification.

AJANSON
9.

Fig. 5-3. Later stages in growth of a long bone.

In the center of the diaphysis, cartilage is eroded away and the *primary marrow cavity* is formed. Bone continues to be added progressively toward each end until the entire shaft is ossified. As the diameter of the bone increases, the diameter of the marrow cavity also increases through action of osteoclasts, which destroy the bone already formed in that area. While ossification is proceeding in the diaphysis, ossification centers develop in the epiphyses. The cartilage in the region between the bone being formed in the diaphysis and the bone being formed in the epiphysis is called the *cartilage plate*. This plate remains relatively constant in thickness inasmuch as it replaces its cells as rapidly as the cartilage at its surface is replaced with bone. When proliferation of cartilage cells ceases and cartilage matrix is replaced with bone, the epiphysis unites with the diaphysis and the longitudinal growth of bone is terminated.

The factors involved in the deposition of bone matrix by osteoblasts are not thoroughly understood. One is a *humoral* factor, pertaining to the concentration of inorganic salts in the blood; the other is a *local* factor, pertaining to the deposition of bone in specific areas.

Vitamin D is essential to the formation of bone in children. In its absence osseous tissue continues to grow but does not calcify. As a result, bone fails to harden, and rickets develops.

Calcium laid down as a bone salt can be made available only by the process of *resorption*, which is regulated by the parathyroid glands. Dysfunction of these glands can bring about serious bone disorders. in hyperparathyroidism the extensive resorption of bone gives rise to osteitis fibrosa. Long-standing calcium deficiency, in which the mineral content of bone is greatly reduced, results in osteomalacia ("adult rickets"). The *hormones* of the parathyroids and of the anterior lobe of the hypophysis are considered to be the regulatory factors.

Phosphorous deficiency and improper balance between phosphorous and calcium are also known to influence the growth of bone unfavorably.

Bone as a Living, Adaptable Structure. Every organ of the body is a complex of tissues arranged in a definite pattern and having the ability to grow, develop, and repair itself. Because a bone has these properties, it must be regarded as a living structure or an *organ of the body*. The more or less definite *form* of each bone is closely correlated with the function or functions which it serves.

Although bone consists largely of inorganic matter, it is nevertheless remarkably *adaptable to environmental influences*. Disuse causes it to tend to atrophy or to lose some of its substance, and its processes become less pronounced. With increased use it tends to hypertrophy, that is, to increase in mass. For example, loss of teeth results in resorption of the bone (alveolar process) which gave them support;

habitual squatting with feet crossed produces "squatter's facets" on the external malleoli of the tibiae; the cradling practice in which the infant is made to rest its head on a hard board usually results in a flat ("Armenoid") occiput.

Descriptive Terms Applied to Bones. All bones have irregular surfaces: *elevations* or *projections* which serve for attachment of muscles, for articulation with other bones, or for protection of vital parts; *depressions*, *grooves*, or *openings* for the passage of blood vessels, nerves, tendons, and ducts of glands; or *concavities* for receiving the articulating surface of other bones. To facilitate description and recognition of these irregularities, the following terms are used:

Elevations, Projections

Condyle	a rounded process, usually smooth, for articulation
Crest	a ridge
Head	the expanded end of a bone, separated from the principal part by a constricted region, the *neck*
Process	a general term for any elevation or projection
Spine	a more or less pointed process
Trochanter	a very large process
Trochlea	a process shaped like a pulley
Tubercle	a small, rounded projection
Tuberosity	a larger, roughened projection

Depressions, Grooves, Openings, Concavities

Aditus	an entrance into a cavity
Alveolus	a deep pit, or socket
Antrum	a sinus
Facet	a small, flat surface
Fissure	a slit-like opening
Foramen	an opening through which blood vessels or other structures pass
Fossa	a depression or concavity
Hiatus	a slit or gap
Meatus	a short canal
Sinus	a cavity, or hollow, in the interior of a bone, lined with mucous membrane and filled with air
Sulcus	a groove, or narrow, elongated concavity

Other Terms

Fontanel	a membranous space between the cranial bones in fetal life and infancy
Ramus	a part of a bone that forms an angle with the body of the bone
Suture	the line of junction between two adjacent bones of the skull

DIVISIONS OF THE SKELETAL SYSTEM

The skeletal system, comprising 206 bones, has two general divisions: the *axial skeleton*, the basic framework of the body; and the *ap-*

pendicular skeleton, the extremities. The subdivisions and the number of bones in each are:

AXIAL SKELETON

Number of Bones

Skull	Cranium 8	
	Face 14	29
	Hyoid bone 1	
	Auditory ossicles..... 6	
Vertebral Column	Vertebrae 26	80
Thorax	Sternum 1	25
	Ribs 24	

APPENDICULAR SKELETON

Number of Bones

Upper Extremity	Pectoral girdle........ 4	
	Arms and hands 60	126
Lower Extremity	Pelvic girdle 2	
	Legs and feet......... 60	

THE AXIAL SKELETON

The axial skeleton includes the bones of the skull, the vertebrae, and the bones of the thorax.

The Bones of the Skull. The 29 bones of the skull comprise those in the cranium and face, the auditory ossicles, and the hyoid bone. They are tabulated here:

	Single Bones	Paired Bones
Cranium...........	Frontal Occipital Sphenoid Ethmoid	Parietal Temporal
Face	Mandible Vomer	Maxillae Zygomatic Lacrimal Nasal Inferior nasal conchae Palatine
Hyoid bone		
Auditory ossicles		Malleus Incus Stapes

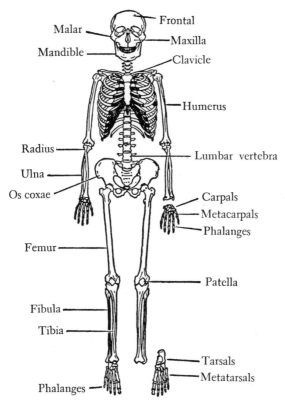

Malar
Mandible
Frontal
Maxilla
Clavicle
Humerus
Radius
Ulna
Os coxae
Lumbar vertebra
Carpals
Metacarpals
Phalanges
Femur
Patella
Fibula
Tibia
Tarsals
Metatarsals
Phalanges

Fig. 5-4. The skeleton, anterior view. (Adapted from figure copyright by General Biological Supply House, Chicago, and used with permission.)

CRANIAL BONES. The cranial bones enclose the brain cavity. Their parts and the interrelations between them follow.

Frontal Bone. Early in its formation the frontal bone develops in two halves, but by the end of the second year of life these halves are fused in 91.5 per cent of whites. This bone forms the anterior portion of the cranial vault and the major portion of the orbit. Its parts are: *glabella,* the most prominent area in the midsagittal plane, situated between the superciliary arches; *superciliary arches,* ridges superior to the orbit, beneath the eyebrows; *supraorbital foramen* (sometimes a notch rather than a foramen), which transmits the supraorbital nerve and blood vessels; and *frontal sinuses,* air cavities enclosed in bone directly over the orbit. *Articulations:* The frontal bone is joined with 12 other bones (the sphenoid, the ethmoid, and the paired parietals, nasals, maxillae, lacrimals, and zygomatics).

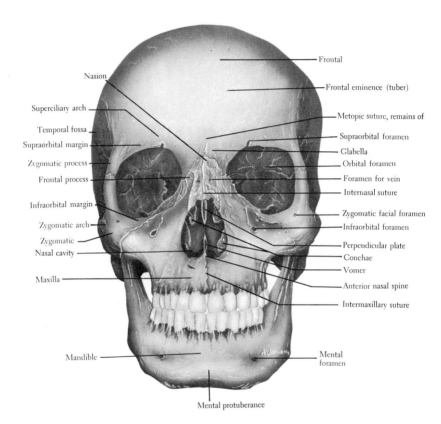

Fig. 5-5. Anterior view of skull.

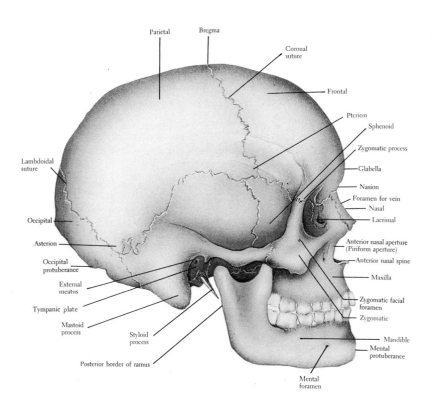

Fig. 5-6. Lateral view of skull.

Parietal Bones. These bones form the roof and part of the sides of the cranium. The *sagittal suture* lies at the junction of the two bones in the midline. The *sagittal sulcus* is a groove on the inner surface at the junction for the superior sagittal sinus. *Articulations:* Each parietal bone articulates with five other bones (the opposite parietal, the temporal on the same side, and the occipital, frontal, and sphenoid).

Temporal Bones. The temporal bones form a part of the sides and base of the skull. Each encloses an ear and bears a fossa with which the lower jaw articulates. Each of these bones has four portions: a *squamous portion,* a flat scale-like plate at the side of the skull, with a zygomatic process extending anteriorly to meet the temporal process of the zygomatic bone and a mandibular (glenoid) fossa on its inferior surface; a *mastoid portion,* lying posterior and inferior to the auditory meatus, which bears the prominent mastoid process and contains air cells that communicate with the middle ear by way of the mastoid aditus; a *tympanic portion,* a curved plate of bone surrounding the external auditory meatus, a canal leading to the middle ear; and a *petrous portion,* projecting medially to form a prominent ridge in the floor of the cranial cavity, containing the middle and inner ear and bearing a sharp, pointed, styloid process which extends downward. *Articulations:* Each temporal bone articulates with five bones (occipital, parietal, sphenoid, zygomatic, and mandible).

Occipital Bone. This bone forms the posterior and inferior portions of the cranial cavity. Its *foramen magnum,* a large opening, transmits the spinal cord. *Occipital condyles,* rounded prominences on each side of the foramen magnum, articulate with the first vertebrae (the atlas). Two prominences (the external occipital protuberance and the external occipital crest) lie in the midline on the posterior surface. Extending laterally from these are the superior and inferior nuchal lines. Two transverse grooves on the inner surface are for transmission of large blood vessels, the right and left *transverse sinuses,* their junction being called the *confluence of sinuses. Articulations:* The occipital bone articulates with six other bones (the sphenoid, the atlas, and the paired parietals and temporals).

Sphenoid Bone. The sphenoid bone (its form resembles that of a bird in flight) comprises the anterior portion of the base of the cranium. Its *body* is a cube-shaped median portion containing two *sphenoidal sinuses* separated by a septum. Lateral extensions from the body (two *great wings* and two *lesser wings*) form part of the walls and floors of the orbits. The *sella turcica* is a concavity of the superior surface of the body; it is occupied by the hypophysis. *Lateral* and *medial pterygoid* plates project inferiorly. Prominent *openings* in this bone are: foramen rotundum, foramen ovale, foramen spinosum, optic foramen, and supraorbital fissure. *Articulations:* The sphenoid bone articulates with 12 other bones (vomer, ethnoid, frontal, occipital, and the paired parietals, temporals, zygomatics, and palatines).

Ethmoid Bone. The ethmoid bone lies between the orbits at the base of the cranium. It forms the principal supporting bone of the nasal cavity. The ethmoid has four parts: (1) *cribriform plate,* a horizontal plate forming the base of the cranium and the roof of the nasal cavity, perforated by numerous openings for olfactory nerves and bearing a median projection, the *cristi galli;* (2) and (3) two *lateral masses* forming the lateral walls of the nasal cavity, each bearing two scroll-like folds, the *superior* and *middle conchae* (turbinate bones) on their median surfaces and containing the *ethmoidal air cells* or sinuses; and (4) the *perpendicular plate,* a thin quadrangular median plate which forms the upper portion of the nasal septum. *Articulations:* The ethmoid bone articulates with 11 other bones (vomer, frontal, sphenoid, and the paired lacrimals, palatines, inf. conchae, and nasals).

Other Cranial Bones. These include the small, irregular bones located in the sutures, called *wormian* or *sutural* bones. *Epipteric* bones are wormian bones found in the region of the sphenoidal fontanel, where the parietal, sphenoid, frontal, and temporal bones meet.

Bones of the Face. The parts and interrelationships of the 14 bones of the face are discussed in the following paragraphs.

Maxillae. The two maxillae constitute the upper jaw, most of the roof of the mouth and floor of the nasal cavity, part of the median surface of each orbit, and the lateral wall of the nasal cavity. The *zygomatic* and *frontal processes* articulate with these bones. On the inferior border of the maxillae is the *alveolar process,* which bears sockets holding the upper teeth. Its *horizontal (palatine) processes* form the hard palate. The *infraorbital foramen* lies beneath the orbit; the *incisive foramen* is located anteriorly between the palatine processes near the incisor teeth. The *lacrimal groove* transmits the nasolacrimal duct. The *maxillary sinus (antrum of Highmore),* an air sinus, lies in the body of a bone beneath each orbit. *Articulations:* Each maxilla articulates with nine other bones (frontal, ethmoid, nasal, zygomatic, lacrimal, inferior nasal conchae, vomer, and the opposite maxilla).

Zygomatic (Malar) Bones. These bones form the prominences of the cheeks and part of the lateral and inferior walls of the orbits. Each bears a *temporal process* which projects posteriorly and articulates with the zygomatic process of the temporal bone to form the *zygomatic arch.* The *frontal process* projects superiorly and articulates with the frontal bone. *Articulations:* Each zygomatic bone articulates with four other bones (frontal, temporal, sphenoid, and maxilla).

Lacrimal Bones. These are thin, flat bones forming part of the median wall of each orbit. Each has a *lacrimal sulcus,* a groove for the lacrimal canal. *Articulations:* Each lacrimal bone articulates with four other bones (the frontal, ethmoid, and maxilla, and inferior nasal concha).

Nasal Bones. These small, flat bones form the bridge of the nose. *Articulations:* The nasal bones articulate with four other bones (frontal, ethmoid, maxilla, and the opposite nasal bone).

Inferior Nasal Conchae. These small, curved bones extend horizontally along the lateral walls of the nasal cavity. Each is curved on itself, in the manner of a scroll, and projects medially into the nasal cavity. *Articulations:* Each inferior nasal concha articulates with four other bones (ethmoid, maxilla, lacrimal, and palatine).

Palatine Bones. These bones form part of the lateral wall and floor of the nasal cavity and part of the roof of the mouth and the floor of the orbit. Their paired *horizontal plates* unite to form the posterior portion of the hard palate. Extending upward from these plates are the *vertical plates.* A *pyramidal process* extends backward and laterally from the junction of the vertical and horizontal plates. An *orbital process,* extending upward and laterally from the vertical plate, usually contains a small sinus which communicates with the sphenoidal and ethmoidal sinuses. A *sphenoid process* extends upward and medially from the vertical plate. *Articulations:* Each palatine bone articulates with six other bones (sphenoid, ethmoid, maxilla, inferior concha, vomer, and opposite palatine).

Vomer. This thin, flat bone lies in the median plane and forms the posterior and inferior portion of the nasal septum. *Articulations:* The vomer articulates with six other bones (sphenoid, ethmoid, and the paired maxillae and palatines) as well as with the septal cartilage.

Mandible. This is a U-shaped bone comprising the lower jaw. It consists of a horizontal *body* and two upward projecting *rami.* The two halves of the body are united at the *symphysis,* the lower portion of which forms the *mental protruberance* (chin prominence). The upper portion of each half of the body forms the *alveolar process.* This process contains eight sockets (*alveoli*) in which are found the roots of the lower teeth. On the lateral surface is the *mental foramen* for transmitting the mental nerve and vessels. (Note that the halves of the mandible unite at the symphysis during the second year.)

Projecting upward from the posterior ends of the body are the two *rami.* Each ramus bears two processes: an anterior *coronoid process,* which serves for attachment of the temporal and masseter muscles; and a *condyloid process,* consisting of a *capitulum* and a *neck.* This latter process articulates with the mandibular fossa of the temporal bone. Where the posterior border of the ramus meets with the inferior border of the body, there is a prominence, the *angle of the jaw.* On the inner surface of each ramus is a *mandibular foramen,* which leads to the *mandibular canal.* These foramina transmit the inferior alveolar vessels and nerve. *Articulations:* The mandible articulates with the two temporal bones.

HYOID BONE. This horseshoe-shaped bone lies in the neck, suspended from the tips of the styloid processes of the temporal bone by two *stylohyoid ligaments*. It has a *body;* two horn-like processes (the *greater cornua*) projecting posteriorly from the lateral surface of the body; and two *lesser cornua* (small, conical eminences projecting upward at the junction of the body and the greater cornua). The hyoid bone has no articulations.

AUDITORY OSSICLES. In the tympanic cavity on each side of the skull lie the three ear bones, or auditory ossicles. They comprise a part of the middle ear.

Malleus. The hammer, or malleus, laterally situated, is attached to the tympanic membrane. It possesses a *head,* with a facet for the incus; a *neck;* and three *processes* (the manubrium and the anterior and lateral processes). The manubrium is attached by its lateral margin to the tympanic membrane.

Incus. The anvil, or incus, located between the malleus and the stapes, has a *body,* with a facet for the malleus; a *short crus;* and a *long crus* with a small *lenticular process.* The incus articulates with the malleus and stapes.

Stapes. The stirrup, or stapes, lies between the incus and the *fenestra vestibuli,* an opening to the inner ear. It has a *head,* with a concavity for the incus; a *neck;* two *crura;* and a *base,* which is fixed to the margin of the fenestra vestibuli. (The fenestra vestibuli is also known as the *fenestra ovalis.*)

SPECIAL FEATURES OF THE SKULL. Certain characteristics of the bone structure of the skull are not encountered elsewhere in the skeleton, and consequently merit special explanation. These are: sutures, fontanels, air sinuses and mastoid cells, and cavities of the skull.

Sutures. The principal cranial sutures are: the *sagittal,* between the parietal bones; the *coronal,* between the *parietal* and *frontal* bones; the *lambdoidal,* between the parietal and occipital bones; the *squamosal,* between the parietal and the temporal; and the *metopic* or *interfrontal,* between the halves of the frontal bone before fusion.

After adolescence, bones begin to unite across the sutures, which gradually become obliterated, the inner surfaces or tables usually fusing earlier than the other surfaces. The degree of obliteration of the sutures plus wear evidenced by the teeth very roughly give an indication of the age of the skull. The sagittal suture begins to close at the age of 22 and is usually well advanced by age 35; the coronal suture begins to close at age 24 and is almost entirely closed by the age of 38, although complete fusion may be delayed for several years. Other sutures begin to close between the ages of 26 and 37 but some of

TIME OF CLOSURE OF EXTERNAL
CRANIAL SUTURES IN MALES

Suture	Commencement and Course (Age in Yrs.)		Termination or Peak
Sagittal	22		35
Sphenofrontal, lesser	22	Slow to 26	64
Sphenofrontal, greater	22		65
Coronal 1 and 2	24		38
Coronal 3	26		41
Lambdoidal 1 and 2	26	Rapid to about 30	42
Lambdoidal 3	26		47
Masto-occipital 3	26		72
Sphenoparietal	29		65
Sphenotemporal 2	30	Slow, at once	67
Sphenotemporal 1	31		67
Masto-occipital	30		81
Parietomastoid 1 and 2	37	Almost inactive until 62	81
Squamous posterior	37		81
Squamous anterior	37		81

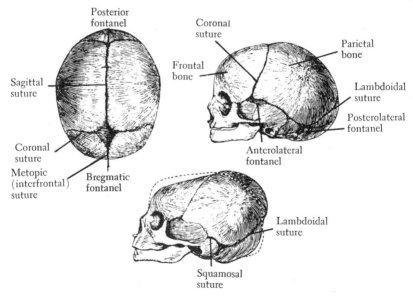

Fig. 5-7. Three views of skull of newborn infant, showing sutures and fontanelles. In lower drawing, the molded head is shown; dotted lines indicate alteration that takes place during birth. (From *Atlas of Human Anatomy*, Barnes & Noble, Inc., 1956.)

these sutures may not become completely obliterated until late in life.

One suture, the metopic (or interfrontal), closes early in life, commencing during the second half of the first year and being completed by the end of the second year. However, its obliteration, as with all other sutures, is variable and in unusual cases may not occur at all. This suture remains unclosed in 8.5 per cent of white adults; in a radiographic view, it has occasionally been mistaken for a fracture.

Fontanels. These are membrane-covered spaces, in the infant, between the parietals and bones adjacent to them. All but one are at the junctions of sutures. The fontanels represent the areas at the angles of the cranial bones, which are last to undergo ossification; the membranes in these areas remain unossified until after birth. They constitute the "soft spots" (of which the *bregmatic fontanel* is the most prominent) in the head of the infant. The names, location, and times of closure of the fontanels are noted in the accompanying table.

LOCATIONS AND TIMES OF CLOSURE OF FONTANELS

Fontanel	*Juncture (Sutures)*	*Time of Closure*
Bregmatic (Anterior)	Coronal and sagittal	During 2nd year
Posterior	Lambdoidal and sagittal	About 2 months after birth
Anterolateral	Coronal and squamosal	About 3 months after birth
Posterolateral	Lambdoidal and squamosal	About end of 1st year
Sagittal	Between sites of parietal foramina	Often at birth, but usually before 4th month after birth

Air Sinuses. The air sinuses are cavities in certain of the skull bones. Those lying adjacent to and communicating with the nasal cavities are the *paranasal sinuses.* The small, irregular spaces in the mastoid processes of the temporal bones are *mastoid air cells.* These communicate with each other and with the middle ear through the *tympanic antrum.* Not infrequently the mastoid air cells invade adjacent bones.

The paranasal sinuses comprise: the *frontal sinus* (usually paired), lying superior to the orbit; the *maxillary sinus* or *antrum of Highmore*, lying inferior to the orbit and lateral to the nasal cavity; *ethmoid air cells* (3 to 18 in number), lateral to the nasal cavity, honeycombing the lateral masses of the ethmoid bone, and sometimes extending into the nasal conchae or adjacent skull bones; and the *sphenoid sinus*, lying superior and posterior to the nasal cavity. These sinuses are lined with a ciliated mucous membrane which is continuous with that of the nasal cavity. The lining, made up of pseudostratified epithelium, is thinner and has fewer glands and goblet cells than the nasal epithelium. The lamina propria is thin and continuous with the periosteum of the bones. Drainage is into the nasal cavity; the ducts open into the meatuses between the conchae. The ducts draining the maxillary and sphenoidal sinuses are disadvantageously placed for efficient drainage because their nasal openings lie above the floor of the sinus drained.

The paranasal sinuses lighten the skull, play a secondary role as resonating chambers in voice production, and, through their mucous secretions, aid in moistening the nasal cavity.

Cavities of the Skull. These cavities are the *orbits*, the *nasal cavity*, the *oral cavity*, and the *cranial cavity*.

The *orbits* contain the eyes and associated structures. Each is formed by parts of the frontal, zygomatic, ethmoid, sphenoid, lacrimal, and palatine bones, and the maxillae, and communicate posteriorly with the cranial cavity by means of the supraorbital fissure and the optic foramen. Anteriorly, each communicates with the nasal cavity through the nasolacrimal canal, laterally and inferiorly with the infra-temporal and pterygo-palatine fossae by the inferior orbital fissure.

The *nasal cavity* consists of two *nasal fossae* (separated by the *nasal septum*) which communicate anteriorly with the outside through the *anterior nares* and posteriorly with the nasopharynx through the *posterior nares*, or *choanae*. The bones enclosing and forming the supporting structures for the nasal cavity are: ethmoid, palatine, vomer, sphenoid, and maxillae.

The *oral cavity* is enclosed by the teeth-bearing mandible and maxillae and by the palatine and sphenoid bones.

The *cranial cavity* contains the brain. The bones that enclose it, comprising the *cranium*, have been described earlier in this chapter.

The Vertebral Column. The vertebral column serves as the main axis of the body, providing general rigidity yet permitting flexibility of movement. It is an enclosing protective case for the spinal cord and the roots of the spinal nerves. It provides surfaces for articulation of the skull, ribs, and pelvic girdle, and for the attachment of muscles and ligaments. The outline of the vertebral column, as seen from the side, shows four *curves*: the cervical, thoracic, lumbar, and sacral. The thoracic and sacral curves are *primary* (present at birth); the cervical and lumbar are *secondary* (developing after birth). The 26 bones of the vertebral column comprise 24 individual vertebrae (7 cervical, 12 thoracic, 5 lumbar), the sacrum (5 fused vertebrae), and the coccyx (3 to 5 rudimentary vertebrae). Although the vertebrae in different regions of the column vary in size and in details of structure, they exhibit a marked uniformity in their fundamental plan of structure. The 6th thoracic vertebra, for example, has the following parts:

Body—a solid, cylindrical part forming the major portion of the vertebra.

Vertebral or *neural arch*—the remaining portion, which, with the

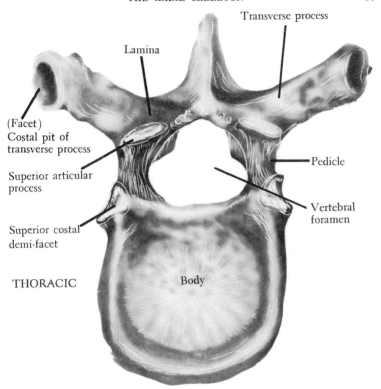

Transverse process

Lamina

(Facet)
Costal pit of
transverse process

Superior articular
process

Superior costal
demi-facet

THORACIC

Pedicle

Vertebral
foramen

Body

Fig. 5-8. A typical vertebra (T6).

body, encloses the vertebral foramen, an opening in which lies the
spinal cord. The neural arch has 2 *pedicles*, which form the sides of
the arch; 2 *lamina*, which form the roof; and 7 processes (2 inferior
articular, 2 superior articular, 2 transverse, and 1 spinous). A pronounced notch on the posterior surface of each pedicle is called the
intervertebral notch. When vertebrae are in normal position, this
notch forms a foramen through which a spinal nerve makes its exit
from the spinal cord.

Between the bodies of successive vertebrae are *invertebral discs*,
flexible elastic connections each consisting of a disc of fibrous cartilage
enclosing a central mass, the *nucleus pulposus*. Strong ligaments (supraspinous, interspinous, and ligamenta flava) hold the vertebrae in
position yet permit a limited degree of movement.

CERVICAL VERTEBRAE. Lying in the neck region, the cervical vertebrae include the atlas, the axis, and five additional vertebrae. For convenience of reference, they are numbered C1 through C7. These ver-

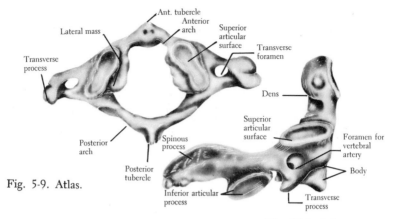

Fig. 5-9. Atlas.

Fig. 5-10. Axis

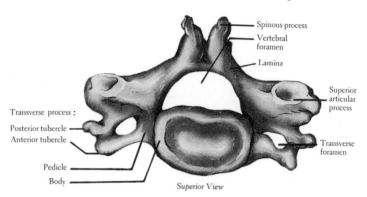

Superior View

Fig. 5-11. C3.

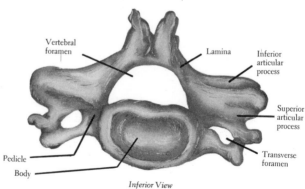

Inferior View

Fig. 5-12. C4.

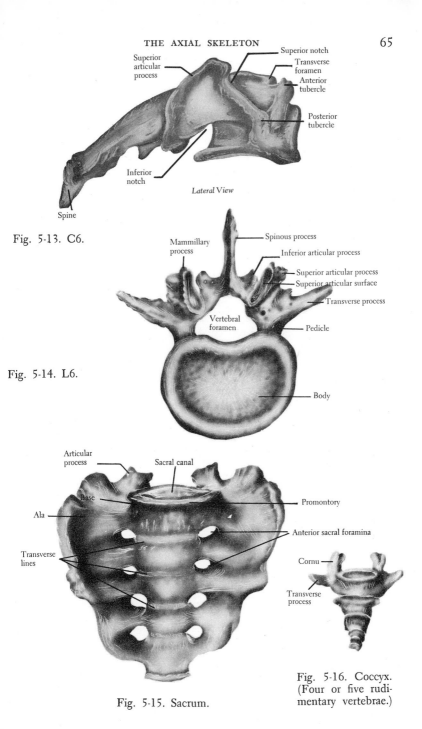

Superior articular process

Superior notch

Transverse foramen

Anterior tubercle

Posterior tubercle

Inferior notch

Lateral View

Spine

Fig. 5-13. C6.

Mammillary process

Spinous process

Inferior articular process

Superior articular process

Superior articular surface

Transverse process

Vertebral foramen

Pedicle

Fig. 5-14. L6.

Body

Articular process

Sacral canal

Base

Ala

Promontory

Anterior sacral foramina

Transverse lines

Cornu

Transverse process

Fig. 5-15. Sacrum.

Fig. 5-16. Coccyx. (Four or five rudimentary vertebrae.)

tebrae have relatively small bodies and large vertebral foramina. Each of their transverse processes possesses an opening, the *foramen transversarium*, which transmits the vertebral artery. A spine is lacking on C1 (atlas); on C2 through C6 the spines are rather blunt and compressed and their free ends are bifid (forked). On C7 the spine is long and thickened at its free end, producing a prominence at the base of the neck.

The *atlas* (C1) is highly modified in that a body and a spinous process are lacking. It is made up of two *lateral masses* and two *arches* (anterior and posterior); each arch bears a *median tubercle*. On the upper surface are two *superior articular surfaces,* cup-shaped concavities which receive the occipital condyles of the skull; they permit nodding movements of the head. Posterior to each process is a groove for the vertebral artery. On the lower surface are two *inferior articular surfaces;* these are flattened and permit turning movements on the axis. The *transverse atlantal ligament* extends across the vertebral foramen, dividing it into two parts, the anterior of which encloses the *dens*.

The *axis* or *epistropheus* (C2) bears the dens on its upper surface. The dens, a prominent elongated odontoid process, forms a pivot for rotation of the atlas and skull, which it supports.

THORACIC VERTEBRAE. Lying in the chest region are the 12 thoracic vertebrae (T1 through T12). Each of their transverse processes bears on its extremity a *facet* for articulation with the tubercle of a rib. On each side of the body are two *demifacets* for articulation with the head of a rib. A *spinous process* is well developed and directed downward. The *vertebral foramen* is generally circular in shape. Articular processes usually lie horizontal to the long axis of the body (the superior ones face upward, the inferior downward).

LUMBAR VERTEBRAE. The five lumbar vertebrae (L1 through L5) lie in the region of the loin. Their *bodies* are large and heavy, their *spines* short and blunt. *Articular processes* are in general vertical to the body (superior ones face inward, inferior outward). Thick, broad spinous processes project horizontally dorsad.

SACRUM. This bone is composed of five sacral vertebrae which fuse and become united into a single bone. The sacrum is curved and wedge-shaped with its *base* directed upward and its *apex* downward. The parts of the sacrum are: two *alae* (wings), processes lying lateral to the *promontory*, a prominence on the superior anterior portion of the body; and two *articular surfaces* for the ilia of the pelvic girdle and two for the 5th lumbar vertebra. A *sacral canal*, a continuation of the vertebral canal, contains sacral nerves (instead of the spinal cord) which make their exit through four pairs of *sacral foramina*.

COCCYX. The coccyx is formed by the fusion of four (sometimes three or five) rudimentary coccygeal vertebrae. The first piece is much

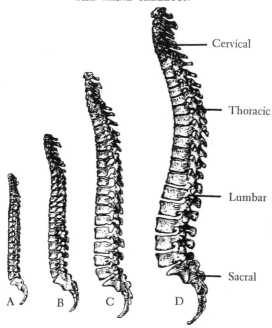

Cervical

Thoracic

Lumbar

Sacral

A B C D

Fig. 5-17. Vertebral column of (A) new-born child; (B) three-year-old child; (C) ten-year-old child; (D) adult. (From *Atlas of Human Anatomy*, Barnes & Noble, Inc., 1956.)

broader than the others; it bears two *cornua*, which articulate with the sacrum, and rudimentary *transverse processes*. All the usual parts of a vertebra, excepting the body, are lacking.

The Skeleton of the Thorax. The thoracic vertebrae, already described under the vertebral column, along with the sternum and the ribs, comprise the skeleton of the thorax.

STERNUM. This is the breastbone. Its most superior portion is called the *manubrium*, with the following articular surfaces: a *clavicular notch*, a *1st costal notch*, and the superior half of the *2nd costal notch*. The middle portion, the *body* (or *gladiolus*) bears costal notches (2nd through 7th). The *xiphoid* (*ensiform*) *process* (the inferior portion of the sternum) is usually cartilaginous, though sometimes it is ossified.

RIBS. There are twelve pairs of ribs. All of them articulate posteriorly with the vertebrae. Their anterior attachment, however, varies. The *true* or *vertebrosternal ribs* (the seven superior pairs) have their anterior ends attached directly to the sternum by *costal cartilages*. The *false* ribs are not attached directly to the sternum. They include the *vertebrochondral ribs* (8th, 9th, and 10th pairs), which have their anterior ends attached by costal cartilages to the cartilage above them,

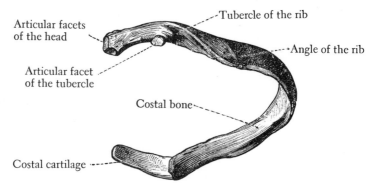

Fig. 5-18. A typical (4th right) rib. (Reprinted with permission of The Mac
millan Company from Toldt, *Atlas of Human Anatomy*, 1948.)

while the anterior ends of the *floating ribs* (11th and 12th pairs) are
free.

The 4th and 5th ribs will serve to illustrate the *parts* of a rib. Each
possesses a *head*, an expanded posterior end which, through its two
facets, articulates with the bodies of two thoracic vertebrae; a *neck*, a
slightly constricted region; and a *shaft*, the remainder of the rib. At
the juncture of the shaft with the neck there is a *tubercle*, which has
a facet for articulation with the end of the transverse process of a
vertebra. The *angle* of a rib is a moderately sharp bend near the pos
terior end. The sternal end of a rib has an oval recess into which the
costal cartilage fits. The *costal groove* is on the inferior border.

Some ribs have *atypical features*: The *1st rib* is very short and broad
and markedly curved, with a prominent tubercle. It has two grooves
on its superior surface for the subclavian artery and vein and the 1st
thoracic nerve, and a scalene tubercle between the grooves. It lacks
an angle and a costal groove. The *2nd rib* has a pronounced eminence
on its posterior surface. The *floating ribs* lack a neck, a tubercle, an
angle, and a costal groove.

THE APPENDICULAR SKELETON

The appendicular skeleton includes the bones of the upper and
lower extremities. The upper extremities are comprised of the bones
of the pectoral (shoulder) girdle, the arms, the forearms, and the
hands. The lower extremities are comprised of the bones of the pelvic
girdle, the thighs, the knees, the legs, and the feet.

The Upper Extremity. The upper extremities have 64 bones. They
are described, along with their parts, in the succeeding paragraphs.

Pectoral (Shoulder) Girdle. The two scapulae and two clavicles
make up the shoulder girdle.

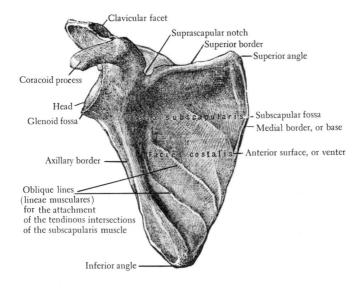

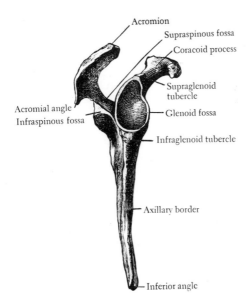

Fig. 5-19. Two views of right scapula. (Reprinted with permission of The Macmillan Company from Toldt, *Atlas of Human Anatomy,* 1948.)

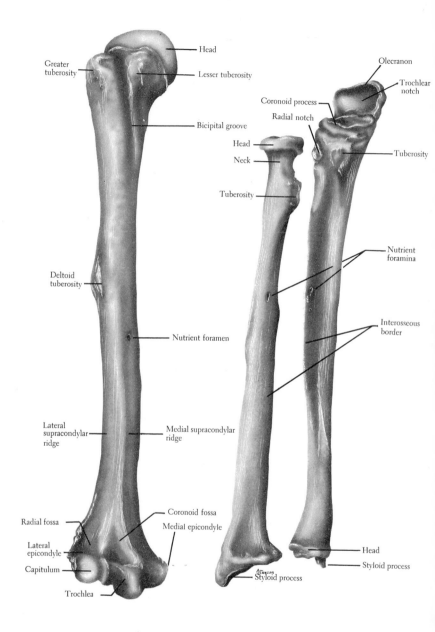

Fig. 5-20. Humerus, radius, and ulna.

Scapula. The *shoulder blade,* or scapula, has medial, lateral, and inferior *angles;* superior, vertebral, and axillary *borders;* and costal and posterior *surfaces.* On its posterior surface there is a *spine,* whose free distal end is the *acromium,* which forms the prominence of the shoulder. There are two *fossae,* a supraspinous and infraspinous, and a *glenoid cavity* (an oval depression at the lateral angle for articulation with the head of the humerus); on the superior border of the glenoid cavity is the *supraglenoid tubercle.* A *coracoid process* extends in a curve anteriorly and superiorly to the glenoid fossa; on its superior border is the *scapular notch.*

Clavicle. The *collar bone,* or clavicle, is a somewhat S-shaped bone that connects with the scapula and the sternum. Its medial or sternal end articulates with the sternum, the lateral or acromial end with the scapula. On the inferior surface near the acromial end there is a roughened elevation, the *coracoid tuberosity,* which bears a *conoid tubercle;* on its inferior surface is a *subclavian groove.*

ARM (BRACHIUM). The *humerus,* sometimes referred to as the bone of the "upper arm," extends from the shoulder to the elbow and consists of a shaft and two extremities. The *shaft* has a *deltoid tuberosity,* an *intertubercular* or *bicipital groove,* and a groove for the radial nerve. The upper extremity of the humerus has a *head,* which articulates with the glenoid cavity; an *anatomical neck,* a shallow constriction; *greater* and *lesser tubercles,* separated by the aforementioned bicipital groove; and a *surgical neck,* a region immediately distal to the tubercles, which is especially susceptible to fracture. The lower extremity of the humerus has a *trochlea,* an articular surface to join with the semilunar notch of the ulna; a *capitulum,* an articular surface for the head of the radius; a *coronoid fossa* to receive the coronoid process of the ulna; *median* and *lateral epicondyles,* prominences on the medial and lateral surfaces which serve for attachment of muscles; and an *olecranon fossa,* a cavity on the posterior surface which receives the olecranon process of the ulna.

FOREARM (ANTEBRACHIUM). The *ulna* and the *radius* are the bones of the forearm.

Ulna. The ulna is slightly longer than and lies medial to the radius. At its proximal end is the *semilunar notch,* which articulates with the trochlea of the humerus. Its *coronoid process* forms the anterior part of the semilunar notch; its *olecranon process* forms the posterior portion (the tip of the elbow). At the base of the coronoid process is the *radial notch,* which accommodates the head of the radius. The *interosseous crest,* on the anterolateral surface, is sharp and prominent. The *head* of the ulna is a small, rounded process at the distal end. It bears two articular surfaces, one for the radius, the other for the wrist bones. The *styloid process* is a small projection on the median dorsal portion of the head. Note that the ulna does not articulate with any of the carpal bones.

Radius. The radius lies lateral to the ulna. It consists of a *shaft* and *two extremities.* The *head,* the enlarged disc-like end of the proximal extremity, has a depression for articulation with the capitulum of the humerus. Its rim, the *articular circumference,* articulates with the radial notch of the ulna. The *neck* is a constricted region distal to the head. A *radial* (or *bicipital*) *tuberosity* provides for the insertion of the biceps muscle. There are two ridges, the *anterior* and *posterior oblique lines* on corresponding surfaces. The *distal extremity* bears a concave articular surface with two facets: a *medial lunate facet* and a *lateral navicular facet.* The *styloid process* is a blunt process on the lateral surface. The *ulnar notch* offers an articulating surface for the head.

HAND. The bones of the hand comprise the *carpals* (wrist), *meta carpals* (palm of the hand), and *phalanges* (digits or fingers).

Carpals. The wrist, or carpus, consists of eight small bones arranged in two rows. The bones are named here in order, from the lateral (radial) side toward the medial (ulnar) side:

Proximal Row	Scaphoid ⎫ Lunate ⎬ articulate with radius Triquetral ⎭ Pisiform (smallest carpal bone)
Distal Row	Trapezium (articulates with metacarpal on thumb side) Trapezoid Capitate (largest carpal bone) Hamate (bears the *hamulus,* a hook-like process projecting toward the volar surface)

Metacarpals. The bones of the palm are numbered I to V, beginning with the thumb side. Each consists of a base (or proximal extremity), a shaft, and a head (or distal extremity). The *base* of each is irregular in shape; it articulates with the carpal bones. The *shaft* has three surfaces: lateral, medial, and dorsal. The *head* is rounded and articulates with the first phalanx of the corresponding digit.

Phalanges. Each of the three bones in a finger (two in the thumb) is called a *phalanx.* It is therefore customary when speaking of the digits (either fingers or toes) to use the term "phalanges" collectively for a digit. In each digit the proximal phalanx is designated the "first phalanx"; the middle phalanx is the "second"; the distal is the "third" or "terminal." Each phalanx consists of a base, a shaft, and a trochlea. The *bases* of the proximal phalanges are concave, to receive the heads of metacarpals; the bases of the other phalanges bear two lateral concavities separated by a ridge. The distal end of each terminal phalanx is flattened and slightly expanded to form the *ungual tuberosity;* that

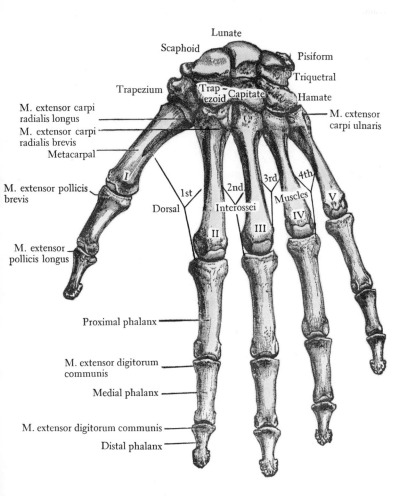

Fig. 5-21. Left hand, dorsal surface. (Reprinted with permission of Blakiston Division, McGraw-Hill Book Company, from *Morris' Human Anatomy*, 11th ed., edited by J. P. Schaeffer, 1953.)

of the other phalanges forms a pulley-like surface called the *trochlea.*

Sesamoid Bones. Embedded in the tendons of the flexor muscles of the hand are several small bones, varying in number. They occur most commonly over the metacarpophalangeal joint of the thumb and the second and fifth digits. (These bones, called sesamoid because of their resemblance to sesame seeds, occur in various tendons that are subject to great pressure.)

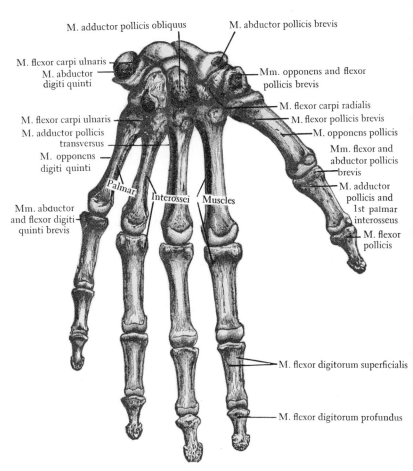

M. adductor pollicis obliquus

M. abductor pollicis brevis

M. flexor carpi ulnaris
M. abductor
digiti quinti

Mm. opponens and flexor
pollicis brevis

M. flexor carpi radialis

M. flexor carpi ulnaris
M. adductor pollicis
transversus
M. opponens
digiti quinti

M. flexor pollicis brevis

M. opponens pollicis

Mm. flexor and
abductor pollicis
brevis

M. adductor
pollicis and
1st palmar
interosseus

M. flexor
pollicis

Palmar Interossei Muscles

Mm. abductor
and flexor digiti
quinti brevis

M. flexor digitorum superficialis

M. flexor digitorum profundus

Fig. 5-22. Left hand, palmar surface. (Reprinted with permission of Blakiston Division, McGraw-Hill Book Company, from *Morris Human Anatomy*, 11th ed., edited by J. P. Schaeffer, 1953.)

Lower Extremity. The lower extremity has 62 bones. They are described, along with their parts, in the succeeding paragraphs.

THE PELVIC GIRDLE. The *hip bone* (*os coxae* or *innominate bone*) is in reality three bones (ilium, ischium, and pubis), which in childhood are distinct but in the adult are fused into a single bone. The three bones unite at a socket-like depression, the *acetabulum*, located on the lateral surface. The acetabulum receives the head of the femur.

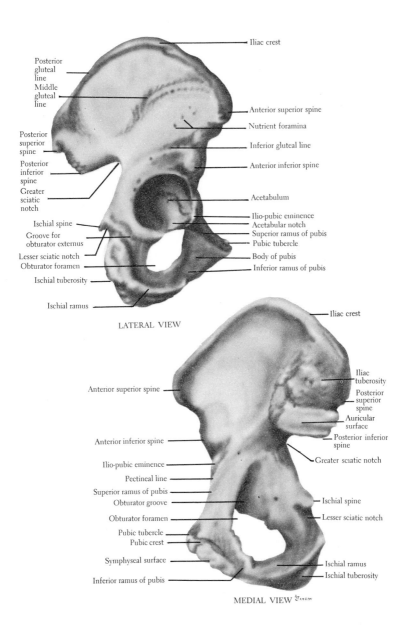

Fig. 5-23. Right innominate bone (Os coxae).

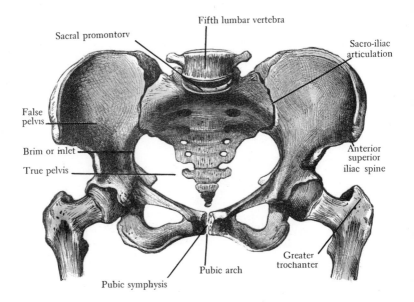

Fifth lumbar vertebra

Sacral promontory

Sacro-iliac articulation

False pelvis

Brim or inlet

True pelvis

Anterior superior iliac spine

Greater trochanter

Pubic arch

Pubic symphysis

Fig. 5-24. The female pelvis. (Reprinted with permission of The Macmillan Company from Toldt, *Atlas of Human Anatomy*, Vol. I.)

The two hip bones form the pelvic girdle: anteriorly, they unite at the *pubic symphysis*; posteriorly, they articulate with the *sacrum*. They form the anterior and lateral walls of the pelvis. A large aperture, the *obturator foramen*, lies between the pubis and ischium.

Ilium. This is the largest of the three bones forming the hip. Each ilium consists of a lower portion or *body*, which occupies about two-fifths of the acetabulum, and a flattened expanded upper portion, the *ala*, whose superior border, the *crest*, forms the prominence of the hip. On the inner surface, the *arcuate line* separates these two divisions. Conspicuous processes are the *anterior* and *posterior superior iliac spines*, which mark the ends of the crest; the *anterior* and *posterior inferior spines*, which lie below the preceding. A deep *greater sciatic notch* transmits the sciatic nerve. On the lateral surface of the ala are the *anterior, posterior,* and *inferior gluteal lines*; on the medial surface are the *iliac fossa* (a shallow concavity), the *arcuate line* (a diagonal prominence), an *articular surface* for articulation with the sacrum, and, above it, the *iliac tuberosity* for attachment of the sacroiliac ligaments.

Ischium. This bone forms the posterior and inferior portion of the innominate bone. It consists of a body and one ramus. The *body* (or main portion) includes about two-fifths of the acetabulum. The inferior portion that extends downward and backward from the aceta-

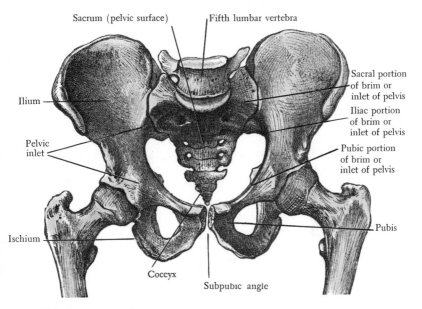

Sacrum (pelvic surface)

Fifth lumbar vertebra

Ilium

Pelvic inlet

Ischium

Coccyx

Subpubic angle

Sacral portion of brim or inlet of pelvis

Iliac portion of brim or inlet of pelvis

Pubic portion of brim or inlet of pelvis

Pubis

Fig. 5-25. The male pelvis. (Reprinted with permission of The Macmillan Company from Toldt, *Atlas of Human Anatomy*, 1948.)

bulum terminates in a large process, the *tuberosity* of the ischium; the *ramus* extends anteriorly from the tuberosity and unites with the inferior ramus of the pubis. The ischium bears a sharp inward projecting *ischial spine*, beneath which is located the *lesser sciatic notch*.

Pubis. The pubic bone forms the anterior portion of the hip bone. It consists of a body and two rami. The *body* forms about one-fifth of the acetabulum. Extending inferiorly and medially from the body is the *superior ramus*, which joins its fellow in the midline to form the *pubic symphysis*. The upper border of the superior ramus forms a ridge which continues on the ilium as the *iliopectineal eminence;* at its anterior end lies the *pubic tubercle*. The *inferior ramus* passes downward and laterally and joins with the inferior ramus of the ischium below the obturator foramen.

The Pelvis. The pelvis is the basin-like ring of bones consisting of the two innominate bones, the sacrum, and the coccyx, and the ligaments which bind these bones together. The cavity within these bones is divided into the greater and lesser pelvic cavities.

The *greater* or *false pelvis* is the expanded portion lying superior to the brim of the true pelvis. It is bounded laterally by the ilia, posteriorly by the lumbar vertebrae, and anteriorly by the muscular wall of the abdomen. The *lesser* or *true pelvis* is the part of the pelvic cavity lying below the margin formed by the sacral promontory and the ileopectineal lines which mark the brim of the pelvis. The opening within the brim is the *inlet* or *superior aperture*. The *outlet*, at the lower limits of the pelvic cavity, is marked by the tip of the coccyx and the spines and tuberosities of the ischia.

The following are noteworthy differences between the pelvis of the male and that of the female:

Feature	In the Male	In the Female
General Feature	Narrow, heavy, compact	Broad, light, capacious
Shape of Inlet	Heart-shaped	Round or oval
Angle of Pubic Arch	Acute, narrow	Obtuse, broader
Ilia	Directed less vertically	More vertical
Iliac Fossa	Deeper	More shallow
Acetabulum	Directed laterally	Directed slightly anteriorly
Ischial Spine	Sharper, directed medially	Blunter, directed more posteriorly
Sacrum	Narrower, longer, set lower between ilia	Broader, shorter, set higher between ilia
Sacral Curve	Pronounced	Less pronounced
Coccyx	Directed anteriorly	Directed inferiorly
Adaptation	For strength, speed	For child-bearing

THE THIGH. The *femur* (thigh bone) consists of a head, neck, shaft, and two extremities.

The *upper or proximal extremity* of the femur comprises the following parts: *head*, the smooth, rounded articulating portion that fits into the acetabulum and has a small pit, the fovea, to which the *round ligament* (*ligamentum teres*) is attached; *neck*, the constricted region; *greater trochanter*, a large process extending laterally; *trochanteric fossa*, a depression of the medial surface of the great trochanter; *lesser trochanter*, situated inferior, posterior, and medial to the greater trochanter; *intertrochanteric crest*, a ridge between the trochanters, on the anterior surface.

On the *shaft* are: *linea aspera*, a pronounced ridge on the posterior surface; and *gluteal tuberosity*, located near the base of the greater trochanter.

At the *lower extremity* or *distal extremity* of the femur are: *lateral* and *medial condyles*, large, rounded processes for articulation with tibia; *lateral* and *medial* epicondyles, slight elevations lying superior to the condyles, the medial one bearing the *adductor tubercle*; *intercondylar fossa*, a deep notch separating the condyles on the posterior surface; and *patellar facet*, the smooth surface between the condyles on the anterior surface, for articulation with the patella.

THE PATELLA. The patella, or kneecap, which is the largest sesamoid bone in the body, develops on the anterior surface of the knee in the

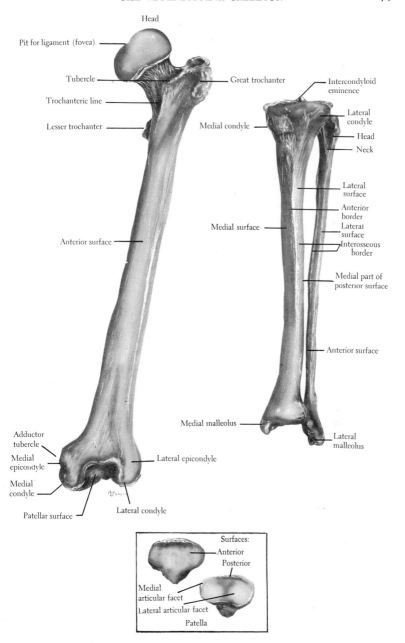

Fig. 5-26. Femur, tibia, and fibula.

extensor tendon of the quadriceps muscle. It is triangular, with its base directed upward and its apex inferiorly. Its anterior surface is rounded and rough; its posterior surface is smooth, bearing *medial* and *lateral articular facets*.

THE LEG. The tibia and the fibula are the bones of the leg.

Tibia. The tibia, or shin bone, consists of a shaft and two extremities. At its proximal extremity are: *two condyles* (lateral and medial), each bearing articular surfaces for the femur; an *intercondyloid eminence*, a prominence between the condyles; a *tuberosity*, a prominent roughened area on the anterior surface inferior to the condyles; and a *fibular facet* (on the lateral condyle) for articulation of the fibula. The *shaft* has an *anterior crest*, the prominent ridge (or shin); a *lateral border*, bearing a thin interosseous crest; a *medial border*, a broad, rounded surface; and a *popliteal line*, a ridge on the upper posterior surface. The *distal extremity* bears a *medial malleolus*, a process that forms the inner prominence of the ankle; a *fibular notch*, an articular surface for reception of the distal end of the fibula; and an *inferior articular surface* for articulation with the talus at the ankle joint.

Fibula. The fibula lies parallel to the tibia on the lateral side. It consists of a shaft and two extremities. At the *proximal extremity* is the *head*, which articulates with the lateral aspect of the lateral condyles of the tibia. The *shaft* bears no distinct processes. Its anteromedial border, or *interosseous crest*, serves for attachment of the interosseous membrane. At the *lower extremity* is the *lateral malleolus*, a substantial process forming the outer prominence of the ankle. Its inner surface articulates with the fibular notch of the tibia and with the lateral surface of the talus.

Note that the ankle is the joint between the leg and the foot. The ankle bone is the talus.

THE FOOT. The bones of the foot are the tarsals, metatarsals, and phalanges of the toes.

Tarsus. The tarsus, or instep, comprises seven bones: calcaneus, talus, navicular bone, cuboid bone, and the medial, intermediate, and lateral cuneiform bones. The *calcaneus*, the largest and most posterior tarsal bone, forms the prominence of the heel. It articulates with the talus and navicular bones. The *talus* has a smooth, rounded superior surface, for articulation with the tibia; its lateral surfaces articulate with the lateral and medial malleoli of the fibula and tibia; inferiorly it articulates with the calcaneus and the navicular bone. The *navicular bone* is a slightly curved bone on the medial side of the foot, which articulates posteriorly with the talus, anteriorly with the three cuneiform bones, and sometimes laterally with the cuboid bones. Medially, it bears a prominent tuberosity. The *cuboid bone*, on the lateral side of the foot, articulates posteriorly with the calcaneus, anteriorly with

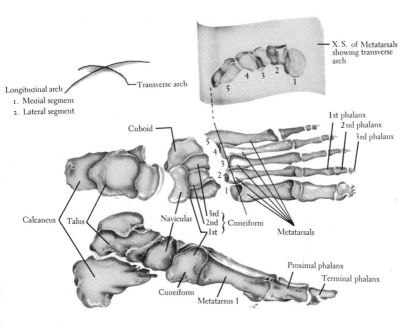

Fig. 5-27. Bones of the foot.

the 4th and 5th metatarsals, and medially with the 3rd cuneiform bone and sometimes with the navicular bones. The three *cuneiform bones* lie anterior to the navicular, medial to the cuboid, and posterior to the first three metatarsals.

Metatarsals. The five metatarsal bones of the foot are numbered I to V, from the medial side outward. Metatarsus I is on the side of the great toe (the hallux). The bases of the metatarsal bones articulate with the three cuneiform bones and the cuboid bone. The heads of the metatarsal bones articulate with the proximal phalanges of the digits. The rounded head of metatarsus I forms the "ball of the foot" at the base of the great toe.

Phalanges. As with the upper extremity, there are two phalanges in the first digit (hallux) and three in each of the remaining toes. Each phalanx consists of a *base* or *proximal extremity;* a *shaft,* the middle portion; and a *head* or *distal extremity.* The distal extremities are expanded and flattened, to form the horseshoe-shaped ungual tuberosities which bear the toe nails.

Sesamoid Bones. Two sesamoid bones are commonly found under the head of the first metatarsal, in the tendon of the flexor hallucis brevis. Additional sesamoids may be present in other tendons of the

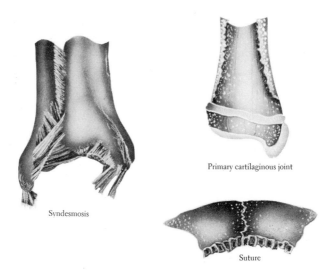

Primary cartilaginous joint

Syndesmosis

Suture

Fig. 5-28. Types of synarthrodial joints.

ARTICULATIONS (JOINTS)

An articulation is a junction between two or more bones, or between cartilage and bone. The two main types are *synarthrosis* and *diarthrosis*, which differ in the degree of movement permitted at the joint, as shown in the table which follows. Diarthroses, or *synovial joints*, possess a cleft containing synovial fluid between the free surfaces of the bones; in synarthroses, or *non-synovial joints*, the cavity is lacking.

CLASSIFICATION OF ARTICULATIONS

Type	Degree of Movement	Example
Synarthrosis		
syndesmosis	slight	between tibia and fibula
synchondrosis	slight	at pubic symphysis
synostosis	none	between cranial bones
Diarthrosis	slightly or freely movable	joints of the limbs and some of their parts

Synarthrosis. This joint has a continuous binding substance, such as ligaments, cartilage, or fibrous tissue between its components. It lacks an articular cavity, and the degree of movement is either limited or entirely absent.

SYNDESMOSIS. In this type of articulation, bones are bound together by fibrous connective tissue in the form of ligaments. *Examples:* junction of the distal ends of the tibia and fibula; junction of the spinous process of a vertebra and adjoining vertebra.

SYNCHONDROSIS. The bones of a synchondrosis are bound together by hyaline or fibrous cartilage. *Examples:* the junction between the diaphysis and epiphysis of a developing bone, in which the cartilage eventually disappears and is entirely replaced with bone; the junction between a rib and costal cartilage.

A *symphysis* is a synchondrosis in which fibrous cartilage binds the bones together. *Examples:* the pubic symphysis; the joint between bodies of vertebrae.

SYNOSTOSIS (SUTURE). In a synostosis the bones are joined directly, with little or no intervening substance. *Example:* the junction between two cranial bones.

Diarthrosis. A diarthrosis is a joint in which articular surfaces are covered with cartilage and separated by an articular cavity. The degree of movement ranges from slight to great.

TYPES OF DIARTHRODIAL ARTICULATIONS

Gliding (arthrodia)	Articular surfaces are flat	Between carpal bones; between articular processes of vertebrae
Hinge (ginglymus)	Convex cylindrical surface articulates with a concave surface	Between humerus and ulna (elbow); interphalangeal joints
Ball-and-socket (enarthrosis)	Head of one bone fits into concavity of another	Hip and shoulder joints
Pivot (trochoid)	Pivot-like process turns within a ring, or a ring turns on a pivot	Between atlas and odontoid process of axis; between head of radius and ulna
Ellipsoidal (condyloid)	Ovoid or rounded surface of a bone fits into a shallow concavity of another	Between occipital condyles and atlas; between carpals and radius
Saddle	The two articulating surfaces are saddle-shaped in one direction, convex in the other.	Between carpal bone and 1st metacarpal of thumb

Diarthrodial articulations may also be classified as: *plane* (same as gliding), *uniaxial* (same as hinge and pivot), *biaxial* (condyloid), and *multiaxial* (ball-and-socket and saddle).

STRUCTURE OF A DIARTHRODIAL ARTICULATION. A typical diarthrodial joint consists of: *articular cartilage*, which covers the articulating surfaces; an *articular capsule*, completely enveloping the joint and

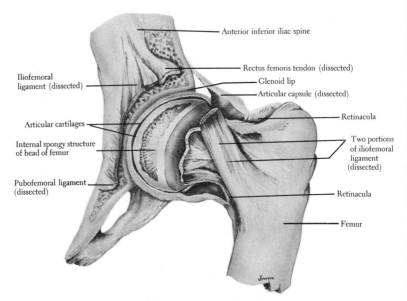

Fig. 5-29. Typical diarthrodial joint.

having two layers, an outer fibrous and an inner synovial; a *joint cavity*, a space within the capsule lined with the *synovial membrane* and containing a small quantity of *synovial fluid* or *synovia*, a clear, watery fluid; *ligaments*, bands of connective tissue which bind the bones together, not generally elastic yet permitting movement and at the same time acting to limit the degree of movement. In some joints an *articular disc* composed of fibrous cartilage divides the cavity (the mandibular-temporal, for example).

Movements in Diarthrodial Articulations. The manner and direction of movement at a diarthrodial joint are referred to in the following terms:

Flexion is movement in an anteroposterior plane, in which the angle between the bones is *decreased* (bending arm at elbow, bending wrist on forearm, bending head forward, bending body forward at hip joint). *Extension,* the opposite of flexion, is movement in an anteroposterior plane, in which the angle between the bones is *increased* (the opposites of the movements mentioned under flexion serve as examples).

Abduction is movement of the part *away from* the median plane of the body or the median plane of a part, as in lateral and upward movement of arm, lateral movement of leg, or movement of digits away from the third digit (in hand) or second digit (in foot). *Adduction* is the opposite of abduction; movement is *toward* the median plane of the body or of a part.

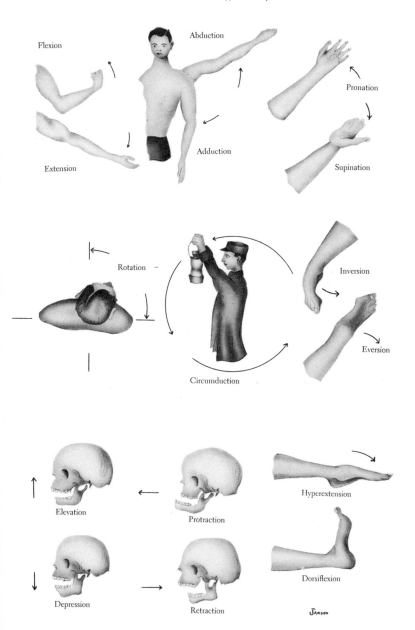

Fig. 5-30. Types of joint movements.

Supination is the turning of the hand so that the palm faces upward. *Pronation* is the turning of the hand so that the palm faces downward.

Rotation is movement in which a part turns on its longitudinal axis, as in turning the head to left or right at the joint between the atlas and the axis or turning the arm or leg outward (lateral rotation) or inward (medial rotation).

Circumduction is movement involving both angular and rotary movements; the proximal end of a limb remains fixed while the distal end describes an arc (swinging the arm in a circle).

Inversion is movement at an ankle joint, in which the sole of the foot is turned inward (medially). *Eversion* is the opposite movement of the same part, that is, turning it outward (laterally).

Elevation is movement in which a part is raised (movement of mandible in closing the jaw, raising of the scapula). *Depression* is movement in which the part is lowered (movement of mandible in opening the jaw, lowering of scapula).

Protraction is movement of a part forward (protrusion of mandible). *Retraction* is backward movement of a part (drawing back of mandible).

Hyperextension describes movements at the wrist, phalangeal joints, and metatarsophalangeal joints, in which the part is extended beyond the straight line formed by normal extension. *Plantar flexion* is extension of the foot. *Dorsiflexion*, the opposite of plantar flexion, is movement of the foot upward (that is, toward the anterior surface of the leg).

DISORDERS AND DISEASES OF THE BONES AND JOINTS

Acromegaly. Hypertrophy of bones of face, hands, and feet; due to hypersecretion of anterior lobe of pituitary gland.

Ankylosis. Fusion or consolidation of bones of a joint; results in reduced movement or complete immobility.

Arthritis. A group of ailments involving joints, muscles, and tendons; formerly referred to as "rheumatism"; some common types are: (1) *infectious arthritis*, a form which accompanies infectious diseases such as tuberculosis, syphilis, gonorrhea, and rheumatic fever; (2) *metabolic arthritis*, commonly called "gout" (due to presence of excessive quantities of uric acid in blood and to deposition of urates in or around joints, especially those of the hallux); (3) *osteoarthritis*, a chronic disease of the joints (generally affects older persons; characterized by degeneration and hypertrophy of bone and cartilage); (4) *rheumatoid arthritis*, either gradual or sudden in onset (may last for years or disappear quickly; in advanced stages joints may swell to twice normal size, cartilage between bones may disappear and joints fuse and become immobile; affects young as well as old).

Bunion (also called *hallux valgus*). Displacement of great toe laterally toward the other toes; often results from wearing of shoes or socks that are too short, the pressure causes enlargement of the metatarsophalangeal joint and thickening of the joint capsule.

Bursitis. Inflammation of a bursa. "Housemaid's knee" (inflammation of the patellar bursa) and "tennis elbow" (inflammation of the olecranon bursa) are examples.

Club foot. See *Talipes.*

Dislocation. Displacement of the ends of the bones of a joint; results in disarrangement of the parts.

Fracture. A break or crack in a bone. Types of fractures are: *Colles',* in which radius is broken about ½ to 1 inch from the wrist; *compound,* in which bone is broken and there is an external wound at the point of fracture; *Greenstick,* in which bone is partially broken, with a splintering effect; *Pott's,* a break of the tibia just above the ankle; and *simple,* in which bone is broken but there is no external wound.

Gout. See *Arthritis.*

Hallux valgus. See *Bunion.*

Kyphosis. Abnormal increase in the thoracic curve of the vertebral column; gives rise to the condition called "hunchback."

Osteitis. Inflammation of a bone; in *osteitis deformans (Paget's disease),* the bones become thickened and softened; in *osteitis fibrosa (von Recklinghausen's disease),* hyperparathyroidism brings about extensive resorption of bone.

Osteoarthritis. See *Arthritis.*

Osteomalacia. "Adult rickets"; softening of bone in which, due to long-standing deficiency of vitamin D in diet, and the mineral content of bone substance becomes greatly reduced.

Osteomyelitis. Inflammation of bone marrow; due to infection by pyogenic microorganisms. It may remain localized, or it may spread and involve the bone and the periosteum.

Paget's disease. See *Osteitis deformans.*

Pott's disease. Tuberculosis of spine; bodies of vertebrae are often eroded, resulting in abnormal curvature.

Rickets. Condition in children in which the bones become bent and distorted; may result in knock-knee (*genu valgum*) or "bowleg" (*genu varum*). It is caused by defective calcification which results from failure (attributed to absence of vitamin D) of the digestive tract to absorb calcium and phosphorus.

Scoliosis. Abnormal increase in lateral curvature of vertebral column.

Spina bifida. A developmental defect in which there is incomplete closure of the vertebral arches; it results in herniation (protrusion) of spinal cord.

Sprain. The wrenching of a joint, with stretching or tearing of its ligaments.

Strain. Excessive stretching of the ligaments of a joint capsule.

Talipes. Any of a number of deformities of the foot, such as *talipes valgus* (flat foot) and *talipes varus* (club foot). They are usually congenital.

Tenesynovitis. Inflammation of a tendon sheath.

6: THE MUSCULAR SYSTEM

The muscular system comprises the organs which, by their contraction and relaxation, produce the movements of the body as a whole and of its parts. The muscles constitute the "red flesh" of the body. They account for 42 per cent of the total body weight in males and 36 per cent in females. Also related to the muscular system are tendons, fasciae, and aponeuroses, all of which serve to secure the ends of the muscles and to determine the direction of their pull.

FUNCTIONS OF MUSCLES

The functions performed by muscles may be regarded as of two kinds: voluntary and involuntary. There is no strict dichotomy between the two; certain functions classed as "voluntary" may also, and quite readily, take place involuntarily, while some of the "involuntary" functions are amenable to conscious (voluntary) control.

Principally Voluntary Functions of Muscles. The functions served by muscular action that are principally voluntary in nature are:

1. *Maintenance of posture*, whereby the general "attitude" of the entire framework of the body is controlled.

2. *Accomplishment of various movements in which action is externally visible*, shown in the table which follows.

limbs	locomotion, exertion of force	*tongue and lips*	food manipulation, vocalization
fingers	grasping, handling, manipulation	*abdominal wall*	respiration, defecation, vomiting
toes	balance, leverage, locomotion	*head*	bringing sense organs into more favorable position
diaphragm	respiration		
pharynx	swallowing	*face*	expression of mood and emotion

Principally Involuntary Functions of Muscles. The functions that are principally involuntary are:

1. *Propulsion of substances through body passages*, as of food through the digestive tract, blood through the vessels, and germ cells through the reproductive ducts.

2. *Expulsion of stored substances*, such as bile from the gallbladder, urine from the kidneys and the urinary bladder, and feces from the

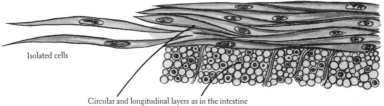

Isolated cells

Circular and longitudinal layers as in the intestine

Fig. 6-1. Smooth muscle cells.

rectum; the last two are also readily capable of voluntary control.

3. *Regulation of the size of openings,* such as the pupil of the eye, the pylorus, the anus, and the neck of the bladder.

4. *Regulation of the diameter of tubes,* such as blood vessels and bronchioles.

TYPES OF MUSCULAR TISSUE

Muscle tissue is classified into three types on the basis of structure and function, namely, smooth, striated, and cardiac.

Smooth Muscle Tissue. Also known as "nonstriated muscle" as well as "plain muscle," this type of tissue constitutes the visceral (involuntary) muscles. It exists as single cells arranged in small groups, in bundles, or in sheets or layers.

The cells or fibers of smooth muscles are spindle-shaped, long, and slender. Each cell has a single nucleus, located in the center. Its cytoplasm consists of *sarcoplasm,* in which lie *myofibrils,* the contractile elements. Cells are bound to each other by an interlacing network of reticular fibers. The fibers do not anastomose or divide.

Smooth muscle cells are of two kinds: (1) those organized into motor units, which contract as do skeletal muscles (muscles of blood vessels, intrinsic muscles of the eye, piloerectors of the skin); and (2) those which are automatic in their activity (muscles of the intestines, uterus, and oviduct).

LOCATION. Smooth muscle tissue is found in the wall of the digestive tract, the trachea and bronchi, the urinary bladder and gallbladder, urinary and genital ducts, walls of blood vessels, the capsule of the spleen, and the iris of the eye. It is also found attached to hair follicles of the skin.

INNERVATION. Smooth muscles are innervated by efferent fibers of the autonomic nervous system.

TYPE OF ACTION. Smooth muscles are not subject to voluntary control; their action is involuntary. They are, however, under the control of the visceral motor centers of the brain.

Striated Muscle Tissue. This type of tissue, also called "striped muscle," characterizes the skeletal or voluntary muscles. It takes on the

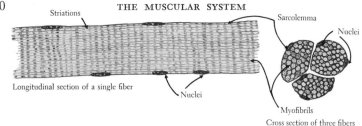

Fig. 6-2. Striated muscle cells.

form of fibers which are made up of large, multinucleated cells. The fibers are grouped in bundles.

Striated muscle fibers vary in length from 1 to 40 mm. and in thickness from 10 to 100 microns. Each fiber consists of a semifluid matrix (*sarcoplasm*) in which the contractile elements (*myofibrils*, or *fibrillae*) are embedded. Each myofibril has alternate light and dark bands which give the fiber its "striped" appearance. The bands of one fibril are at the same level as those of adjoining fibrils, so that striations seem to cross the entire fiber. The membrane surrounding the fiber is the *sarcolemma*. The nuclei are located near the periphery of each fiber. Fibers may be red or white, the color being due to the presence of the pigment *myoglobin*.

Such muscle fibers grouped together form a *primary bundle* or *fasciculus*, which is surrounded by a connective tissue membrane, the *perimysium*. The connective tissue which surrounds the individual fibers within a fasciculus constitutes the *endomysium*. A *muscle* is a group of these primary bundles. It is enclosed in a sheath, the *epimysium*.

LOCATION. Striated muscle tissue comprises all muscles attached to the skeleton, the muscles of the tongue and the soft palate, those that move the scalp, those in the pharynx and the upper part of the esophagus, and those in the extrinsic eye muscles.

INNERVATION. Striated muscle tissue is innervated by efferent fibers of cerebrospinal nerves. Each nerve fiber divides into several branches each of which enters a muscle fiber and terminates in an enlargement called a *motor end-plate* or *myoneural junction*. A single nerve fiber and the muscle fibers it supplies constitute a *motor unit*. Afferent fibers carrying sensory (proprioceptive) impulses are also present; these end in *neuromuscular spindles*.

TYPE OF ACTION. Striated muscles are under voluntary control. There are a few exceptions, among them the muscles in the upper third of the esophagus.

Cardiac Muscle Tissue. Cardiac muscle (*heart muscle*) consists of fibers which branch and anastomose with adjoining fibers, forming a *syncytium*. The fibers or cells are striated, as are those of skeletal muscles, but the striations are less pronounced. The nuclei occupy a cen-

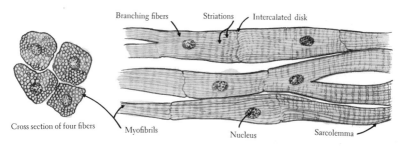

Fig. 6-3. Cardiac muscle.

tral position in each fiber. At intervals fibers show transverse markings called *intercalated discs*.

Atypical fibers, called *Purkinje fibers*, serve to provide an impulse-conducting system; these are found just under the endocardium. Purkinje fibers differ from the usual muscle fibers in having fewer fibrils, less distinct striations, considerable sarcoplasm about the nuclei, and a large amount of glycogen. Such fibers are concentrated in the S–A node, the A–V node, the atrioventricular bundle (*bundle of His*), and branches of these structures, all of which are described in chapter 10, The Circulatory System.

LOCATION. Cardiac muscle is found only in the heart.

INNERVATION AND TYPE OF ACTION. Cardiac muscles are innervated by fibers from the autonomic nervous system. Their action is involuntary, automatic, and rhythmic.

PHYSIOLOGY OF MUSCLES

Properties of Muscle Tissue. Four properties of muscle tissue facilitate the functioning of muscles: contractility, extensibility, elasticity, and irritability.

CONTRACTILITY. Muscle tissue has the capacity to become shorter—a property of protoplasm which is exhibited to its highest degree in muscle cells. When stimulated, muscle fibers may shorten to one-sixth of their length at rest; striated fibers may shorten to one-tenth of their normal length. The rhythmic contraction of cardiac and smooth muscle is due to a property inherent within these cells, which will continue to contract even when removed from the body, provided that they be kept in a favorable environment.

EXTENSIBILITY. Muscle tissue also has the ability to stretch upon the application of force. Smooth muscle cells of the visceral organs, such as the stomach, urinary bladder, and uterus, can stretch to a remarkable degree as these organs become filled. Cardiac muscles and muscles of the blood vessels stretch when these structures become filled with blood. Striated muscles stretch when the opposing muscles contract, as when the flexor muscle of the arm contracts, forcing the extensor muscle to extend. This permits movement at a joint.

ELASTICITY. This property of muscle tissue enables muscles to regain their original size and shape after having been stretched. Through elasticity, muscle tone is maintained in skeletal muscles, and organs such as the urinary bladder and the uterus resume their minimum size after they have been emptied. When the arteries (aorta and its branches) have been stretched by the blood forced into them by contraction of the heart (systole), they tend to resume their normal size during the diastole. The resultant pumping action maintains a steady flow of blood through the circulatory system.

IRRITABILITY. Muscle tissue has the property of being able to respond to a stimulus. This stimulus is ordinarily a nerve impulse transmitted through the cranial and spinal nerves, but other stimuli may induce muscle contraction. Examples of the latter are: the application of electrical shock, the action of irritating chemical substances, and a mechanical stimulus.

Contraction of an Individual Muscle (Experimental Observations). The contraction of a muscle can be studied experimentally by removing a single muscle from the body of an animal, subjecting it to various stimuli, and recording the results obtained. For this purpose, the gastrocnemius of a frog is the most generally used muscle.

Four types of stimuli are commonly employed:

1. *Mechanical*: tapping, pinching, stretching.
2. *Chemical*: agents such as an acid or a salt.
3. *Thermal*: application of heat by various means.
4. *Electrical*: application of various strengths of electric current.

For experimental purposes, the electrical type of stimulus is most frequently used because its strength, duration, and frequency are easily controlled and there is a minimum of injury to the tissues.

INTENSITY OF A STIMULUS. To provoke a response (in this case, muscle contraction) a stimulus must possess a certain intensity. A weak stimulus will elicit no contraction; such a stimulus is said to be *subminimal*. Should the intensity of the stimulus be increased gradually, a point will be reached at which the muscle will barely respond; this is called a *threshold* or *minimal stimulus*. Now, if the intensity of the stimulus is gradually increased further, the extent of contraction will also increase gradually until a point is reached beyond which further increase in intensity of the stimulus produces no increase in the extent of contraction; this is called a *maximal stimulus*.

THE ALL-OR-NONE PRINCIPLE. If cardiac muscle is stimulated, the whole muscle contracts to its fullest extent. This illustrates the "all-or-none principle," namely, that *each contraction is maximal for the conditions under which the muscle is stimulated*. The principle holds

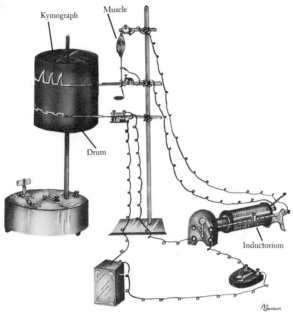

Fig. 6-4. Kymograph, inductorium, and nerve-muscle preparation.

true also for a *single striated muscle fiber*. When a single fiber is stimulated, it contracts to its fullest extent. A muscle consisting of a great many individual fibers does not follow this principle. A minimal stimulus applied to an entire muscle may cause one or a few of the fibers to contract, and the result is a slight response. But as the stimulus is increased, more and more fibers are stimulated, and a greater contraction of the muscle is brought about. Finally, a point may be reached at which all the fibers are being stimulated, and, since each is then contracting to its fullest extent, a *maximal response* has been attained, with no further contraction possible.

It is not to be inferred from the foregoing remarks that under the all-or-none principle the response of a muscle to a stimulus is always the same. Not only do muscle cells vary but the physiological conditions under which they respond may change. In brief, then, the all-or-none principle means that *for a given muscle the degree of response is independent of the strength of the stimulus.*

RECORDING OF MUSCLE RESPONSE. For obtaining records of many types of physiological activity a *kymograph* is used. The kymograph is an apparatus consisting of a revolving drum activated by a spring or an electrical motor. The speed of revolution of the drum can be regulated. Plain, graph, or smoked paper is placed on the drum and a writing stylus is so positioned that it traces the record on the paper.

ELECTRICAL STIMULATION. Electricity is applied directly from a battery to stimulate a muscle tissue. The current is galvanic, and the stimuli coming from it are continuous. The customary method of stimulation requires use of an induction coil, or *inductorium*—an apparatus consisting of two coils (a primary and a secondary). The direct current from the battery is led through a primary coil and flows continuously as long as the circuit is closed. The secondary coil is so arranged that its position can be altered in relationship to the primary coil. When the circuit is closed (the "make"), a current flows through the primary coil and sets up (induces) for a brief instant a current of high intensity in the secondary coil. This produces a *single induced shock*. Repeated induced shocks constitute a *faradic current*. When the circuit is broken (the "break"), a second shock of slightly higher intensity occurs. In the primary circuit between battery and primary coil, a signal magnet with a writing stylus may be placed. This indicates on smoked paper the exact time when the stimulus is applied. In some instances, a tuning fork or an interval timer may be included in the circuit.

MUSCLE-NERVE PREPARATION. To prepare a muscle for experimental purposes, a frog in good physical condition is secured and "pithed" (the brain destroyed). The skin is removed from the hind legs, exposing the muscles. The gastrocnemius (calf) muscle and its tendon of Achilles (which passes under the foot) are carefully separated from the shank. The sciatic nerve is then separated from the surrounding thigh muscles. All muscles and other tissues are cut away until only the gastrocnemius and the lower end of the femur (from which it originates) and the nerve remain. The femur is then placed in a muscle clamp and the tendon of Achilles is attached by a hook to a writing lever. A weight is fixed to the lever to provide tension such as occurs normally in the body.

PHENOMENA OF MUSCLE CONTRACTION OBSERVED. Some of the phenomena of muscle contraction that have been observed experimentally are: (1) effect of gradually increasing the strength of the stimulus; (2) a single muscle twitch recorded on a rapidly moving drum; (3) effects of rapidly repeated stimuli; and (4) fatigue, or the effects of long-continued stimulation.

Effect of Increasing the Strength of a Stimulus. Subminimal stimuli (those with insufficient strength) fail to elicit any muscular response. A threshold stimulus is one which produces a minimal response. In experiments stimuli of gradually increasing strength are applied to a muscle. As the stimuli increase in strength, muscular reactions increase up to a point of maximal response. A further increase in the strength of the stimulus does not increase the response beyond this point, but merely continues to elicit the same maximal reaction.

A Single Muscle Twitch Recorded on a Rapidly Moving Drum. A single muscle twitch can be recorded on a rapidly moving drum; thus the result may be shown by means of a wavy line representing the vibration of a tuning fork oscillating at the rate of 100 double vibrations per second and another line (made by a signal magnet) indicating the time of stimulation. In experiments the results for the gastrocnemius of a frog at 21° C. show that the muscle twitch lasts about 0.1 second. The twitch can be divided into three periods or phases:

A *latent period*—the lapse of time (about 0.01 second) from the application of the stimulus to the beginning of a response.

A *period of contraction*—the period during which the muscle is shortening; this lasts about 0.04 second.

A *period of relaxation*—with a duration of about 0.05 second.

The times of duration will vary according to the type of muscle, the physiological condition of the muscle, and the environmental conditions.

Effects of Rapidly Repeated Stimuli. Rapidly repeated stimuli produce summation, tetanus, a refractory period, and a "staircase" effect.

When a single subminimal stimulus does not elicit a contraction, rapidly repeated subminimal stimuli may do so; this effect is called *summation.*

When stimuli above threshold strength are repeated fairly rapidly and only partial relaxation occurs, *incomplete tetanus* exists. When, however, the stimuli are repeated very rapidly, so that no relaxation takes place and the muscle twitches are blended into a single sustained contraction, the condition is known as *complete tetanus.* Practically all skeletal muscle contractions are tetanic in nature. Even a rapid movement, such as the blinking of an eyelid, involves tetanus.

After a muscle has been stimulated, for a very short period it loses its irritability and will not respond to a second stimulus while in this condition. This is known as the *absolute refractory period.* It is brief for striated muscles, longer for cardiac muscles, and longest for nonstriated muscles.

Following the application of repeated stimuli it is sometimes noted that the contractions are successively higher even though there is no increase in the strength of the stimulus. The resultant reading on the kymograph record resembles a staircase; hence it is called the "staircase" effect. It is believed that with each contraction the irritability of the muscle protoplasm increases, resulting in a slightly increased contraction at each successive stimulus. This is the basis of the "warming up" period required of athletes.

Fatigue. When a muscle has been maintained in a state of sustained contraction through repeated stimulation, it gradually loses its ability to contract, and relaxation occurs. This is the mechanism of *fatigue,* a condition characterized by decreased irritability and contractility. During fatigue the fibers tend to resume their original state and contractions are reduced in extent or fail to occur, even though the muscle is still being stimulated. In the latter condition the muscle is regarded as being completely fatigued. *Fatigue, then, is the reduced capacity or inability of a muscle to perform work.*

Factors in Fatigue. The sensation of fatigue, experienced in the brain, is projected to (localized in) specific muscles. As already noted, it is followed by diminished capacity or total inability of a muscle to perform work. The significant factors giving rise to fatigue are: (1) excessive activity; (2) malnutrition; (3) circulatory disturbances; (4) respiratory disturbances; (5) infections; (6) endocrine disturbances; (7) psychogenic factors; and (8) incorrect posture and eyestrain.

EXCESSIVE ACTIVITY. Energy-producing substances may be used up faster than the restorative processes can replenish them or faster than the circulatory system can supply essential raw materials or remove waste products. Recovery is achieved through rest.

MALNUTRITION. Lack of essential food materials, especially proteins, minerals, or vitamins, may deprive muscle cells of the chemical substances which are vital to contraction. Depletion of salt is a common factor in fatigue.

CIRCULATORY DISTURBANCES. Circulatory disturbances prevent the adequate supply of oxygen and energy materials (e.g., glucose) to muscles and the effective removal of waste products. This is seen in anemia, in which fatigue is a consequence of reduction in the amount of hemoglobin.

RESPIRATORY DISTURBANCES. In respiratory illness, the supply of oxygen and the elimination of carbon dioxide are upset. An example is tuberculosis.

INFECTIONS. In nearly all infectious diseases, fatigue is one of the commonest symptoms. It is thought to be due to the presence of metabolic or toxic products manufactured by invading organisms. Fatigue is also thought to be a protective mechanism whereby bodily energy is directed toward overcoming the infection; the enforced rest facilitates operation of restorative processes.

ENDOCRINE DISTURBANCES. Hormone imbalance which interferes with normal metabolism may result in symptoms of fatigue. Examples are the fatigue states which accompany the menopause, diabetes, and thyroid disorders.

PSYCHOGENIC FACTORS. Conditions that have a psychological or psychosomatic background, such as emotional conflicts, frustration, grief, worry, and boredom, are often characterized by fatigue. Neurasthenia serves as an example, as does the lack of muscle tone in grief.

OTHER FACTORS. Incorrect posture and eyestrain are also regarded as factors in the causation of fatigue. Incorrect posture makes it difficult for muscles to counteract the force of gravity and places additional strain on ligaments and muscles. The improper functioning of eye muscles, sometimes because of inadequate illumination, may cause ocular fatigue.

Changes Occurring during Contraction of Striated Muscle. When a striated muscle contracts, the following types of changes occur: changes in structure and shape, chemical changes, electrical changes, and thermal changes.

CHANGES IN STRUCTURE AND SHAPE. During contraction, a striated muscle becomes shorter and thicker, but there is no change in its over-all volume. Certain structural changes occur in the light and dark bands which constitute the striations.

The means by which the energy released in muscle contraction brings about changes in the shape and structure of muscles are not fully known. It has been postulated that the fibers shorten as the result of sudden heating. It has also been suggested that changes occur in the shape of the molecules within muscle cells as the result of changes in surface tension, or that water molecules shift their position as a consequence of osmotic changes or electrolytic dissociation.

The foregoing changes have proved inadequate to explain all the facts of muscle contraction. Recent studies indicate that muscle contraction may result from changes in the shape of protein molecules and that they involve particularly the protein *myosin*. According to Astbury, rod-like submicroscopic micellae composed of long, slender molecules of myosin shorten by a *folding* process. It is the opinion of Szent-Györgi that the chief muscle proteins involved in contraction are *myosin* and *actin*, acting together as *actomyosin*, and that contraction is due to a shortening of the micellae which is brought about by a twisting or rolling up of long chains of the molecules that comprise these proteins. Ultramicroscopic studies by X-ray and double-refraction methods have shown that protein molecules of many animal products are arranged in parallel fashion and consist of more or less folded chains. Since this folding permits stretching, when tension is applied, shortening takes place by a refolding of the long chains of amino-acid molecules.

It is also postulated that muscle contraction is brought about by a change in the chemical environment of the molecules within a muscle fiber which causes their folding and shortening, with resultant shortening of the muscle fibers. The change in chemical environment is believed to be produced by the breakdown, with explosive rapidity, of adenosine triphosphate (ATP) to phosphoric acid and adenosine diphosphate (ADP).

CHEMICAL CHANGES. The energy utilized by a muscle during contraction comes from chemical changes within the muscle tissue. A resting muscle contains the following substances:

	Per Cent		Per Cent
Water	75.	Ash	1.5
Proteins	20.	Hexosephosphate	0.05
Glycogen	1.	Adenylpyrophosphate, cyto-	
Lactic acid	0.5	chrome, myoglobin, fat,	
Phosphocreatin	0.3	lecithin, cholesterol, en-	
		zymes	trace

Liberation of Energy. Chemical analysis shows that after contraction of a muscle, certain compounds (especially the inorganic phosphates and lactic acid) increase in quantity, while others (especially the organic phosphates and glycogen) decrease in quantity. Oxygen is utilized in the process; carbon dioxide and water are liberated. The exact nature of these chemical changes is not known, but the essential processes in the liberation of energy are believed to be the following:

1. Adenosine triphosphate⇄ { Phosphoric acid and Adenosine diphosphate (ADP) } — Energy immediately available for contraction
   (ATP)

2. Phosphocreatine ⇄ { Phosphoric acid and Creatine } — Energy for resynthesis of adenosine triphosphate

3. Glycogen * ⇄ Lactic acid — Energy for resynthesis of phosphocreatine and phosphoric acid

4. ⅕ of the lactic acid, → H_2O and CO_2 — Energy for resynthesis of
   plus O_2 — the remaining ⅘ of lactic acid to glycogen

* This process, called *glycolysis*, is very complex, involving several intermediary reactions and several enzymes. Certain phosphoric compounds play indispensable roles.

Oxygen Debt. The release of energy for muscle contraction is an *anaerobic* process. This means that it does not directly require the presence of oxygen. Since oxygen is not stored in muscle tissue, it must be brought to muscle cells by the blood stream as it is needed. When skeletal muscles are contracting continuously, as in strenuous exercise, the chemical changes involving energy release require little or no oxygen. The organic phosphates provide the energy needed for contraction. Their supply is, however, soon exhausted and must be replenished. This is accomplished by their resynthesis. The energy for the reactions in this process comes primarily from the oxidation of lactic acid (an aerobic process) to carbon dioxide and water (as in Step 4 in the preceding table). The consequence is that, during active contraction, the muscle acquires an *energy debt* (which is repaid after contraction and during the resting period) through the utilization of oxygen. This energy debt is regarded, and is usually referred to, as *oxygen debt*. The commonest manifestation of it is the increased respiratory activity which occurs and persists for some time after energy has been released in vigorous muscular activity (as in running or climbing).

THERMAL CHANGES. Of the total energy expended in muscle contraction, only about 35 per cent is utilized for the performance of work; the balance is liberated in the form of heat, which is employed to maintain body temperature. In cold weather, the production of body heat can be increased through voluntary muscular activity (rubbing hands together, walking) or involuntarily by shivering. Conversely, in warm weather, muscular activity is deliberately curtailed to reduce heat production.

Initial heat is the heat produced in the contraction of muscles; *delayed* or *recovery heat* is that produced in the restorative processes.

ELECTRICAL CHANGES. When a muscle fiber contracts, or a nerve conducts an impulse, or a gland secretes, electrical changes are manifested. These changes can be detected and recorded by suitable apparatus.

In effect, a muscle is like a tiny battery; when it is stimulated to contract, it generates a current, called the *action current*. This current flows from the positive to the negative pole. (The active region of a muscle is electrically negative to the inactive regions.) When the muscle is resting, no current is generated.

The current generated by the human heart is strong enough to be detected by a galvanometer. When electrodes are attached to the arm and the leg, the current generated by cardiac activity can be conducted to an *electrocardiograph*, which records the nature of the impulses. Its printed record, the electrocardiogram, enables a physician to analyze the heart beat and to detect and diagnose various types of cardiac dysfunction.

Factors Which Affect Muscle Function Unfavorably. There are several sites which may be the seat of the trouble in muscle failure or muscle malfunction: (1) the muscle itself; (2) the connection between nerve and muscle; (3) the nerve supplying the muscle; (4) the spinal cord; and (5) the brain.

THE MUSCLE ITSELF. Factors which may involve the muscle directly are: improper development, injury (as from a cut or blow), improper or inadequate nutrition, the presence of an abnormal structure (such as a tumor), the presence of infectious organisms (such as bacteria or trichinella), and the effects of toxic substances.

THE CONNECTION BETWEEN NERVE AND MUSCLE. A factor in muscular dysfunction is the failure of acetylcholine to be formed at the myoneural junction, a condition which prevails in myasthenia gravis. Curare, a drug used by South American Indians for poison darts and arrows, produces its effects by acting on this junction.

THE NERVE SUPPLYING THE MUSCLE. Muscle function depends on the maintenance of normal nerve functioning. Injury to, or severance of, motor nerve fibers results in paralysis and in muscle atrophy.

THE SPINAL CORD. Impulses originating in the brain pass through nerve tracts in the spinal cord and thence through nerves to the muscle. Injury to, or disease in, the conducting pathways of the cord, or destruction of motor cells in the gray matter of the cord (as in poliomyelitis), leads to muscle dysfunction.

THE BRAIN. Organic disorders in the motor centers of the brain, where impulses initiating movement arise, may bring about abnormal muscle functioning.

In general, the foregoing factors, which form the basis for diagnosis of any condition in which the disturbance of muscular functioning is an element, underlie dysfunction of any organ or organ system.

Measurement of Muscle Effectiveness. Aside from maintaining body heat and metabolic activities within the cells (secondary functions), the energy liberated in muscle contraction serves in the *performance of work* (primary function). The amount of work performed by striated muscles can be measured in the following manner: In a muscle-nerve preparation, the muscle is loaded with a 10-gm. weight and stimulated to contract. Thus it is found that the muscle will lift the weight a certain number of millimeters. The "work performed" is the product of *grams × millimeters moved.*

It should be noted that a muscle functions with maximum efficiency when it is *moderately* loaded. When the load is too light or too heavy, the muscle does not perform to its maximum capacity.

Isometric and Isotonic Contractions. If a muscle is overloaded, when stimulated it contracts but does not shorten. Such a contraction is called an *isometric contraction.* Although tension is developed, no work is performed, all of the energy being expended as heat. However, if the load is below the maximum and the muscle contracts, the load is moved and mechanical work is performed. In the process, the muscle shortens, and its contraction is called an *isotonic contraction.*

Muscle Tone (Tonus). Both nonstriated and striated muscles are normally in a mild state of contraction, the condition called *tonus,* or *muscle tone.* Muscle tone depends on a steady stream of impulses to the muscles. Its basis is apparently a reflex action in which impulses initiated in receptors in muscles and tendons are being continually carried by afferent nerves to the central nervous system, where connections are made with efferent fibers. These efferent fibers then conduct impulses to muscles, stimulating them to contract slightly.

Muscle tone varies in accordance with existing conditions. It disappears when the nerves leading to a muscle are severed or destroyed. It is diminished or may be entirely lacking during sleep or in anesthesia. Emotional states have a profound effect on muscle tone, increasing it in periods of excitement, anticipation, and anxiety, decreasing it in grief, worry, or depression. The state of health also greatly affects tonus, which is lower in ill health. Muscle tone is also amenable to conscious regulation, as when one "braces" himself for a leap or to receive a shock (increase in tonus), or in relaxation (decrease in tonus).

Effects of Training and Work on the Muscles. Activity of skeletal muscles brings about profound effects in nearly every other system of the body. The rate and force of the heart beat, the rate of respiration, the amount of perspiration produced, the appetite, and the development of the skeletal framework all respond to activity by the skeletal muscles. The effects are either temporary or permanent, depending on the intensity or the duration of the activity. But of equal importance is the fact that the amount of training and work performed by a muscle is reflected in the muscle itself: in its size and structure, its strength, and its efficiency.

EFFECT OF TRAINING ON SIZE AND STRUCTURE OF MUSCLES. Muscles that remain unused tend to atrophy; those that are used excessively tend to hypertrophy. This is due to changes in the *sarcoplasm* of the individual fibers and *not* to an increase in the *number* of fibers. Muscle fibers that have been destroyed can regenerate only to a limited degree. In injuries of extensive nature, muscle tissue is replaced by connective (scar) tissue. In muscles that are used excessively, the amount of connective tissue between the fibers increases, making the surrounding structure tougher.

EFFECT OF TRAINING ON STRENGTH OF MUSCLES. Strength (capacity to do work) is increased by training. This is accounted for in several ways: (1) increase in size of the muscle; (2) improved coordination, in which antagonistic muscles are completely relaxed at the proper time and thus do not impede the functioning of the acting muscles; (3) improved functioning in the cortical region of the brain, where the impulses are initiated that bring about contraction of the muscles.

EFFECT OF TRAINING ON EFFICIENCY OF MUSCLES. Muscular efficiency is attained by (1) performance of work at the proper rate and with average loads, (2) improved coordination of all muscles involved in an activity, (3) improved adjustments of the circulatory and respiratory systems to the requirements of the muscular activity, (4) im-

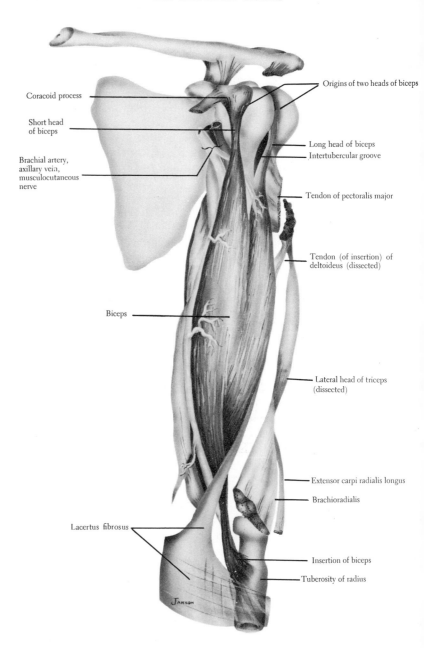

Coracoid process

Short head
of biceps

Brachial artery,
axillary vein,
musculocutaneous
nerve

Biceps

Lacertus fibrosus

Origins of two heads of biceps

Long head of biceps

Intertubercular groove

Tendon of pectoralis major

Tendon (of insertion) of
deltoideus (dissected)

Lateral head of triceps
(dissected)

Extensor carpi radialis longus

Brachioradialis

Insertion of biceps

Tuberosity of radius

JANSON

Fig. 6-5. An entire muscle.

proved movement at joints involved in the activity, and (5) elimination of excess fat.

THE SKELETAL (STRIATED) MUSCLES

The skeletal (voluntary) muscles include all the muscles that are attached to and that move the skeletal parts. Striated muscles also form the walls of the oral, abdominal, and pelvic cavities, and are attached to such movable structures as the lips, the eyelids, and eyeballs, the skin, and the tongue. As previously shown, there are *two principal muscle groups:*

1. *Axial muscles:* those of the head, face, neck, and trunk.
2. *Appendicular muscles:* those of the limbs (or extremities).

Structure of a Skeletal Muscle. A skeletal muscle contains many fibers bound together in primary bundles called *fasciculi.* The fibers are held together by a fibrous connective tissue, the *endomysium;* the sheath of connective tissue which surrounds the bundle is the *perimysium.* Primary bundles are grouped together to form secondary bundles, and these form tertiary bundles. The entire muscle is enclosed in a sheath of connective tissue, the *epimysium,* a part of the *deep fascia.*

Blood and Nerve Supply of Skeletal Muscles. Muscles are abundantly supplied with *blood vessels.* Capillaries entwine the individual fibers and, through anastomoses, form an interlacing network throughout the muscle. In general, the vessels run parallel to the muscle fibers. *Nerve fibers* are very numerous in striated muscles; they are myelinated afferent and efferent fibers from the cerebrospinal nerves.

Attachments of Skeletal Muscles. To perform its work, a muscle requires attachment at two points: an *origin,* the relatively fixed point of attachment (usually the one nearer to the midline of the body); and an *insertion,* the movable end of the muscle (usually the one farther from the midline). When a muscle contracts, the insertion is brought nearer to the origin. In some instances, the origin is fixed absolutely and only one type of movement is possible in contraction. An example of this is the temporalis muscle, which closes the jaw. In other instances, either end of the muscle can act as the insertion, depending on which is held in a fixed position. An example is the biceps muscle; in ordinary activity, when the biceps contracts, the radius, on which it is inserted, is supinated and flexed on the arm (humerus). But when one is "chinning" himself on a bar, the radius remains fixed and the arm is flexed on the forearm. In general, however, the origin and the insertion are predetermined on the basis of the customary or normal movement performed by the muscle.

The *means* of attachment are: *direct* and *indirect.* In direct attachment, the perimysium or fascia is attached directly to the periosteum of a bone or the perichondrium of cartilage. Indirect attachment is achieved through tendons or aponeuroses. *Tendons* are dense, round or flat cords of collagenous fibers, white in color and varying in length; they are extremely strong and inelastic. *Aponeuroses* are broad, flat sheets of connective tissue, white in color and similar in structure to tendons.

FASCIAE. The fasciae, superficial and deep, differ in structure and in function.

Superficial Fascia. Underneath the skin and over most of the surface of the body there is a more or less continuous sheath of connective tissue, the superficial fascia. It contains a considerable amount of fat, the amount varying in different parts of the body. When fat cells predominate, it becomes *adipose tissue.* In some places the fascia is dense; in others it is loose. In some regions of the body it can be separated into layers (as in the lower abdominal wall); in others it is closely bound to the surrounding tissue.

The superficial fascia serves the following *functions:* (1) connects the skin with underlying parts; (2) forms a protective and insulating covering for the body; (3) plays an important role in inflammatory processes by which foreign or noxious agents are counteracted; and (4) provides a principal reservoir for the storage of food and water.

Deep Fascia. The deep fascia is the usually dense, inelastic fibrous tissue that forms the investing sheaths of muscles. In certain parts of the body, the fascia is continued between the individual muscles as *intermuscular septa.* It is thick and well developed in some regions; in others it is thin and hardly distinguishable from the epimysium.

The splitting and fusing of deep fascia into compartments, planes, and clefts makes it possible to predict the course of the movement of pus, the localization of pathology, and surgical procedure.

The deep fascia serves the following *functions:* (1) forms investing coverings for the muscles; (2) in some cases, attaches the muscle to bone or cartilage; (3) separates individual muscles, thus facilitating their movement by avoiding mutual interference; and (4) encloses blood and lymphatic vessels and nerves.

The deep fascia is given a specific name appropriate to the region of the body in which it is found: *axillary fascia* of the armpit, *orbital fascia* of the eye, *cervical fascia* of the neck, *palmar fascia* of the hand.

Subserous Fascia. The subserous fascia or visceral fascia forms the fibrous layer of serous membranes (pleura, pericardium, peritoneum), covering and supporting the viscera and serving to attach the parietal layer of the serous membranes to the deep fascia of the internal surface of the body wall.

Bursa. A bursa ("pocket") is a space within areolar connective tissue forming a closed sac which contains a small amount of fluid (*synovia*). Bursae are generally located at places where muscles or tendons

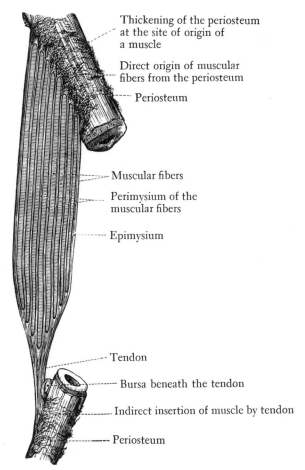

Thickening of the periosteum at the site of origin of a muscle

Direct origin of muscular fibers from the periosteum

Periosteum

Muscular fibers

Perimysium of the muscular fibers

Epimysium

Tendon

Bursa beneath the tendon

Indirect insertion of muscle by tendon

Periosteum

Fig. 6-6. Bursa and tendon sheaths. (Reprinted with permission of The Macmillan Company from Toldt, *Atlas of Human Anatomy*, 1948.)

pass over hard structures. They lessen friction and facilitate movement. Bursae are classified as follows:

Subtendinous. Found where tendons rub against bone, cartilage, or other firm structures.

Articular. Found between bones in certain joints (e.g., between the dens and the transverse ligament of the atlas).

Subcutaneous. Found between the skin and bony prominences (tip of the elbow, over the kneecap).

Submuscular. Found between muscles and bony prominences.

Tendon Sheath. When a tendon passes over a bony surface or traverses an area of possible friction or compression before attaching to its insertion, it may pass through a tubular bursa called a *tendon sheath*. Such a sheath is actually a double tube whose inner section (the *visceral* tube) lies next to and adheres to the tendon and is separated from the outer or *parietal* tube by a space filled with synovial fluid. Tendon sheaths are found in the hands and the feet and in the intertubercular groove.

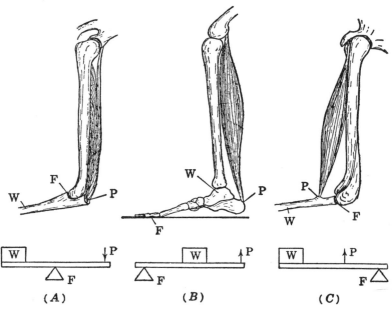

Fig. 6-7. Simple levers. (A) First class lever (triceps muscle extending arm at elbow. (B) Second class lever (gastrocnemius muscle raising weight of body on toes. (C) Third class lever (biceps muscle flexing arm at elbow). Abbreviations: F, fulcrum; P, power W, weight. From Alexander, *Biology*, College Outline Series, copyright, 1954, by Barnes & Noble, Inc.)

The Mechanics of Skeletal Muscular Action. To recapitulate, muscles produce movement by contraction. When a muscle shortens (contracts), ordinarily the insertion is pulled nearer to the origin and the part on which the muscle is inserted moves. If the part is a bone of the skeleton, movement will occur at the joint located between the origin and the insertion.

LEVERAGE. Most skeletal muscles involve the principle of leverage. A *lever* consists of a bar-like structure which moves on a fixed point or *fulcrum*. There are three classes of levers: Class I—Fulcrum lies between point where force is applied and point where resistance is met or weight is lifted. Class II—Point of resistance lies between fulcrum and point where force is applied. Class III—Force is applied at a point between fulcrum and point of resistance.

The *advantages* gained through leverage, depending of course on the position of the fulcrum in relation to the point where force is applied, are: (1) Speed may be gained at the expense of power. (2) Power may be gained at the expense of speed. (3) A change in the direction of movement may be achieved.

CLASSIFICATION OF SKELETAL MUSCLES AS TO TYPE OF ACTION. In accomplishing their primary objective of performing work, muscles fall into four classes: prime mover, antagonist, synergist, and fixator.

Prime Mover. This muscle bears the principal responsibility for a specific action (e.g., deltoid muscle in abduction of arm).

Antagonist. This muscle produces the opposite movement. The latissimus dorsi and pectoralis, for example, are antagonists of the deltoid.

Synergist. When a prime mover passes over two joints, this muscle helps to stabilize the movement of one joint so that the force can be applied at the desired joint. Synergists inhibit undesirable or encumbering movements. As an example, when the fingers are being flexed by the flexor muscles, the muscles that inhibit bending at the wrist act as synergists.

Fixator. This muscle "fixes" the position of a limb when movement is occurring in the distal portion. In the illustration given under "Synergist," the biceps and triceps muscles are fixators; they hold the shoulder and the elbow in position.

WAYS OF DETERMINING THE SPECIFIC ACTION OF MUSCLES. Muscular action can be determined in the following ways:

1. Watch or feel the contraction of a muscle in a living subject and note resulting movement.

2. Isolate a muscle in an animal cadaver, then pull the muscle or its tendon and note the resulting movement.

3. Note the clinical effects of paralysis of a certain muscle.

4. Note the results of surgery in which tendons have been transplanted.

5. Stimulate electrically the motor point of a nerve leading to a specific muscle in a living subject, and observe the movement that results.

6. Stimulate electrically living muscle from an experimental animal and note the electrical changes in action potentials when it contracts.

Language for Description of Skeletal Muscles. For the sake of universal understanding and ease of reference, it is essential to adopt a special terminology and a uniform pattern of presentation in describing specific muscles.

DESCRIPTIVE TERMINOLOGY. The special terminology for the description of muscles includes the names of the muscles and terms referring to their action.

Names of Muscles. The etymologic background of the name of a muscle often reveals one or more facts about it, as in the following examples:

> Shape—rhomboideus, trapezius, serratus, deltoid
> Position—pectoralis, intercostal, latissimus dorsi, supraspinatus
> Shape and Position—external oblique, rectus femoris
> Size and Position—vastus lateralis
> Structure, or Number of Parts—biceps, triceps
> Origin and Insertion—stylohyoideus, sternothyroideus
> Action—levator scapulae, flexor carpi radialis, tensor tympani

Terms for Muscular Action. The action of a muscle is identified by the nature of the movement that occurs when it contracts. For explanations of the principal terms, see page 84.

PATTERN OF PRESENTATION. Ease of reference is attained when the elements of description are presented consistently in the same sequence. The correct sequence is seen in the following description of the biceps brachii.

Name. Biceps brachii.

Location. The biceps brachii lies in the (upper) arm, anterior to the humerus. It forms the bulk of the arm.

Origin. By two heads arising from the scapula. The *short head* arises by a flat tendon from the tip of the coracoid process. The *long head* arises from the supraglenoid tuberosity and glenoid ligament by a long tendon which passes over the head of the humerus within the joint capsule. It continues distally within the intertubercular groove of the humerus.

Insertion. By a large tendon which passes over the anterior surface of the elbow joint and is inserted on the tuberosity of the radius.

Action. Flexion and supination of the forearm. The latter of these actions is especially pronounced when the forearm is flexed and pronated. The position of the muscle is such that it can bring about movements at three joints: the shoulder, elbow, and radio-ulnar articulations. In addition to the foregoing, which are its principal actions, the biceps brachii can act as a flexor and medial rotator of the humerus. It also acts to pull the humerus toward the scapula, thus stabilizing the head of the humerus in the glenoid cavity. The long head, acting alone, abducts the humerus; the short head adducts the humerus.

Nerve Supply. The biceps brachii is innervated by the musculocutaneous nerve, a branch of it supplying each head. The nerve fibers come from the 5th and 6th cervical nerves.

Blood Supply. The biceps brachii is supplied with blood by arteries that branch from the brachial artery. Branches of the axillary vein carry blood away from the muscle.

Table of Skeletal Muscles. There are 656 muscles (327 pairs, 2 unpaired muscles) in the body. The actual number varies with different authorities, some listing as separate muscles what others regard as parts of a single muscle. The table which follows on several pages is organized in main divisions and subdivisions in the following manner:

  I. *Muscles of the Head*
    A. Muscles of expression
    B. Muscles of mastication
    C. Muscles of the tongue
    D. Muscles of the pharynx
    E. Muscles of the soft palate
 II. *Muscles of the Neck*
    A. Muscles that move the head
    B. Muscles that move the hyoid bone and the larynx
    C. Muscles that act on the upper ribs
III. *Muscles of the Trunk and the Extremities*
    A. Muscles that move the vertebral column
    B. Muscles that move the scapula
    C. Muscles of respiration
    D. Muscles that act on the humerus
    E. Muscles that act on the forearm
    F. Muscles that act on the hand and the fingers
    G. Muscles of the pelvic outlet
    H. Muscles that act on the femur
    I. Muscles that act on the leg
    J. Muscles that act on the foot and the toes

In the table that follows, only the principal muscles of each group are listed. The data included are: location, origin, insertion, and action. Under *location*, the position or a brief description will be found; under *origin*, the attachment which remains relatively fixed during contraction; and under *insertion*, the attachment which during contraction is pulled toward the point of origin. The *action* is the movement performed as though the muscle were acting alone. In activities involving widely distributed areas of the body, several muscles or their parts are usually involved. As a rule, a muscle does not act alone, its action being modified by the following factors or conditions: (1) whether all or a part of the muscle is contracting (trapezius may adduct, elevate, or depress the scapula); (2) the position of the part acted upon (brachioradialis may be either a pronator or a supinator, depending on the position of the forearm); (3) the action of fixators and synergists; and (4) the number of joints over which the muscle passes.

I. MUSCLES OF THE HEAD

A. Muscles of Expression. These muscles are used in the expression of fear, anger, pleasure, pain, joy, grief, and other emotions.

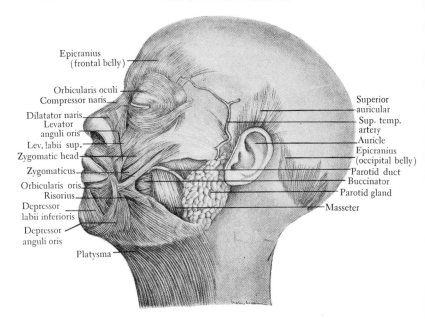

Fig. 6-8. Muscles of expression. (Reprinted with permission of C. V. Mosby Company and the author from Francis, *Introduction to Human Anatomy*, 2nd ed., 1954.)

Name, *Action*	Location	O—Origin I—Insertion
Epicranius frontalis *Elevates eyebrow; wrinkles forehead*	On each side of forehead	O—By galea aponeurotica I—Skin of eyebrow and root of nose
Epicranius occipitalis *Tenses aponeurotica and pulls scalp backward*	On occipital bone above superior nuchal line	O—Superior nuchal line I—Galea aponeurotica
Corrugator supercilii *Pulls eyebrow medially and downward; wrinkles forehead vertically*	Under frontalis, on medial side of eyebrow	O—Frontal bone, near junction with nasal bone I—Skin of eyebrow
Orbicularis oculi *Closes eyelids; tightens skin of forehead*	Encircles orbit, underlying eyebrow	O—1. Lacrimal bone, 2. Frontal and maxillary bones, 3. inner canthus of eye
Orbicularis oris *Closes oral orifice and protrudes lip*	Encircles mouth, forming fleshy portion of lips	(A sphincter muscle with no definite origin and insertion)
Zygomaticus *Elevates corner of mouth*	Extends diagonally upward from corner of mouth	O—Zygomatic arch I—Corner of mouth
Triangularis (Depressor anguli oris) *Depresses corner of mouth*	Extends along side of chin	O—Oblique line of mandible I—Orbicularis oris muscle

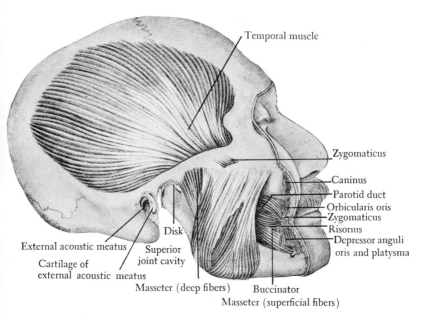

Temporal muscle

Zygomaticus

Caninus

Parotid duct

Orbicularis oris

Zygomaticus

Risorius

Depressor anguli oris and platysma

External acoustic meatus

Cartilage of external acoustic meatus

Superior joint cavity

Disk

Masseter (deep fibers)

Buccinator

Masseter (superficial fibers)

Fig. 6-9. Muscles of mastication. (Reprinted with permission of C. V. Mosby Company and the author from Francis, *Introduction to Human Anatomy*, 2nd ed., 1954.)

Name, *Action*	Location	O—Origin I—Insertion
Risorius *Draws corner of mouth laterally*	Extends across middle of cheek	O—Fascia over masseter muscle I—Corner of mouth
Quadratus labii inferioris (Depressor labii inferioris) *Depresses lower lip*	Extends along chin beneath lower lip	O—Oblique line of mandible I—Lower lip
Buccinator *Compresses cheek and retracts angle of mouth*	Deep within skin of cheek	O—Alveolar process of mandible and maxilla, and pterygomandibular raphe I—Lips near angle of mouth
Platysma *Draws corner of mouth downward and backward; depresses mandible*	A broad, thin sheet of muscle covering side of neck and lower jaw	O—Fascia over deltoid and pectoralis muscles I—Angle of mouth, inferior border of mandible, and skin of cheek

B. Muscles of Mastication. These muscles act on the mandible, elevating it to close the jaw, depressing it to open the jaw. The elevators include the temporalis, masseter, and pterygoideus internus. The ptery-goideus externus is the depressor.

Name, *Action*	Location	O—Origin I—Insertion
Temporalis *Elevates mandible (closes jaw); its posterior fibers retract the mandible*	Occupies temporal fossa of skull	O—Bones forming the temporal fossa, except zygomatic I—Coronoid process of mandible
Masseter *Elevates mandible; fibers in deep portion assist in retraction, and those in superficial portion assist in protraction*	Covers lateral surface of ramus of mandible	O—Zygomatic bone and arch I—Ramus, angle, and posterior portion of body of mandible
Pterygoideus internus *Elevates and protracts mandible*	Lies on medial side of ramus of mandible	O—Pterygoid fossa of sphenoid and palatine bones I—Medial surface of ramus of mandible
Pterygoideus externus *Protracts and depresses mandible; assists in opening mouth*	Lies medially to temporalis	O—Great wing and lateral pterygoid plate of sphenoid bone I—Neck of condyloid process of mandible

C. Muscles of the Tongue. The movements of the tongue are complex. Protraction, retraction, elevation, depression, and lateral movements are possible. Changes in the shape of the tongue, whereby it becomes broad or narrow, flattened or pointed, or grooved, are accomplished to a considerable extent by intrinsic musculature of the tongue itself. The following muscles, part of the extrinsic musculature, produce the larger movements of this organ.

Name, *Action*	Location	O—Origin I—Insertion
Genioglossus *Posterior fibers protract and depress tongue; anterior fibers retract it. Hyoid bone is elevated by this muscle*	Lies beneath anterior portion and forms bulk of tongue	O—Superior genial tubercles of mandible (posterior surface of symphysis) I—On dorsum of tongue; some fibers extend to hyoid bone
Hyoglossus *Retracts and depresses tongue*	Lies beneath posterior portion of tongue	O—Hyoid bone, body and greater cornu I—On dorsum of tongue
Styloglossus *Retracts tongue; unilateral contraction pulls tongue laterally*	Lies along lateral ventral surface of tongue	O—Styloid process of temporal bone I—Sides of tongue

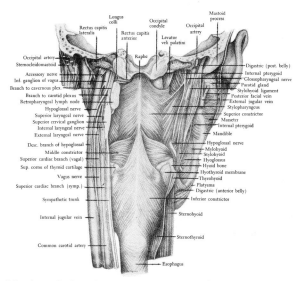

Fig. 6-10. Muscles of the pharynx. (Reprinted with permission of C. V. Mosby Company and the author from Francis, *Introduction to Human Anatomy*, 2nd ed., 1954.)

D. Muscles of the Pharynx. The muscles of the pharynx constitute the muscular portions of its wall and bring about swallowing by their constricting action.

Name, *Action*	Location	O—Origin I—Insertion
Constrictor pharyngis superior *Constricts pharynx during swallowing*	Wall of pharynx	O—Pterygoid processes of sphenoid bone, pterygomandibular ligament, and mylohyoid ridge of mandible I—Posterior median line of pharynx; occipital bone
Constrictor pharyngis medius *Constricts pharynx in swallowing*	Wall of pharynx	O—Greater and lesser cornua of hyoid and stylohyoid ligaments I—Posterior median line of pharynx
Constrictor pharyngis inferior *Constricts pharynx in swallowing*	Wall of pharynx	O—Thyroid and cricoid cartilages of larynx I—Posterior median line of pharynx
Stylopharyngeus *Elevates larynx and pharynx during swallowing*	Wall of pharynx	O—Styloid process of temporal bone I—Lateral wall of pharynx; posterior border of thyroid cartilage

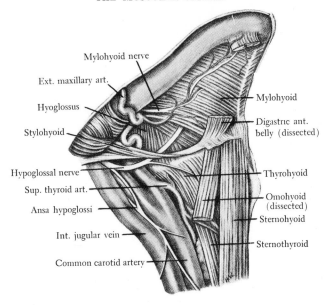

Fig. 6-11. Extrinsic muscles of the larynx. (Reprinted with permission of C. V. Mosby Company and the author from Francis, *Introduction to Human Anatomy*, 2nd ed., 1954.)

E. Muscles of the Soft Palate. These muscles play an important role in swallowing (deglutition) in that they (1) constrict the isthmus of the fauces, thus preventing the bolus of food from re-entering the buccal cavity, and (2) close off the nasal portion of the pharynx, thus preventing food from entering the nasal cavity.

Name, *Action*	Location	O—Origin I—Insertion
Palatoglossus *Constricts faucial isthmus*	In anterior palatine pillar (glossopharyngeal arch), the anterior border of tonsillar recess; and lateral border, isthmus of fauces	O—Lateral side of tongue I—Soft palate
Palatopharyngeus *Constricts fauces and elevates larynx and pharynx in swallowing*	In posterior palatine pillar (pharyngopalatine arch), which forms posterior border of tonsillar recess; and lateral border of pharyngeal isthmus	O—Soft palate and cartilage of auditory tube I—Lateral wall of larynx and posterior border of thyroid cartilage of larynx
Levator veli palatini *Elevates palate, closing off nasal pharynx*	In dorsolateral portion of soft palate	O—Petrous portion of temporal bone and cartilage of auditory tube I—Soft palate

Name, *Action*	Location	O—Origin I—Insertion
Tensor veli palatini *Tenses velum of soft palate and opens auditory tube*	Lateral to levator veli palatini	O—Scaphoid fossa and angular spine of sphenoid bone and cartilage of auditory tube I—Soft palate
Musculus uvulae *Draws uvula upward; assists in closing nasal pharynx*	Within the uvula	O—Posterior nasal spine of palatine bone I—Uvula

II. MUSCLES OF THE NECK

A. Muscles that Move the Head. Flexion, extension, and rotation are the principal movements of the head. Flexion and extension occur at the atlanto-occipital articulation (between the occipital bone and the atlas); lateral flexion (bending the head and neck sideways) is also possible. Rotation occurs at the atlanto-epistrophic articulation.

Name, *Action*	Location	O—Origin I—Insertion
Sternocleidomastoideus *When both muscles contract, head is extended (i.e., tipped backward); if head is fixed, vertebral column is flexed in cervical region (head and neck pulled forward). Unilateral contraction turns face toward opposite side*	Large muscles extending diagonally across sides of the neck; when head is rotated, one of them stands out prominently	O—Clavicle (median third) and sternum (manubrium) I—Mastoid process of temporal bone
Splenius capitis *When both contract, head is extended; when one contracts, head is rotated and face tipped upward*	Extends diagonally across posterolateral side of neck	O—Spinous processes of lower cervical and upper thoracic vertebrae I—Mastoid process of temporal bone and lateral portion of superior nuchal line
Semispinalis capitis *When both contract, head is extended; when one contracts, head is rotated slightly and face tipped upward*	A band of muscles consisting of several slips, which lie alongside spines of cervical and thoracic vertebrae under splenius capitis	O—Transverse and spinous processes of lower cervical and upper thoracic vertebrae I—On lower surface of occipital bone between superior and inferior nuchal lines
Longissimus capitis *When both contract, head is extended; when one contracts, head is rotated and inclined*	A long, band-like muscle lying under the splenius capitis and lateral to the semispinalis capitis	O—Transverse processes of upper four thoracic vertebrae and articular processes of last four cervical vertebrae I—To mastoid process by a short tendon

B. Muscles that Move the Hyoid Bone and the Larynx. These muscles, which play an important role in swallowing movements, are classified as either suprahyoid or infrahyoid. The *suprahyoid group*, which lies superior to the hyoid bone, comprises the stylohyoid, digastricus, mylohyoideus, and geniohyoideus. When the *hyoid bone* is fixed, they depress the mandible (open the mouth); when the *mandible* is fixed, they elevate the hyoid and with it the larynx, thus raising the base of the tongue and forcing the food into the pharynx, the first step in deglutition; when both the hyoid bone and the mandible are fixed, these muscles assist in flexing the head. The *infrahyoid group*, which lies below the hyoid bone, comprises the sternohyoideus, omohyoideus, sternothyreoideus, and thyreohyoideus. The action of these muscles is to move the hyoid and the larynx downward.

Name, *Action*	Location	O—Origin I—Insertion
Stylohyoideus *Pulls hyoid bone upward and posteriorly*	A long, slender muscle located within the angle of the mandible	O—Styloid process of temporal bone I—Body of hyoid bone
Digastricus *Anterior belly pulls hyoid upward and forward; depresses mandible if hyoid is fixed. Posterior belly pulls hyoid upward and posteriorly; assists in extending head if hyoid is fixed*	Possess two bellies with a common rounded tendon which perforates the stylohyoideus and lies below the mandible on the mylohyoid and hyoglossus muscles in the anterior triangle	O—Anterior belly on inner surface of mandibular symphysis; posterior belly on medial surface of mastoid process of temporal bone I—By an intermediate tendon to body and cornua of the hyoid
Mylohyoideus *Elevates hyoid bone and raises floor of mouth; when hyoid is fixed, depresses mandible*	A thin, flat muscular sheet forming floor of mouth	O—Medial surface of body of mandible I—Hyoid bone and median raphe; extends from mandibular symphysis to hyoid
Geniohyoideus *Elevates hyoid bone and pulls it anteriorly*	Parallels anterior belly of digastricus; is covered by mylohyoideus	O—Inferior mental spine of mandible I—Body of hyoid bone
Sternohyoideus *Depresses hyoid bone; in forced inspiration, assists in raising sternum*	Medially located in anterior portion of neck	O—Medial end of clavicle and posterior surface of manubrium of sternum I—Inferior border of body of hyoid bone
Omohyoideus *Depresses hyoid bone*	A slender muscle lying lateral to sternohyoideus and obliquely crossing sternothyroideus	O—Superior border of scapula I—Body of hyoid bone
Sternothyroideus *Depresses larynx and hyoid bone*	Lies lateral and internal to sternohyoideus; lower end partially covered by sternocleidomastoideus	O—Posterior surface of manubrium and first costal cartilage I—Thyroid cartilage of larynx

Name, *Action*	Location	O—Origin I—Insertion
Thyrohyoideus *Draws hyoid bone toward larynx, or vice versa*	A short, broad muscle lying between hyoid bone and larynx	O—Thyroid cartilage of larynx I—Body and greater cornua of hyoid bone

C. Muscles that Act on the Upper Ribs. These include the scalenus anterior, scalenus medius, and scalenus posterior. All three of them are located in the neck beneath the sternocleidomastoideus. When the neck is fixed, these muscles elevate the first two ribs, assisting in forced inspiration. When the thorax is fixed, bilateral action flexes the neck, and unilateral action bends the neck and head to the side.

Name	Location	O—Origin I—Insertion
Scalenus anterior (See above)		O—Transverse processes of third to sixth cervical vertebrae I—First rib
Scalenus medius (See above)	The three muscles together constituting a triangular mass extending from the first two ribs to the transverse processes of the fifth to the sixth cervical vertebrae	O—Transverse processes of third to sixth cervical vertebrae I—First and second ribs
Scalenus posterior (See above)		O—Transverse processes of fifth and sixth cervical vertebrae I—Second rib; sometimes also third rib

III. MUSCLES OF THE TRUNK AND EXTREMITIES

A. Muscles that Move the Vertebral Column. The principal movements of the vertebral column are flexion (forward movement or "bending") and extension (backward movement or "straightening"). These movements occur mainly in the cervical and lumbar regions. Unilateral contraction results in a sidewise movement or lateral flexion.

Name, *Action*	Location	O—Origin I—Insertion
Iliopsoas *When femurs are fixed, this muscle acts to flex vertebral column on hips*	(This muscle is a flexor of the femur and as such is described under Muscles that Act on the Femur, on page 130.)	

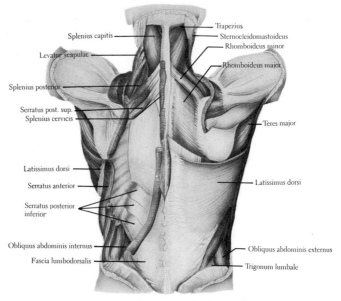

Fig. 6-12. Intermediate back muscles.

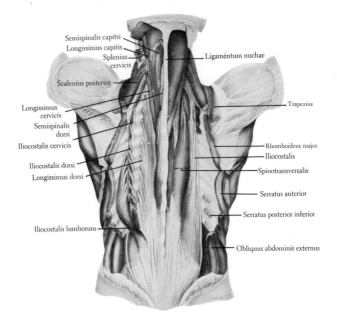

Fig. 6-13. Deep back muscles.

Name, *Action*	Location	O—Origin I—Insertion
Quadratus lumborum *Bilateral action extends vertebral column; unilateral action bends vertebral column sidewise*	A quadrilateral-shaped muscle forming portion of posterior wall of abdomen between pelvis and thorax	O—Crest of ilium and transverse processes of lower lumbar vertebrae I—Transverse processes of upper lumbar vertebrae and inferior surface of twelfth rib
Erector spinae (sacrospinalis) *Extends vertebral column; unilateral action bends vertebral column sidewise or rotates it; assists in expiratory movements by depressing ribs*	A long muscular mass extending alongside vertebral column from sacrum to skull. Consists of two main portions: *iliocostalis* (lateral) and *longissimus* (medial)	O—Ilium, sacrum, and lumbar and thoracic vertebrae I—Lumbar, thoracic, and cervical vertebrae. The whole has a common origin, but its insertion is through numerous parts, some of which are given special names

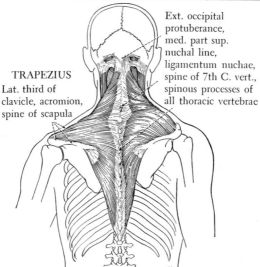

Ext. occipital protuberance, med. part sup. nuchal line, ligamentum nuchae, spine of 7th C. vert., spinous processes of all thoracic vertebrae

TRAPEZIUS
Lat. third of clavicle, acromion, spine of scapula

Fig. 6-14. Trapezius. (Reprinted with permission of W. B. Saunders Company from Millard, King, and Showers, *Human Anatomy and Physiology*, 4th ed., 1956.)

B. Muscles that Move the Scapula. Movements of the scapula are principally abduction (away from the midline) and adduction (toward the midline). The scapula may also be elevated and depressed, or rotated. The abductors include the serratus anterior and pectoralis minor. The adductors include the trapezius and rhomboideus. The elevator is the levator scapulae.

Name, *Action*	Location	O—Origin I—Insertion
Serratus anterior 　*Pulls scapula laterally and forward (abduction); elevates ribs when scapula is fixed*	Lies on lateral surface of thoracic wall covering posterior portions of ribs. Its anterior border has a serrated or notched appearance	O—Lateral surface of first nine ribs I—Vertebral border of scapula
Pectoralis minor 　*Abducts scapula and pulls it downward*	Lies under pectoralis major	O—Sternal end of second to fifth ribs I—Corocoid process of scapula
Trapezius 　*The three portions acting as a whole adduct scapula; superior portion alone elevates and rotates scapula, raising shoulder; inferior alone depresses and rotates scapula, lowering shoulder. When scapula is fixed, contraction of superior portion extends head and pulls it laterally.*	The most superficial muscle on upper surface of back. A large triangular muscle consisting of three portions: superior, middle, and inferior	O—External protuberance and superior nuchal line of occipital bone, ligamentum nuchae, spinous processes of seventh cervical and all thoracic vertebrae I—Lateral third of clavicle; spine and acromion of scapula
Rhomboideus major 　*Elevates and pulls scapula medially; rotates scapula so that point of shoulder is depressed*	A thin, flat rhombus-shaped muscle lying under trapezius. Fibers run obliquely downward and laterally from their origin	O—Spinous processes of first four thoracic vertebrae I—Vertebral border of scapula
Levator scapulae 　*Elevates scapula*	A long, narrow muscle lying in neck under trapezius	O—Transverse processes of first four cervical vertebrae I—Vertebral border of scapula

C. Muscles of Respiration. The muscles involved in respiration are those which either directly or indirectly bring about changes in the volume of the thoracic cavity. Any muscle attached to the thoracic cage may be involved, such as the scalenes and the sternocleidomastoid. Those which increase the volume bring about *inspiration*; those which decrease it bring about *expiration*. The inspiratory muscles include the diaphragm and the external intercostals. The expiratory muscles include four abdominal muscles (rectus abdominis, obliquus abdominis externus, obliquus abdominis internus, and transversus abdominis) and the internal intercostals.

DIAPHRAGM. The location and description, origin, and action of the diaphragm are as follows.

Location and Description. The diaphragm is a musculofibrous structure separating the thoracic and abdominal cavities. The convex por-

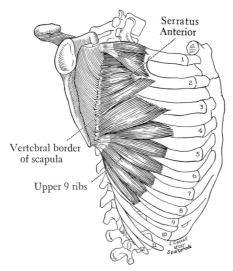

Serratus
Anterior

Vertebral border
of scapula

Upper 9 ribs

Fig. 6-15. Serratus anterior.

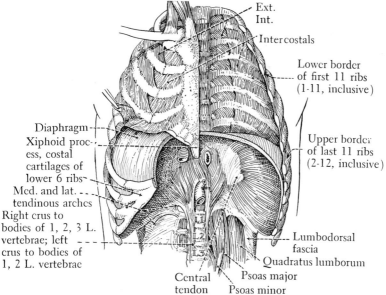

Ext.
Int.

Intercostals

Lower border
of first 11 ribs
(1-11, inclusive)

Diaphragm
Xiphoid process, costal
cartilages of
lower 6 ribs
Med. and lat.
tendinous arches
Right crus to
bodies of 1, 2, 3 L.
vertebrae; left
crus to bodies of
1, 2 L. vertebrae

Upper border
of last 11 ribs
(2-12, inclusive)

Lumbodorsal
fascia
Quadratus lumborum
Psoas major
Psoas minor

Central
tendon

Fig. 6-16. Diaphragm and intercostal muscles.

(Figs. 6-15 and 6-16 reprinted with permission of W. B. Saunders Company from Millard, King, and Showers, *Human Anatomy and Physiology*, 4th ed., 1956.)

tion forms the floor of the thorax; the concave portion forms the roof of the abdominal cavity. The central portion is fibrous, consisting of the *central tendon*. The diaphragm has three large openings: (1) the *aortic opening*, through which pass the aorta, thoracic duct, and azygous vein; (2) the *esophageal opening*, through which pass the esophagus and vagal nerve; and (3) the *caval opening*, through which pass the inferior vena cava and branches of the phrenic nerve. Smaller openings transmit the splanchnic nerves and hemiazygous vein.

Origin. Inner surfaces of six lower ribs and their costal cartilages; bodies of lumbar vertebrae; posterior surface of xiphoid process of sternum.

Insertion. Central tendon of diaphragm.

Action. Depresses central tendon so that the diaphragm as a whole descends, thus increasing vertical diameter of the thoracic cavity. This reduces intrathoracic pressure, and *inspiration* occurs; it also increases intra-abdominal pressure, which assists in expulsion of substances from the organs within the abdominal cavity, as in defecation, urination, vomiting, and childbirth.

Name, *Action*	Location	O—Origin I—Insertion
Intercostal Muscles **Intercostales externi** (external intercostals) 　*Elevate ribs, assisting in* 　*inspiration*	In intercostal spaces from tubercles of ribs to intercostal cartilages. Fibers pass obliquely forward and downward	O—Lower margin of each rib external to costal groove I—Upper margin of the next lower rib
Intercostales interni (internal intercostals) 　*Action questionable; they* 　*probably depress the ribs,* 　*assisting in expiration*	Same as preceding, except that fibers pass obliquely downward and posteriorly	O—Lower margin of each rib. Near angles of ribs from internal lip of costal groove; near distal ends of ribs from both internal and external lips of groove I—Upper margin of the next lower rib

MUSCLES OF THE VENTRAL ABDOMINAL WALL. With the exception of the rectus abdominis, these are thin sheets of muscle tissue whose fibers run at right angles to each other. They act to support the abdominal viscera and to bring about changes in intra-abdominal pressure. Compression of the abdominal viscera causes a pressure to be exerted on the underside of the diaphragm which results in expiration.

The rectus abdominis is a larger paired band of muscles which depresses the sternum and ribs and pulls the thorax downward, flexing the vertebral column.

Name, *Action*	Location	O—Origin I—Insertion
Obliquus abdominis externus (external oblique) *Compresses abdomen and depresses ribs. Unilateral contraction assists in flexion and rotation of vertebral column*	Most superficial layer. Fibers pass diagonally, ventrally, and medially from their origin	O—Surfaces of lower eight ribs I—By an extensive aponeurosis * to linea alba and iliac crest. Lower border of aponeurosis forms *inguinal ligament*, a band extending from anterior superior iliac spine to pubic tubercle
Obliquus abdominis internus (internal oblique) (Same as *external oblique*)	Lies directly beneath external oblique, its fibers running in the opposite direction (*i.e.*, from their origin cranially and medially)	O—Lumbodorsal fascia, iliac crest, lateral portion of inguinal ligament I—By an extensive aponeurosis to lower three ribs, linea alba, pubic tubercle, and symphysis
Transversus abdominis *Compresses abdomen and depresses sternum*	Lies directly beneath internal oblique, fibers running transversely	O—Costal cartilages of lower six ribs, lumbodorsal fascia, iliac crest, and inguinal ligament
Rectus abdominis *Depresses sternum and ribs, thus increasing intra-abdominal pressure; flexes vertebral column by pulling thorax downward. When sternum is fixed, pelvis is flexed on trunk*	A paired band of muscles extending from sternum to pubis on either side of linea alba	O—Crest of pubis I—Xiphoid process of sternum, and costal cartilages of fifth to seventh ribs

* In males, this aponeurosis is pierced by an opening, the *subcutaneous inguinal ring*, through which passes the spermatic cord. In females, it transmits the *round ligament* of the uterus.

D. Muscles that Act on the Humerus. Owing to the laxness of the ligaments and the shallowness of the glenoid fossa, the degree of mobility at this joint is great and a wide range of movements is possible. The principal movements and the primary muscles by which they are accomplished are:

Abduction: deltoideus, supraspinatus
Adduction: pectoralis major
Flexion: coracobrachialis
Extension: teres major

External rotation: infraspinatus
teres minor
Internal rotation: latissimus dorsi
subscapularis

Note the multiple action of some of these muscles, as shown in the table on page 124. For example, the deltoideus and supraspinatus, which abduct the arm, assist in lateral rotation. The pectoralis major, which adducts the arm, flexes and rotates it medially.

Name, *Action*	Location	O—Origin I—Insertion
Deltoideus *Abduction of humerus; anterior portion, acting singly, flexes and rotates humerus medially; posterior portion extends humerus and brings about lateral rotation*	A thick triangular muscle forming the shoulder prominence	O—Acromium, spine of scapula, and lateral third of clavicle I—Deltoid tuberosity of humerus
Supraspinatus *Abduction and lateral rotation of humerus*	Occupies supraspinous fossa of scapula	O—Surface of supraspinous fossa I—Uppermost facet of greater tubercle of humerus
Pectoralis major *Adduction of humerus; also flexes and rotates arm medially*	A large fan-shaped muscle covering upper portion of chest	O—Medial half of clavicle; sternum, costal cartilages of second to sixth ribs; aponeurosis of external oblique muscle
Infraspinatus *Lateral or external rotation of humerus*	Lies in infraspinous fossa of scapula	O—Surface of infraspinous fossa I—Greater tubercle of humerus
Teres minor *Lateral rotation and adduction of humerus*	A small muscle lying along axillary border of scapula	O—Axillary border of scapula I—Greater tubercle of humerus distal to insertion of infraspinatus
Latissimus dorsi *Medial or internal rotation; also extends arm when arm is flexed and adducts it when arm is abducted*	A large, flat triangular muscle superficially located on lateral posterior surface of back	O—By lumbodorsal aponeurosis (fascia) to spinous processes of lower six thoracic and all lumbar vertebrae, posterior surface of sacrum, crest of ilium, and lower four ribs
Subscapularis *Rotates humerus medially*	Occupies subscapular fossa on costal surface of scapula	O—Surface of subscapular fossa I—Lesser tubercle of humerus
Coracobrachialis *Flexor of humerus; also serves as an adductor*	A flat band-like muscle lying in proximal portion of upper arm alongside short head of biceps	O—Coracoid process of scapula I—Medial surface of humerus about middle of shaft
Teres major *Extensor of arm assisting latissimus dorsi; also adductor and medial rotator*	Lies along axillary border of scapula	O—Axillary border of scapula at inferior angle I—Along medial lip of intertubercular groove just below lesser tubercle of humerus

E. Muscles that Act on the Forearm. These muscles bring about flexion and extension at the humero-ulnar joint and pronation and supination at the radio-ulnar joint.

Flexors: biceps brachii, brachialis
      brachioradialis
Extensors: triceps brachii

Pronators: Pronator teres, pronator
      quadratus
Supinators: Biceps brachii, supinator

Name, *Action*	Location	O—Origin I—Insertion
Biceps brachii *Flexor and supinator of forearm; latter action is especially pronounced when arm is flexed. Acting singly, long head abducts humerus, short head adducts it. Biceps acts to stabilize head of humerus in glenoid cavity*	A large spindle-shaped muscle forming the major portion of the bulge on the anterior surface of the upper arm. Formed by union of two distinct heads	O—*Long head*, by a long, slender tendon into supraglenoid tuberosity of scapula (tendon passes through intertubercular groove). *Short head*, by a tendon to coracoid process of scapula I—Into tuberosity of radius at proximal end and by an aponeurosis (semilunar fascia) to fascia of forearm
Brachialis *Flexes forearm*	On anterior surface of humerus; partially covered by biceps	O—Anterior surface of distal half of humerus I—Inferior portion of coronoid process of ulna
Triceps brachii *Extension of forearm; long head extends and adducts arm*	A large muscle occupying entire posterior surface of arm	O—By three heads: middle or *long head* into infraglenoid tuberosity of scapula; outer or *lateral head* onto posterior surface of humerus above intertubercular groove; inner or *medial head* onto posterior surface of distal half of humerus I—Olecranon process of ulna
Brachioradialis *Flexes forearm. When forearm is extended and pronated, it acts as a supinator; when forearm is flexed and supinated, it acts as a pronator*	A long spindle-shaped muscle lying along lateral surface of radius on volar aspect of forearm	O—Upper two-thirds of epicondylar ridge of humerus I—Proximal portion of base of styloid process of radius
Supinator *Supinates forearm*	A short, flat rhombus-shaped muscle on proximal, lateral surface of forearm	O—Lateral epicondyle of humerus and proximal portion of ulna I—Volar and lateral surface of radius proximal to oblique line
Pronator teres *Pronates and flexes forearm*	A spindle-shaped muscle extending diagonally across proximal surface of forearm on volar aspect	O—Median epicondyle of humerus I—Lateral surface of radius
Pronator quadratus *Pronates forearm*	A short, square muscle lying at distal end of forearm. Fibers are crossed by tendons of all flexors of hand	O—Distal end of ulna, volar surface I—Distal end of radius, volar surface

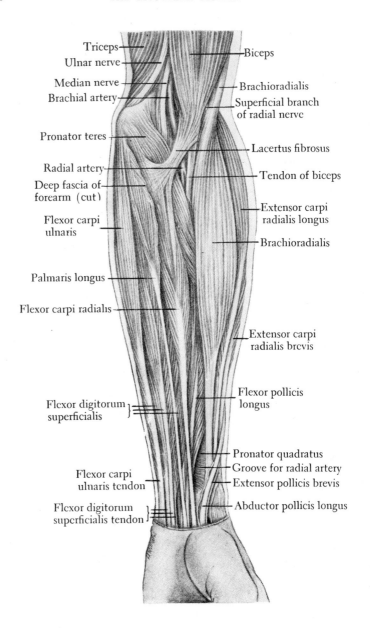

Triceps
Ulnar nerve
Median nerve
Brachial artery
Pronator teres
Radial artery
Deep fascia of forearm (cut)
Flexor carpi ulnaris
Palmaris longus
Flexor carpi radialis
Flexor digitorum superficialis
Flexor carpi ulnaris tendon
Flexor digitorum superficialis tendon

Biceps
Brachioradialis
Superficial branch of radial nerve
Lacertus fibrosus
Tendon of biceps
Extensor carpi radialis longus
Brachioradialis
Extensor carpi radialis brevis
Flexor pollicis longus
Pronator quadratus
Groove for radial artery
Extensor pollicis brevis
Abductor pollicis longus

Fig. 6-17. Superficial muscles of left forearm. (Reprinted with permission of C. V. Mosby Company and the author from Francis, *Introduction to Human Anatomy*, 2nd ed., 1954.)

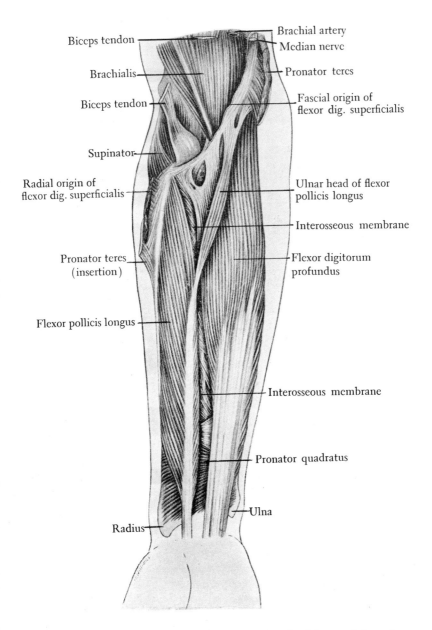

Fig. 6-18. Deep muscles of right forearm. (Reprinted with permission of C. V. Mosby Company and the author from Francis, *Introduction to Human Anatomy*, 2nd ed., 1954.)

F. Muscles that Act on the Hand and Its Digits. There are many muscles in this group. Only a few of the superficial ones will be listed here. Flexion and extension may occur at the wrist and at the metacarpophalangeal and interphalangeal joints. Abduction and adduction of the hand may take place at the wrist; abduction and adduction of the digits may occur at the metacarpophalangeal joints. These muscles may be grouped as to their general location, as follows: those on the anterior aspect of the forearm (brachioradialis, flexor carpi radialis, palmaris longus, flexor carpi ulnaris); those on the dorsal aspect of the forearm (extensor carpi ulnaris, extensor digitorum communis, extensor pollicis brevis); and the intrinsic muscles of the hand (adductor pollicis brevis, flexor pollicis brevis, abductor digiti minimi).

Name, *Action*	Location	O—Origin I—Insertion
Flexor carpi radialis *Flexes hand at wrist; flexes forearm*	Medially located on anterior surface of forearm	O—Median epicondyle of humerus I—Base of second metacarpal
Palmaris longus *Flexes hand and tightens palmar aponeurosis; a weak flexor of forearm*	Lies medial to flexor carpi radialis	O—Median epicondyle of humerus I—By palmar aponeurosis to volar surface of hand
Flexor carpi ulnaris *Flexor and adductor of hand at wrist; flexor of forearm*	The most medial muscle of volar aspect of arm	O—Median epicondyle of humerus and proximal two-thirds of ulna I—Chiefly on pisiform bone but with tendinous extensions to palmar aponeurosis and bases of third, fourth, and fifth metacarpals
Extensor carpi ulnaris *Extends and adducts hand; assists in extending and supinating forearm*	Along dorsal surface of ulna	O—Lateral epicondyle of humerus and proximal portion of ulna I—Base of fifth metacarpal
Extensor digitorum communis *Extends wrist and fingers; produces movements at all joints; extends forearm*	A broad, flat muscle on posterior surface of arm. Gives rise to four tendons	O—Lateral epicondyle of humerus I—By four tendons into dorsal surface of phalanges of fingers
Extensor pollicis brevis *Extends thumb; abducts first metacarpal*	A deep muscle lying under extensor digitorum communis. Becomes a superficial muscle in distal portion of arm	O—Midportion of radius on dorsomedian surface I—Base of first phalanx of thumb
Adductor pollicis brevis *Adducts thumb; at same time, flexes first phalanx and extends second or terminal phalanx*	Forms prominent portion of *thenar eminence* (fleshy portion of thumb)	O—Trapezium and scaphoid bones of carpus; transverse carpal ligament

Name, *Action*	Location	O—Origin I—Insertion
Flexor pollicis brevis *Flexes and adducts thumb*	Lies medial to and is partially covered by adductor pollicis brevis	O—Distal row of carpal bones and transverse carpal ligament I—Base of first phalanx of thumb
Abductor digiti minimi *Abducts little finger*	Principal muscle of hypothenar eminence (fleshy portion on medial surface of palm)	O—Pisiform bone I—Base of first phalanx of little finger

G. Muscles of the Pelvic Outlet. These muscles can be placed in three groups: those of the *pelvic diaphragm* (coccygeus, levator ani, sphincter ani externus); those of the *urogenital diaphragm* (transversus perinei superficialis and profundus, sphincter urethrae); *external genital muscles* (bulbocavernosus, ischiocavernosus).

MUSCLES OF THE PELVIC DIAPHRAGM. These muscles are as follows.

Name, *Action*	Location	O—Origin I—Insertion
Coccygeus *Flexes sacrum and coccyx; assists levator ani in supporting pelvic and abdominal organs*	A triangular muscle lying between spine of ischium and sacrum and coccyx	O—Spine of ischium I—Sacrum and coccyx
Levator ani *Supports pelvic organs; flexes coccyx; elevates rectum during defecation. In female it constricts the vagina*	A broad muscular sheet forming major portion of pelvic floor. Has three parts: *iliococcygeal, pubococcygeal,* and *puborectal*	O—On inner side of pubis along a *tendinous arch* extending from pubic symphysis to spine of ilium I—Coccyx and raphe between coccyx and anus
Sphincter ani externus *Closes anal canal and anus and fixes central tendinous point of perineum*	External sphincter of anus	O—Anococcygeal raphe I—On central tendinous point of perineum

MUSCLES OF THE UROGENITAL DIAPHRAGM. The *urogenital diaphragm* consists of the transversus perenei profundus covered above by the fascia diaphragmatis urogenitalis superior and below by the fascia diaphragmatis urogenitalis inferior (membrana perenei). The transversus perenei profundus originates from the junction of the pubic and ischial rami and unites with its fellow in a median raphe below and behind the membranous part of the urethra. It acts as a sphincter compressing the membranous portion of the urethra in the male and the supra-vaginal portion of the urethra in the female.

EXTERNAL GENITAL MUSCLES. The principal external genital muscles are:

Bulbocavernosus, consisting of two symmetrical halves. In the *male* it surrounds the corpus cavernosum penis and is inserted by an aponeurosis onto its superior surface. It compresses the urethra, acting to empty it; it also compresses the erectile tissue, thus assisting in bringing about an erection. In the *female* its two halves lie on each side of the vestibule. By contraction they act to close the vaginal orifice. They assist in bringing about erection of the clitoris.

Ischiocavernosus, a spindle-shaped muscle arising from the inferior ramus and tuberosity of the ischium. It is inserted into the crura of the penis and clitoris near the pubic symphysis. It assists in bringing about an erection of these organs by compressing the crura. The muscles are larger in the male than in the female.

H. Muscles that Act on the Femur. Movements at the hip joint include flexion and extension, abduction and adduction, and lateral and medial rotation.

Flexors: iliacus, psoas major (combined, known as iliopsoas)
Extensor: gluteus maximus
Adductors: pectineus, adductor longus, adductor brevis, adductor magnus
Abductors: tensor fascia latae, gluteus medius
Lateral rotator: piriformis
Medial rotator: gluteus minimus

Name, *Action*	Location	O—Origin I—Insertion
Iliacus (See Psoas major, below)	A triangular muscle occupying iliac fossa	O—Iliac fossa and base of sacrum I—Lesser trochanter of femur
Psoas major *Flexes femur; adducts and rotates it medially. When thighs are fixed, this and iliacus act together to flex vertebral column and pelvis on femurs. Unilateral action tends to rotate vertebral column and pelvis to opposite side*	Fuses with iliacus, with which it has common tendon for insertion. They are commonly grouped together as the *iliopsoas muscle*	O—Bodies, transverse processes, and intervertebral discs of lumbar vertebrae I—Lesser trochanter of femur
Gluteus maximus *Extends femur; rotates it laterally. When thighs are fixed, pelvis is drawn dorsally*	A large fleshy muscle forming prominence of buttock	O—Posterior portion of iliac crest and lateral surface of ilium posterior to posterior gluteal line; posterior surface of sacrum and coccyx and sacroiliac ligaments I—Iliotibial band and gluteal tuberosity of femur

Name, *Action*	Location	O—Origin I—Insertion
Pectineus *Adducts and flexes femur*	On inner side of thigh. Most superior of the adductor muscles	O—Crest of pubis I—Pectineal line of femur
Adductor longus *Adducts and flexes femur; also rotates it laterally*	A flat triangular muscle lying medial to pectineus	O—Superior ramus of pubis I—On medial portion of linea aspera
Adductor brevis *Adducts femur; also rotates it laterally*	A short muscle lying beneath pectineus and adductor longus	O—Inferior ramus of pubis I—Upper third of linea aspera of femur
Adductor magnus *Adducts femur; also rotates it laterally. Lower portion extends thigh*	A large triangular muscle lying beneath the other adductor muscles	O—Inferior ramus and tuberosity of ischium I—Along entire length of linea aspera, medial supracondylar line, and adductor tubercle of medial epicondyle
Tensor fasciae latae *Tenses the fascia lata; when leg is free, it flexes, abducts, and medially rotates the thigh*	A flat muscle lying along lateral upper surface of thigh. Fibers pass about one-third the length of the thigh	O—By a flat tendinous band to anterior portion of crest of ilium I—Iliotibial band, which passes down lateral side of thigh where it is closely fused with fascia lata to its termination on anterolateral surface of upper end of tibia
Gluteus medius *Abductor of femur. Superior portion may flex and rotate femur medially; posterior portion may extend and rotate femur laterally*	On lateral surface of ilium	O—Anterior three-fourths of iliac crest and iliac surface between anterior and posterior gluteal lines I—Greater trochanter of femur
Piriformis *Lateral rotator and abductor of thigh; also a weak extensor*	Lies underneath posterior portion of gluteus medius	O—Anterior surface of sacrum, sciatic notch of ilium, and sacrotuberous ligament I—Tip of greater trochanter of femur
Gluteus minimus *Medial rotator of femur; also an abductor*	A deep-lying muscle of hip, covered by gluteus medium and piriformis	O—Lateral surface of ilium between anterior and inferior gluteal lines; capsule of hip joint I—Anterior surface of greater trochanter of femur

I. Muscles that Act on the Leg. The principal actions produced at the knee joint are extension and flexion. However, some of the muscles have their insertions on the pelvic bone and consequently may bring about rotation, abduction, and adduction movements.

Flexors: quadriceps femoris. Includes four muscles listed below.

Extensors: sartorius, the "hamstring" muscles, gracilis, popliteus.

QUADRICEPS FEMORIS: a large muscular mass forming the anterior portion of the thigh. It is composed of four heads, each of which is considered a separate muscle. All four heads converge into a common tendon and have a single insertion. The quadriceps is one of the largest and most powerful muscles of the body.

Name	Location	O—Origin I—Insertion
Rectus femoris	Most anterior of the group	O—By two tendons, one to the anterior inferior iliac spine, the other to the rim of acetabulum
Vastus lateralis	Lies lateral and posterior to rectus femoris	O—Along medial lip of upper half of linea aspera
Vastus medialis	Lies medial and posterior to rectus femoris	O—Medial lip of linea aspera throughout its entire length
Vastus intermedius	Lies deep to rectus femoris and vastus medialis, adjacent to femur	O—From anterolateral surface of femur and distal half of lateral margin of linea aspera I—All four muscles insert by a common tendon which passes over the knee enclosing the patella and inserting on the tuberosity of the tibia. The tendon from the apex of the patella to the tuberosity is called the *patellar ligament*.

All four muscles have extension of the leg for their action. The rectus femoris also acts as a flexor of the femur.

Name, *Action*	Location	O—Origin I—Insertion
Sartorius *Flexes leg at the knee; flexes thigh at hip and rotates it laterally; functions in crossing of legs*	A long, strap-like muscle that passes diagonally across anterior and medial surfaces of thigh. Called "tailor's muscle"	O—The anterior superior spine of ilium I—On medial surface of tibia at proximal end near tuberosity

THE "HAMSTRING" MUSCLES: three flexor muscles located on the posterior side of the thigh; antagonists of the quadriceps femoris.

Name, *Action*	Location	O—Origin I—Insertion
Biceps femoris *Flexor of leg; external rotator; long head extends and adducts thigh*	Lies on posterior lateral aspect of thigh	O—Long head from ischial tuberosity; short head from middle third of linea aspera
Semitendinosus *Flexes leg and rotates it medially; extends thigh; also adducts thigh and rotates it medially*	Lies medial to biceps femoris, its upper end being partially covered by it	O—Ischial tuberosity I—Medial surface of proximal end of tibia
Semimembranosus *Flexes leg and rotates it medially; extends thigh; also adducts thigh and rotates it medially*	Lies internal to and is partially covered by biceps femoris and semitendinosus	O—Ischial tuberosity I—Posterior surface of medial condyle of tibia

Name, *Action*	Location	O—Origin I—Insertion
Gracilis *Adducts and flexes thigh; also rotates it medially; flexes leg at knee*	A long, thin muscle located on medial aspect of thigh	O—Inferior rami of pubis and ischium I—On medial surface of thigh just below medial condyle
Popliteus *Flexor of leg; also medial rotator*	A short, flat triangular muscle, deeply situated and hidden by heads of gastrocnemius	O—Lateral epicondyle of femur I—On posterior surface of proximal end of tibia

J. Muscles that Act on the Foot and Its Digits. *Movements of the foot* occur at the ankle and the tarsal joints. Extension or *plantar flexion* is the downward motion in which the foot is "straightened"; flexion or *dorsiflexion* is the movement in which the foot is bent upward. These movements take place at the ankle joint between the malleoli of the tibia and fibula and the talus. Other movements of the foot are those in which the foot is turned inward and the sole partially upward (*inversion*) and the opposite movement in which the foot is turned outward (*eversion*). These movements take place mainly between the tarsal bones. *Movements of the digits of the foot* occur at the metatarsal-phalangeal joints or the interphalangeal joints. The movements are flexion and extension. Abduction moves other digits away from the second digit; adduction is the opposite movement.

MUSCLES THAT ACT ON THE FOOT. These may be grouped into extensors (plantar flexors) and flexors (dorsiflexors):

Extensors: gastrocnemius, soleus, plantaris, tibialis posterior, peroneus longus, peroneus brevis.

Flexors: tibialis anterior, peroneous tertius.

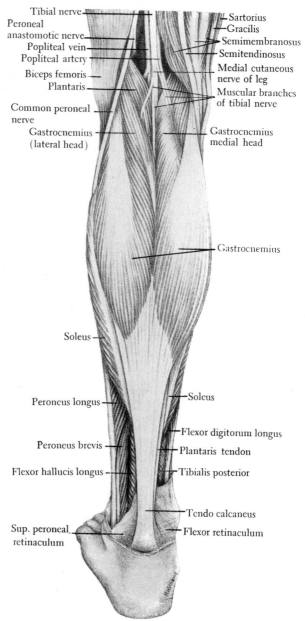

Fig. 6-19. Muscles for lower leg. (Reprinted with permission of C. V. Mosby Company and the author from Francis, *Introduction to Human Anatomy*, 2nd ed., 1954.)

Name, *Action*	Location	O—Origin I—Insertion
Gastrocnemius *Extends foot; flexes leg at knee joint*	A large superficial muscle forming major portion of calf of leg	O—By two heads from lateral and medial condyles of femur I—Into tuberosity of calcaneus bone by *tendon of Achilles*
Soleus *Extends foot*	A broad, flat muscle lying under the gastrocnemius	O—From posterior surface of head and upper portion of shaft of fibula; medial surface of upper end of tibia below popliteal line I—Into calcaneus by tendon of Achilles with gastrocnemius
Plantaris *Extends foot; flexes leg*	A long, slender muscle lying under the gastrocnemius	O—Just above lateral condyle of femur I—By a long, slender tendon lying alongside tendon of Achilles, to fibrous tissue about calcaneus
Tibialis posterior *Extends and inverts foot; supports the arches*	A deeply placed muscle of posterior side of leg	O—Over an extensive area of posterior surfaces of interosseous membrane and proximal portions of tibia and fibula I—By a long tendon which passes through a groove behind medial malleolus to insert on tuberosity of navicular bone. Fibrous extension connects with cuboid and cuneiform bones and with the bases of second and fourth metatarsals
Peroneus longus *Extends and everts the foot; supports the arches*	A superficial muscle lying on lateral side of leg	O—Lateral surface of head of tibia; lateral surface of proximal two-thirds of fibula I—By a long tendon passing behind the lateral malleolus; inserts on plantar surface of first cuneiform and base of first metatarsal
Peroneus brevis *Extends and everts foot*	Lies distal and internal to peroneus longus	O—Middle third of lateral surface of fibula I—By a long tendon that passes behind lateral malleolus to insert on base of the fifth metatarsal

Name, *Action*	Location	O—Origin I—Insertion
Tibialis anterior *Flexes and inverts foot*	A superficial muscle lying lateral to shaft of tibia	O—Lateral surface of head and proximal end of shaft of tibia I—By a long tendon that passes over anterior medial surface of foot to insert on first cuneiform and base of first metatarsal
Peroneus tertius *Flexes and everts foot*	Lies lateral to extensor digitorum longus, with which it functions	O—Distal third of fibula and interosseous membrane I—By a long, slender tendon to base of fifth metatarsal

MUSCLES THAT ACT PRIMARILY ON THE DIGITS. Some of these muscles lie in the lower leg and may assist in movements of the entire foot as well as acting on specific digits. Others are intrinsic muscles that lie entirely within the foot. Flexion, extension, abduction, and adduction are possible.

Name, *Action*	Location	O—Origin I—Insertion
Flexor digitorum longus *Flexes toes; extends and inverts foot*	Lies on medial side of leg, beneath soleus	O—Posterior surface of shaft of tibia I—By long tendon that passes behind medial malleolus and continues obliquely forward and laterally into sole of foot. It divides into four tendons which insert on terminal phalanges of four lateral toes
Flexor hallucis longus *Flexes great toe; extends and inverts foot*	Parallels flexor digitorum on lateral side of leg	O—Distal two-thirds of posterior surface of fibula I—By long tendon which passes posterior to medial malleolus and along lateral surface of sole of foot. Inserted on the hallux
Extensor digitorum longus *Extends toes; flexes and everts foot*	On anterolateral surface of leg, lateral to tibialis anterior. In region of ankle, passes under *transverse crural* and *cruciate ligaments* and divides into four tendons which pass on dorsum of foot to digits	O—Lateral condyle of tibia; proximal two-thirds of fibula and interosseous membrane I—Dorsal surface of phalanges of lateral four toes

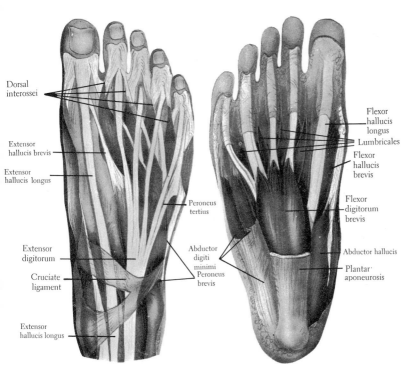

Dorsal interossei

Extensor hallucis brevis

Extensor hallucis longus

Extensor digitorum

Cruciate ligament

Extensor hallucis longus

Peroneus tertius

Abductor digiti minimi
Peroneus brevis

Flexor hallucis longus

Lumbricales

Flexor hallucis brevis

Flexor digitorum brevis

Abductor hallucis

Plantar aponeurosis

Fig. 6-20. Dorsal aspect of right foot.   Fig. 6-21. Plantar view of right foot.

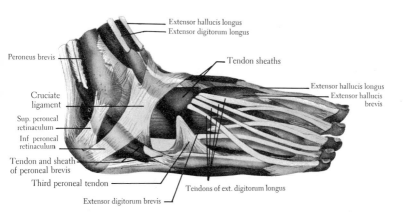

Extensor hallucis longus
Extensor digitorum longus

Peroneus brevis

Tendon sheaths

Cruciate ligament

Sup. peroneal retinaculum

Inf. peroneal retinaculum

Tendon and sheath of peroneal brevis

Third peroneal tendon

Extensor digitorum brevis

Tendons of ext. digitorum longus

Extensor hallucis longus
Extensor hallucis brevis

Fig. 6-22. Lateral view of right foot.

Name, *Action*	Location	O—Origin I—Insertion
Extensor hallucis longus *Extends great toe; flexes and inverts foot*	Lies internal to and between tibialis anterior and extensor digitorum longus	O—Middle portion of fibula; interosseous membrane I—By long tendon to base of distal phalanx of great toe
Abductor hallucis *Abducts and flexes great toe; assists in maintaining longitudinal arch*	A large superficial muscle lying along medial border of foot	O—Calcaneus and adjacent ligaments I—On medial side of base of proximal phalanx of great toe
Adductor hallucis *Adducts great toe and flexes proximal phalanx; aids in supporting arches*	A muscle consisting of two heads lying on plantar surface of foot	O—*Oblique head*, from bases of 2nd, 3rd, and 4th metatarsals, cuboid, and 3rd cuneiform; *transverse head*, from capsules of 2nd to 5th metatarsophalangeal joints I—To base of proximal phalanx and sheath of tendon of flexor hallucis longus
Flexor digitorum brevis *Flexes second row of phalanges on first row; supports longitudinal arch*	A superficial muscle on sole of foot beneath plantar aponeurosis	O—Tuberosity of calcaneus and plantar aponeurosis I—Into bases of phalanges of the four lateral toes
Extensor digitorum brevis *Extends first four toes; abducts second, third, and fourth toes*	A broad, thin muscle on dorsal surface of foot	O—Calcaneus and cruciate ligaments I—Base of proximal phalanx of great toe. Lateral surface of 2nd, 3rd, and 4th toes
Flexor hallucis brevis *Flexes proximal phalanx of great toe*	A short muscle on medial side of plantar surface of foot. Consists of two bellies which lie under first metatarsal bone	O—1st, 2nd, and 3rd cuneiform bones and a fibrous extension of the tendon of the tibialis posterior I—Proximal phalanx of great toe
Extensor hallucis brevis	The most medial portion of extensor digitorum brevis	O—Dorsal and lateral surface of calcaneus I—Base of proximal phalanx of great toe
Quadratus plantae (Flexor accessorius) *Flexes terminal phalanges of four small toes; as accessory to flex. dig. long. alters oblique pull of that muscle to pull in line with the long axis of foot*	A two-headed muscle 2nd layer of planter surface of foot	O—By a muscular head from medial surface of calcaneus, and by a flat tendinous head from lateral border of inferior surface of calcaneus and from the long plantar ligament I—Into the lateral half of the flexor digitorum longus

Name, *Action*	Location	O—Origin I—Insertion
Lumbricales *Flex the proximal pha-* *langes and extend the two* *distal phalanges slightly of the* *four small toes*	Four small muscles in 2nd layer of plantar surface of foot on medial sides of four small toes	O—From angles of division of flexor digitorum longus, each arising from two tendons except the first I—By tendons into dorsal surfaces of first phalanges of four small toes
Interossei dorsales *Flex proximal pha-* *langes, extend middle and* *distal phalanges slightly;* *abduct toes from longitu-* *dinal axis of second toe*	Four muscles situated between the metatarsals	O—From adjacent sides of the metatarsals I—The first into medial side of second toe; the other three into lateral sides of second, third, and fourth toes
Interossei plantares *Adduct the three lateral* *toes toward axis of second* *toe; otherwise, same ac-* *tion as dorsales*	Three muscles lying beneath the lateral three metatarsals	O—From bases and medial sides of bodies of lateral three metatarsals I—Into medial sides of bases of first phalanges of lateral three metatarsals

DISORDERS AND DISEASES OF THE MUSCULAR SYSTEM

"Charley horse." An injury common among athletes, in which a muscle is bruised or torn. It is accompanied by cramps and severe pain.

Cramp. A sustained spasm usually accompanied by severe pain.

Hernia. Protrusion of an organ or a part of an organ through the wall of the cavity that normally contains it. Also referred to as *rupture.* In an *inguinal hernia* (most common type of hernia) the intestine protrudes through the inguinal canal. Among the causative factors are: extremely severe coughing, straining at defecation, lifting of heavy weights and other physical overexertion, all of which may put excessive pressure on the abdominal contents. Other types of hernia take their names from the opening through which the protrusion occurs: *umbilical, diaphragmatic, femoral,* or *scrotal hernia.*

A *reducible hernia* is one which can be corrected by manipulation alone. A *strangulated hernia* is one in which the herniated structure is so tightly constricted that necrosis of tissue results if the condition is not relieved.

Myasthenia gravis. A condition in which there is great muscular weakness without atrophy. It especially affects the muscles of the face and neck. Symptoms are lack of facial expression, difficulty in swallowing and breathing, extreme muscular weakness and fatigue, and general prostration. It is due to the inability of nervous impulses to initiate contraction of muscle fibers. This inability is thought to result from the failure of the myoneural junction to produce acetylcholine or from the presence of excessive quantities of cholinesterase, the enzyme which removes or destroys acetylcholine.

Myositis. Inflammation of voluntary muscles.

Progressive muscular atrophy. A form of muscular atrophy characterized by progressive wasting away of muscle tissue. Apparently due to a disorder in motor nerve endings. Cause unknown.

Spasm. A sudden, involuntary contraction of a muscle. (When persistent, it is called a *tonic spasm.*) The term is also applied to constriction of a tube or of an opening: pyloric spasm, spasm of the bronchioles.

Tetanus. A sustained contraction of a muscle. Also the name of a disease, commonly called *lockjaw*, which is characterized by sustained contraction of certain voluntary muscles. It is caused by the toxin of an infectious bacterium (*Clostridium tetani*).

Torticollis (*Wryneck*). A condition resulting from a spasm of the neck muscles, especially the sternocleidomastoideus. Characterized by twisting of the neck, resulting in an unnatural position of the head.

7: THE DIGESTIVE SYSTEM

The digestive system comprises the organs that act on ingested food, both mechanically and chemically, so that it may be absorbed and provide nutrition for the body. Digestion begins in the mouth with mastication and the mixing of food with saliva containing enzymes secreted by salivary glands. The passages and spaces from this point to the anus make up the alimentary canal, in which the complex compounds are reduced to soluble, absorbable substances, the usable food substances being absorbed and the indigestible and waste materials eliminated. The digestive glands secret enzymes and other chemical components that are essential to the breakdown of food substances and their absorption into the blood stream.

ORGANIZATION OF THE DIGESTIVE SYSTEM

The two general divisions of the digestive system are: the *alimentary canal* and the *accessory glands*. The following tabulation shows the subdivisions and organic units within each of them:

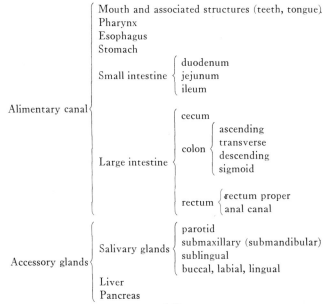

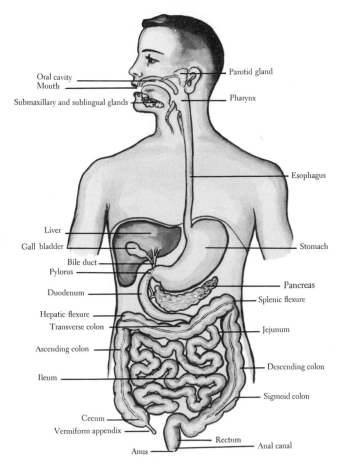

Fig. 7-1. The digestive system.

THE BODY CAVITY AND ITS LININGS

Inasmuch as the digestive organs bear an intimate relationship to the body cavity, this cavity and its linings will be described here. In the embryo the body cavity, or *coelom*, develops by a splitting of the mesoderm. It is at first a single cavity, but with the development of the diaphragm it becomes separated into two parts, which form the *thoracic* and *abdominal cavities*. Subsequently, the thoracic cavity is further divided into two *pleural cavities* (containing the lungs) and the *pericardial cavity* (enclosing the heart). Each of the foregoing cavities is lined with a thin layer of epithelium called *mesothelium*.

In the pleural cavities this layer is further identified as *pleura*, in the pericardial cavity as *pericardium*, and in the abdominal cavity as *peritoneum*.

Mesenteries, Ligaments. The peritoneal lining of each cavity is continuous with and reflected over the organs occupying the cavity. The layer which lines the body wall is the *parietal* or *somatic* layer; that investing the organs is the *visceral* or *splanchnic* layer. A double layer of peritoneum with some connective tissue connects the parietal and visceral layers; this double layer is referred to as *mesentery*. A mesentery acts to support organs and hold them in position. It contains blood and lymph vessels, nerves, and sometimes considerable adipose tissue. Mesenteries are designated by special names, formed by prefixing the name of the organ to which they are attached with *meso-* (for example, mesocolon, mesorectum, mesoduodenum). When a mesentery connects one organ with another, it is called a *ligament*; examples are the gastrosplenic ligament and the round ligament of the uterus.

Omenta. The portion of the peritoneum which connects the stomach with the liver is called the *lesser omentum*. The *greater omentum* is a double-walled layer of peritoneum attached to the stomach and extending inferiorly a considerable distance to cover the intestines in the manner of an apron. The greater omentum is abundantly supplied with fat and forms an important protective and heat-conserving organ. It also plays a role in localizing inflammation within the abdominal cavity. The lesser and greater omenta enclose a space behind the stomach called the *omental bursa* or *lesser peritoneal sac*. This space connects with the true peritoneal cavity by means of an opening, the *epiploic foramen* (*foramen of Winslow*), which lies between the liver and the duodenum.

Organs in Relation to Peritoneum. Some organs are *completely* invested with peritoneum (stomach, jejunum, ileum, transverse colon); others are *partially* covered by it (liver, cecum, ascending colon, descending colon, rectum, uterus); still others lie *behind* the peritoneum (urinary bladder, kidneys, pancreas, duodenum, and the great blood vessels, the aorta and the inferior vena cava) and are said to be *retroperitoneal*.

Peritoneal surfaces are moistened by a serous fluid which minimizes friction between the various organs and between the organs and the linings of the body wall.

LAYERS OF THE ALIMENTARY CANAL

The alimentary canal from the esophagus on possesses four layers: mucous layer (mucosa), submucous layer (submucosa), muscular coat (muscularis externa), and a fibrous or serous layer (serosa).

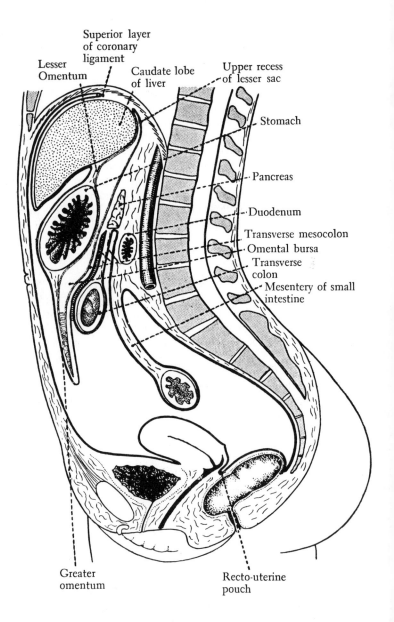

Fig. 7-2. Diagram to show peritoneal relationships. Longitudinal section of body.

Mucous Layer. The innermost layer of the alimentary canal, the mucosa, consists of a layer of epithelium (stratified or columnar), which forms a continuous layer from mouth to anus. Over its great length it is much invaginated to form tubular glands. Directly beneath this epithelium is the *lamina propria*, a thin layer of areolar tissue, on which the epithelium rests. Beneath the lamina propria is a thin layer of smooth muscle, the *muscularis mucosa*, consisting principally of longitudinal fibers.

Submucous Layer. This layer of loose connective tissue contains the blood and lymph vessels and the nerves (*submucous plexus of Meissner*). Mast cells, lymphoid "wandering" cells, and eosinophils are present among the collagenous fibers. Sometimes glands from the mucosa extend into the submucosa. The submucosa provides an adjustable basis for movements and changes in size of the tube.

Muscular Coat. The muscularis externa consists of cells arranged to form an inner *circular* layer and an outer *longitudinal* layer. A third (*oblique*) layer may be present. Between the circular and longitudinal layers lie nerve cells and fibers constituting the *myenteric plexus of Auerbach*.

Serous Layer. A serous membrane, the serosa, forms the outermost layer of the alimentary canal. It consists of a layer of mesothelium lying on a thin layer of loose connective tissue. It is continuous with the mesentery which supports the intestines, and it contains blood and lymph vessels and sometimes adipose tisue. The serosa is lacking in the esophagus, the outer coat there being a fibrous coat, the *fibrosa*.

PARTS OF THE ALIMENTARY CANAL

The parts of the alimentary canal include the mouth and associated structures, pharynx, esophagus, stomach, small intestine, and large intestine.

The Mouth. The *buccal cavity* or *mouth* comprises two regions: the *vestibule* (region between the lips, cheeks, teeth, and gums) and the *oral cavity* (region posterior to the teeth and gums). It is bounded anteriorly and laterally by the lips and cheeks, superiorly by the hard and soft palates, and inferiorly by the tongue, jaws, and intervening mucous membranes.

Floor and Walls of the Mouth. The *floor* of the mouth is formed by the mylohyoid muscles. The tongue is attached to the floor by its root and by a median fold, the *frenulum*. On each side of the frenulum there is a fimbriated fold. The cheeks serve as the *walls* of the buccal cavity.

Within the cavity of the mouth are the teeth and the tongue, accessory digestive organs.

Teeth. These hard structures, whose function in digestion is mastication, appear in two sets: first, the *deciduous* (temporary or "milk") teeth, of which there are ten in each jaw and which are shed at the age levels shown in the accompanying table; later, the *permanent* teeth, the 32 that replace the deciduous teeth.

Eruption and Shedding of Teeth. The approximate age level at which deciduous teeth erupt and are shed and the period over which the permanent teeth erupt are as follows:

| TEETH | DECIDUOUS | | PERMANENT |
	Erupt	*Shed*	*Erupt*
Central incisors	7½ mos.	7 yrs.	6–8 yrs.
Lateral incisors	7–9 mos.	8 yrs.	7–9 yrs.
Canines	16–18 mos.	10 yrs.	9–11 yrs.
First premolars			9–10 yrs.
Second premolars			10–12 yrs.
First molars	12–14 mos.	10 yrs.	6–7 yrs.
Second molars	20–24 mos.	12 yrs.	11–13 yrs.
Third molars			17–21 yrs.

The Permanent Teeth. In each jaw the following permanent teeth are found: 4 incisors (chisel-like in form), 2 canines (cuspids), 4 premolars (bicuspids), and 6 molars ("wisdom teeth"). A *cusp* is a raised portion on the chewing surface of a tooth.

Structure of a Typical Tooth. The *crown* of a tooth is the portion above the gum; the *root* is the portion embedded in a socket (alveolus) of a jawbone (mandible or maxilla). The *neck* is the slightly constricted region between the root and the crown; it is covered by the *gum* or *gingiva.* When a tooth has been cut in longitudinal section, the following parts can be seen:

Hard parts, including enamel, dentine or "ivory," and cementum. *Enamel* is the material covering the crown. It consists of thin prisms or rods, twisted in form, which stand upright on the surface of the dentine. Enamel is the hardest substance in the body. *Dentine* forms the bulk of the tooth. It contains *canaliculi* and *dentinal canals,* but lacunae and bone cells are absent. Although it resembles bone in structure, it is harder than any bone. *Cementum,* another bone-like structure, covers the dentine of the root. It is continuous with enamel at the neck of the tooth, forming a *cemento-enamel junction.*

Soft parts, including the pulp and the periodontal membrane. The *pulp* consists of connective tissue containing a dense network of capillaries, lymph, vessels, and nerve fibers; a layer of *odontoblasts* lies adjacent to the dentine. The *periodontal membrane* covers the root and lines the alveolus, where it serves as the periosteum. The periodontal membrane holds the tooth firmly in its socket.

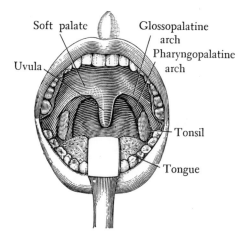

Fig. 7-3. The mouth cavity as seen from the front. (Gerrish.) (Reprinted with permission of The Macmillan Company from Kimber et al., *A Textbook of Anatomy and Physiology*, 13th ed., 1955.)

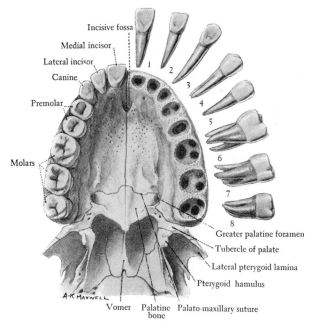

Fig. 7-4. Palate seen from below. Teeth on left side removed to show sockets for roots. (Reprinted with permission of St. Martin's Press and The Macmillan Company Ltd. from Hamilton, *Textbook of Human Anatomy*, 1956.)

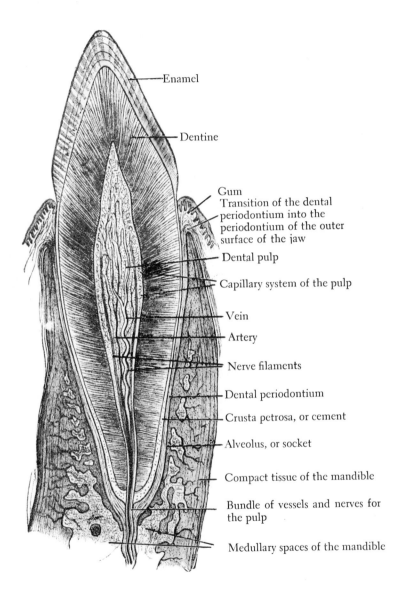

Enamel

Dentine

Gum
Transition of the dental
periodontium into the
periodontium of the outer
surface of the jaw

Dental pulp

Capillary system of the pulp

Vein

Artery

Nerve filaments

Dental periodontium

Crusta petrosa, or cement

Alveolus, or socket

Compact tissue of the mandible

Bundle of vessels and nerves for
the pulp

Medullary spaces of the mandible

Fig. 7-5. Longitudinal section of tooth (lower canine). (Reprinted with permission of The Macmillan Company from Toldt, *Atlas of Human Anatomy*, 1948.)

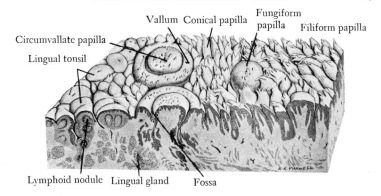

Fig. 7-6. Surface view of tongue to show papillae. (Based on Braus.) (Reprinted with permission of St. Martin's Press and The Macmillan Company Ltd. from Hamilton, *Textbook of Human Anatomy*, 1956.)

TONGUE. The tongue is a freely movable muscular organ lying on the floor of the mouth. It consists of a *body* and a posterior *root*.

Functions of the Tongue. The tongue performs the following functions: (1) manipulation of food, (2) initiation of swallowing movements, (3) cleansing of the teeth and gums, (4) production of certain sounds in speech, and (5) provision of the sensation of taste through the taste buds on its surface.

Attachments of the Tongue. Posteriorly, the tongue is attached to the hyoid bone by its root, to the epiglottis by the glosso-epiglottic fold, and to the soft palate by the glossopalatine arches. *Anteriorly* and *inferiorly,* it is attached to the floor of the mouth by the frenulum (*frenulum linguae*). When the frenulum is unusually short, the person is said to be "tongue-tied" because of the speech defect to which this anomaly gives rise.

Surfaces of the Tongue. The upper surface of the tongue is rough and covered with many elevations called *papillae.* The lower surface is covered with a smooth thin mucous membrane and is devoid of papillae.

Papillae of the Tongue. The papillae of the tongue are of three types: filiform, fungiform, and circumvallate.

The *filiform papillae* are 2 to 3 mm. long and conical in shape, some of them having a double tip. Each consists of a slender core of connective tissue covered by stratified squamous epithelium the superficial cells of which become transformed into hardened, scale-like structures which are constantly being shed. These papillae are quite numerous. They are arranged in more or less diagonal rows, extending laterally from the middle of the tongue.

The *fungiform papillae*, relatively few in number, measure 0.7 to 1.8 mm. in length and 1.0 mm. in thickness. Their distal portions are rounded and broader than their bases. They have a central core of connective tissue that is richly supplied with blood vessels, which gives the papillae a reddish color. Taste buds are present on some of these papillae.

The *circumvallate papillae* (papillae vallatae) are 1 to 3 mm. in diameter; they are 6 to 16 in number, the average number being 9 or 10. Each is surrounded by a deep circular cleft and a wall. The circumvallate papillae are arranged in a V-shaped row on the posterior dorsal surface of the tongue. They contain a core of connective tissue and may bear secondary papillae. The stratified epithelium covering these papillae is smooth and, on their lateral walls, contains many taste buds; the number of buds on a single circumvallate papillae is estimated at about 250.

The *foramen cecum*, a small pit at the apex of the V formed by the circumvallate papillae, indicates the embryonic point of origin of the thyroid gland. The *terminal sulcus*, a groove roughly paralleling the circumvallate papillae, marks the junction of embryonic portions that gave rise to the body and root of the tongue. Lateral to the terminal sulcus lie two masses of lymphoid tissue, the *lingual tonsils*.

Musculature of the Tongue. The muscles of the tongue are of two kinds, extrinsic and intrinsic. The *extrinsic muscles* are inserted into the tongue and have their origins on the bones of the skull. They include the *genioglossus, styloglossus,* and *hyoglossus.* The *intrinsic muscles* are contained entirely within the tongue. Muscle bundles extend in all directions, but fibers run in three more or less distinct planes: longitudinally, laterally, and vertically. The bundles are embedded in areolar connective tissue. Adipose tissue is fairly abundant.

Glands of the Tongue. These glands, called *lingual glands,* are of three types: *mucous glands,* found principally in the posterior region; *serous glands* (glands of Von Ebner), found deeply embedded in muscles and whose ducts empty into the furrows surrounding the circumvallate papillae; and *mixed glands* (glands of Nuhn) which lie near the tip of the tongue, their ducts emptying on the inferior surface.

Innervation of the Tongue. The anterior two thirds is innervated by the lingual nerve containing fibers from the trigeminal and facial nerves; the posterior third is innervated by the glossopharyngeal and vagus nerves, fibers of the latter being restricted to the region near the epiglottis. These nerves carry both sensory and motor impulses.

THE HARD PALATE. The hard palate is supported by portions of the maxillae and the palatine bones. The *incisive papilla*, a small fold of mucous membrane, is situated just posterior to the incisor teeth; openings of incisor canals are often found on either side. Other parts are:

median raphe, the median line, usually somewhat lighter in color than the rest of the hard palate; *palatine rugae* (*plicae palatinae transversae*), transverse ridges in the anterior region; and *palatine glands*, lying in the submucosa under the mucous membrane.

THE SOFT PALATE. The soft palate is a muscular fold covered with mucous membrane extending posteriorly and laterally from the hard palate. Its free edge (*velum*) projects posteriorly and inferiorly and bears a median finger-like projection, the *uvula*. The lateral portion of the soft palate forms the palatine arches. When swallowing occurs, the soft palate moves upward and closes the opening to the nasopharynx.

THE ISTHMUS OF THE FAUCES. This is the opening between the oral cavity and the oral portion of the pharynx. Its *boundaries* are: superiorly, the soft palate; inferiorly, the dorsum of the root of the tongue; laterally, the *glossopalatine arches*. These arches (also called *pillars of the fauces*) are downward continuations of the soft palate. The glossopalatine arch (anterior pillar) contains the glossopalatine (palatoglossus) muscle; the pharyngopalatine arch (posterior pillar) contains the pharyngopalatine (palatopharyngeus) muscle. A depression between them (the *tonsillar fossa*) lodges the palatine tonsil.

THE PALATINE (FAUCIAL) TONSILS. Two masses of lymphoid tissue, the faucial tonsils, lie between the two aforementioned pillars or arches. Each tonsil is enclosed in a connective tissue capsule. The free surface is covered with stratified squamous epithelium often infiltrated with leucocytes and containing several deep indentations, the tonsillar crypts. Adjacent to the crypts are nodules of lymphatic tissue similar to those in lymph nodes. Mucous glands are present. The only known function of the faucial tonsils is the formation of lymphocytes. Their removal, a practice usually inspired by anxiety over focal infection, is often unnecessary.

The Pharynx. The pharynx is the second main component of the digestive tract. It serves as a common passageway for food and air. The pathways for these substances cross, but automatically controlled mechanisms operate to prevent the passage of food into the windpipe. The pharynx is a vertical, tubular structure extending downward from the base of the skull above, to the openings of the larynx and esophagus (at about the level of the 5th vertebra) below. It lies immediately anterior to the spinal column. The pharynx is lined with mucous membrane; the epithelium in the upper portion is pseudostratified ciliated, and that in the middle and lower portions is stratified squamous.

REGIONS OF THE PHARYNX. The pharynx is divided into three regions: nasal, oral, and laryngeal.

The nasal portion or *nasopharynx* lies behind the nose above the level of the soft palate. It communicates anteriorly with the nasal

cavity through the two posterior nares or *choanae*. In its lateral walls
are the openings to the *auditory tubes* and on its posterior wall is a
mass of lymphatic tissue, the *pharyngeal tonsil*. In childhood this frequently hypertrophies, forming an enlarged mass referred to as "adenoids."

The oral portion or *oropharynx* is that portion which lies below the
soft palate and above the epiglottis. It communicates anteriorly with
the oral cavity through the *isthmus of the fauces*. In its lateral walls
between the two palatine arches are the palatine tonsils lying in the
tonsillar fossae.

The laryngeal portion or *laryngopharynx* is the lowermost portion,
communicating directly with the larynx and the esophagus. The opening to the larynx, roughly triangular in shape, lies in its anterior wall
immediately behind an upward-projecting cartilaginous flap, the *epiglottis*. The *aryepiglottic folds* form its lateral boundaries. Inferiorly
at the level of the cricoid cartilage the pharynx narrows and becomes
continuous with the esophagus.

MUSCULATURE OF THE PHARYNX. The principal muscles of the
pharynx are:

Constrictor muscles (superior, middle, and inferior), which form
the external or circular layer. *Action:* Decrease the size of the pharynx,
causing food particles to be grasped and forced downward into the
esophagus (the act of swallowing).

Stylopharyngeus, with its origin on the styloid process and its insertion on the side of the pharynx and the thyroid cartilage. *Action:*
Raises the pharynx and increases its diameter.

Esophagus. The esophagus is a muscular tube about 10 inches in
length extending from the pharynx to the stomach. It lies between the
levels of the 6th cervical and 7th thoracic vertebrae. The esophagus is
situated in the neck, anterior to the bodies of the cervical vertebrae
and posterior to the trachea. It passes inferiorly into the thoracic cavity, continuing through the mediastinal space to the diaphragm,
through which it passes, and, turning to the left, enters the stomach.

The histologic structure of the esophagus is as follows: The *mucosa*
consists of thick stratified epithelium thrown into folds and having a
stellate lumen. A lamina propria is present. In the upper and lower
portions, cardiac glands are usually found. The *submucosa* is a relatively thick layer containing collagenous and elastic fibers. In it lie
the esophageal glands proper, blood vessels, and nerves. The *muscular
coat* consists of two layers, an outer longitudinal and an inner circular,
with Auerbach's plexus between them. Fibers are striated in the upper
third, smooth in the lower third. A *fibrous coat* of loose connective
tissue connects the esophagus to surrounding structures. Inasmuch as
the peritoneal covering is lacking, there is no serosa.

Stomach. The stomach is an expanded portion of the alimentary canal lying in the upper left portion of the abdominal cavity. Its form is variable but roughly J-shaped.

PRINCIPAL PARTS AND OPENINGS OF THE STOMACH. The principal parts and openings of the stomach include: the cardiac orifice, body, fundus or fornix, pyloric orifice, and pyloric portion.

Cardiac Orifice. This is the opening from the esophagus. It is guarded by the cardiac sphincter. At this point the stratified epithelium of the esophagus undergoes transition into the columnar epithelium of the stomach.

Body of the Stomach. This is the main portion of the stomach.

Fundus or *Fornix.* This is the dilated portion lying to the left of the cardiac orifice.

Pyloric Orifice. This is the opening into the duodenum of the small intestine. It is guarded by the *pyloric sphincter.*

Pyloric Portion. The region nearest the pyloric orifice consists of a dilated portion, the *pyloric antrum,* and a narrower *pyloric canal.* The antrum is set off from the body of the stomach by a slightly constricted area, the *incisura angularis.* At this point there is a band of circular muscle fibers, the *prepyloric sphincter.*

SURFACES AND BORDERS OF THE STOMACH. The anterior surface of the stomach faces forward and upward; the posterior surface faces backward and downward. The *lesser curvature* forms the concave medial border and is directed to the right; the *greater curvature* forms the convex lateral border and is directed to the left.

The *histologic structure* of the stomach is as follows: In an empty, contracted stomach, the innermost coat, the *mucosa,* is thrown into numerous longitudinal folds called *rugae,* which disappear when the stomach is full. The surface epithelium, consisting of simple columnar epithelial cells, contains many invaginations, the *gastric pits* or *foveolae,* into the bottom of which the gastric glands open. Goblet cells and villi are lacking. The *submucosa* of the stomach consists of areolar connective tissue containing blood and lymph vessels and nerves. It is situated between the mucosa and the muscular coat, and it binds them together. The *muscular coat* comprises three layers: an outer longitudinal, a middle circular, and an inner oblique. The *serosa,* the outermost coat of the stomach wall, consists of a thin layer of connective tissue covered with mesothelium. It is continuous with the peritoneum of the greater and lesser omenta.

GASTRIC GLANDS. These are simple or branched tubular glands, each with a very narrow neck which opens into a gastric pit. They are confined entirely to the mucosa. It is estimated that there are 30 to 40 million such glands. Four types of *cells* are found: *chief* or *zymogenic cells,* which secrete pepsin; *parietal cells,* triangular in shape and

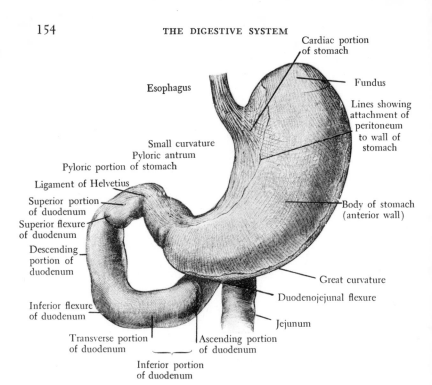

Cardiac portion of stomach

Esophagus

Fundus

Lines showing attachment of peritoneum to wall of stomach

Small curvature
Pyloric antrum
Pyloric portion of stomach

Ligament of Helvetius

Superior portion of duodenum

Superior flexure of duodenum

Descending portion of duodenum

Inferior flexure of duodenum

Body of stomach (anterior wall)

Great curvature

Duodenojejunal flexure

Jejunum

Transverse portion of duodenum

Ascending portion of duodenum

Inferior portion of duodenum

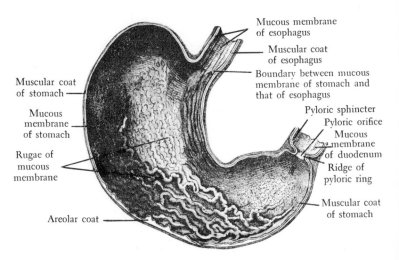

Mucous membrane of esophagus

Muscular coat of esophagus

Boundary between mucous membrane of stomach and that of esophagus

Muscular coat of stomach

Mucous membrane of stomach

Rugae of mucous membrane

Pyloric sphincter
Pyloric orifice
Mucous membrane of duodenum
Ridge of pyloric ring

Muscular coat of stomach

Areolar coat

Fig. 7-7 Two views of stomach. Above: ventral view. Below: anterior half (divided in two) seen from inside. (Reprinted with permission of The Macmillan Company from Toldt, *Atlas of Human Anatomy*, 1948.)

peripherally located, more numerous in the neck region, which secrete hydrochloric acid; *mucous neck cells*, which lie in the neck region of the gland between the parietal cells; and, occasionally, *argentaffine cells*, which occur singly and are possibly concerned with the production of the antianemia factor.

Gastric glands are named according to the region in which they occur. *Cardiac glands* occupy a limited area adjacent to the cardia. *Fundic glands*, shorter and more branched than the cardiac, occupy the superior two-thirds of the stomach. *Pyloric glands* occupy the pyloric region. These last-named glands contain only one type of cell, which is similar to the mucous neck cells. The lumen of pyloric glands is larger, and their secretory portion is more coiled.

There is no sharp demarcation between the glands of one region of the stomach and those of another region. The glands of one type mix freely with those of another at the borders.

Small Intestine. The small intestine is a much-coiled tube extending from the pylorus to the ileocecal valve. Its total length averages about 22.5 feet. The *duodenum* is about 10 inches long; into it open the bile and pancreatic ducts, at the ampulla of Vater. The *jejunum* is about 9½ feet long; it is continuous with the duodenum. The *ileum* is about 12½ feet long; it lies between the jejunum and the large intestine. The above figures apply to the intestine immediately after death and before embalming. In a living subject, however, it is much shorter; in fact, in radiographic examinations, if a flexible radioopaque tube is passed from the mouth to the anus, the part of the tube in the small intestine averages only 5 to 6 feet in length.

Histologically, the wall of the small intestine consists of four layers: mucosa, submucosa, muscular coat, and serosa.

Mucosa. The innermost coat of the small intestine, the mucosa, is lined with simple columnar epithelium containing many goblet cells. Argentaffine cells are also present in the crypts of Lieberkühn (see page 160). The absorbing surface of the mucosa is increased by *circular folds* (*plicae circulares*) or *valvulae conniventes*, constant, well-developed structures which disappear about the midregion; and by *villi*. Villi (sing. *villus*) are finger-like outgrowths of the mucosa averaging 0.5 to 1.5 mm. in length. In the duodenum the villi are broad; in the jejunum they are elongated and narrow; in the ileum they are short and club-shaped. In the core of the villi are argyrophil fibers, a capillary net, a lacteal, strands of smooth muscle cells and free cells such as lymphocytes, plasma cells, and granular leucocytes, especially eosinophils. Villi are most numerous in the jejunum, sparer in the lower portion of the ileum. A lamina propria supports the epithelium and glands and forms the core of a villus.

The mucosa also contains *lymphatic tissue* in the form of nodules

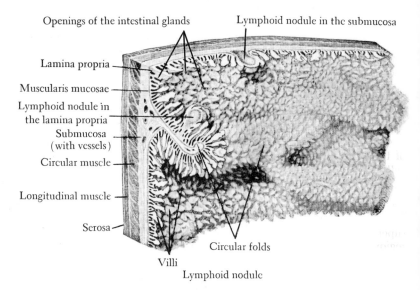

Openings of the intestinal glands — Lymphoid nodule in the submucosa

Lamina propria

Muscularis mucosae

Lymphoid nodule in the lamina propria

Submucosa (with vessels)

Circular muscle

Longitudinal muscle

Serosa

Villi

Circular folds

Lymphoid nodule

Fig. 7-8. Portion of small intestine. (After Braus.) 17x. (Reprinted with permission of W. B. Saunders Company from Maximow and Bloom, A *Textbook of Histology*, 6th ed., 1952.)

located in the lamina propria. These nodules are of two types: solitary and aggregated. The *solitary nodules*, varying in size from 0.6 mm. to 3 mm., are fewer in number in the duodenum but become progressively more numerous in the jejunum, with villi and glands usually absent over the elevated area. The *aggregated nodules* (better known as *Peyer's patches*) are groups of 20 to 30 solitary nodules, found almost exclusively in the ileum. They appear as slightly elevated masses on the side opposite the attachment of the mesentery. Their surface is free of villi and crypts.

SUBMUCOSA. This consists of compact areolar connective tissue with many blood vessels. In the duodenum, Brunner's glands form a thick layer. A nerve plexus (*submucous plexus of Meissner*) is present.

MUSCULAR COAT. This consists of two well-developed layers: an outer longitudinal layer, with fibers running longitudinally in a spiral course, and an inner circular layer, with fibers running circularly in a closer spiral than that of the outer layer. Between these two layers of the muscular coat is the *myenteric plexus of Auerbach*, consisting of nerve fibers and ganglion cells of the autonomic nervous system.

SEROSA. The serosa or peritoneum consists of a layer of squamous epithelium (mesothelium) resting on a thin layer of loose connective tissue. It is continuous with the mesentery supporting the intestine.

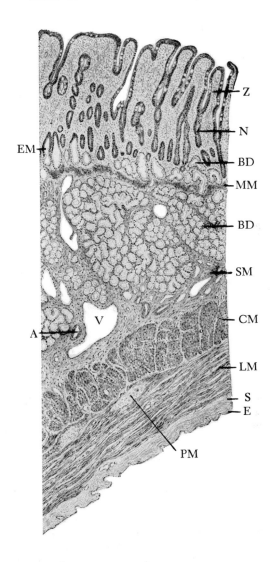

Fig. 7-9. Longitudinal section of duodenum. (A) artery. (BD) Brunner's glands in submucosa. (BD¹) Brunner's glands in mucosa. (CM) circular muscle cut across. (E) mesothelium of serosa. (EM) emptying of a Brunner gland into a crypt. (K) crypt of Lieberkuhn. (LM) longitudinal muscle layer. (MM) muscularis mucosae. (PM) plexus myentericus with a ganglion cell in cross section. (S) serosa. (SM) submucosa. (Z) villus. 30x. (After Schaffer.) (Reprinted with permission of W. B. Saunders Company from Maximow and Bloom, A Textbook of Histology, 6th ed., 1952.)

Large Intestine. The large intestine, about 1.5 meters (5 feet) in length, consists of the cecum, colon, and rectum. The colon has four portions: ascending, transverse, descending, and sigmoid.

GENERAL CHARACTERISTICS. The mucous membrane of the large intestine is not thrown into folds, as is the small intestine, except in the rectum. Villi are lacking. The longitudinal layer of muscles consists of three bands called *taeniae*, which are visible macroscopically; only two such bands are present in the sigmoid colon and the rectum. Each band is about 1 cm. wide. Large sacculations called *haustra* protrude from the wall of the large intestine, and hanging from these are small peritoneal pouches containing fat (*appendices epiploicae*). Lymphatic tissue is present in the form of solitary nodules.

CECUM. The cecum, the first portion of the large intestine, is a large, blind pouch situated on the right side below the ileocecal valve. It averages about 6.5 cm. in length and 7.5 cm. in width. Its blind end is directed downward and projecting from it is a narrow, worm-shaped tube, the *vermiform process* or *appendix*, which averages about 8.5 cm. in length. Histologically, the cecum and the appendix possess the same four coats as does the colon, with which they are continuous. A characteristic feature of the appendix, however, is the large amount of lymphoid tissue present in the mucous layer. This is in the form of a ring of solitary nodules projecting into the submucosa. The lumen is small and presents an irregular and angular form.

ILEOCECAL VALVE. The lower portion of the ileum ends at an opening at the junction of the cecum and the colon. It is guarded by a valve, the ileocecal valve (colic valve), consisting of two folds or lips which project slightly into the lumen of the large intestine. The valve prevents the reverse passage of food from the cecum into the ileum and also acts as a sphincter muscle controlling passage of food into the large intestine.

COLON. The colon passes superiorly from the cecum as the *ascending colon* to the region of the liver, where it turns sharply to the left as the *transverse colon*. This bend is called the *right colic* or *hepatic flexure*. The transverse colon passes to the left, then turns downward (*left colic* or *splenic flexure*) and continues as the *descending colon*. At the level of the crest of the ilium the large intestine makes an S-turn, forming the portion known as the *sigmoid flexure* or *sigmoid colon*. It then passes into the true pelvis and continues to the level of the 3rd sacral vertebra, where it continues as the rectum.

RECTUM. The rectum consists of the *rectum proper* and the *anal canal*.

Gross Structure of the Rectum. The rectum proper, about 5 inches long, follows the curve of the sacrum and coccyx. When distended, it shows three dilated portions formed by inward projecting folds. The

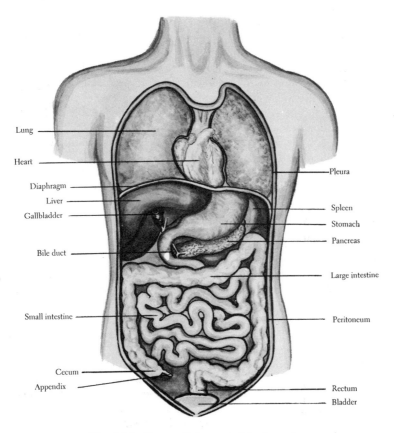

Fig. 7-10. Organs of the ventral body cavity.

lowermost and largest of these dilations is the *ampulla*, which joins the anal canal. The anal canal extends from the pelvic floor downward and posteriorly to the *anus*, the exterior opening. On the inner surface of the canal are from five to ten vertical folds, the *anal columns* or valves, behind which are spaces called *anal sinuses*.

Muscles of the Rectum. The circular muscle layer of the rectum is much thickened and forms the *internal sphincter*, which surrounds the anal canal for a distance of about 1 inch; this sphincter is innervated by autonomic nerves. The *external sphincter*, which is amenable to voluntary control, is a layer of striated muscle tissue surrounding the terminal portion of the anal canal. Its fibers are attached to the coccyx and the surrounding skin. Also forming a part of the pelvic floor is the *levator ani*, whose action is voluntary. Its fibers surround the rectum in such a way as to compress it; some of the fibers enter its wall and merge with those of the sphincters. The *function* of the sphincters is to keep the anal canal closed.

HISTOLOGIC STRUCTURE OF THE LARGE INTESTINE. The same four layers that are found in the small intestine are present in the large intestine, with the following differences: The *mucosa* is relatively smooth and lacking in villi; tubular pits or glands are present; the epithelium is of the simple columnar type, containing many goblet cells which secrete mucus. Lymphatic tissue occurs only in the form of solitary nodules which lie in the mucosa and the submucosa. The *muscular coat* includes an inner circular layer and an outer longitudinal layer, the fibers of which are grouped in three bands, the *taeniae coli*. In the serosa are found pendulous *appendices epiploicae*, extensions of the peritoneum containing masses of fat.

Intestinal Glands. There are two types of intestinal glands: the *crypts of Lieberkühn* and the *duodenal glands* (*Brunner's glands*).

CRYPTS OF LIEBERKÜHN. These are simple tubular glands located in the mucosa and opening between the bases of the villi. They are found in all portions of the intestine. They extend downward through the lamina propria to the muscularis mucosa. Large *cells of Paneth* containing chromophil substance occur in the bases of the glands, and goblet cells are numerous in the epithelium. These glands produce *intestinal juice* (*succus entericus*).

DUODENAL GLANDS. Brunner's glands are abundant near the pylorus, decreasing in number and disappearing in the lower portion of the duodenum. The terminal portions of these glands consist of much-branched and coiled tubes, each with a conspicuous lumen. The glands are most numerous in the submucosa. Their excretory ducts open into the bottom or the side of a crypt of Lieberkühn. They are thought to secrete mucus.

ACCESSORY DIGESTIVE GLANDS

The accessory digestive glands include the salivary glands, the liver, and the pancreas.

Salivary Glands. Numerous glands contribute to the secretion of saliva. Many are small glands located in the mucosa or submucosa of the mouth cavity. These are named according to their location (lingual, buccal, labial). The major portion of the saliva, however, is produced by the *salivary glands proper*, i.e., the parotid, submaxillary (submandibular), and sublingual glands, which are located outside the mouth cavity. All three of these are compound tubuloalveolar glands. Salivary secretion by these glands is under nervous control, occurring reflexly when (*a*) mechanical, chemical, or thermal stimuli act on sensory receptors in the mouth and other parts of the digestive tract, (*b*) olfactory stimuli act on the same sensory receptors, or (*c*) psychic stimuli arise within the higher nervous centers.

Saliva. A viscous, colorless, opalescent fluid, saliva is about 98 per cent water. The balance is made up of mucin, inorganic salts, enzymes, organic compounds, and miscellaneous cells. Foreign substances, such as iodides or bromides, which have been introduced by mouth or injected into the blood may appear in the saliva; this accounts for the taste of morphine following its injection. The normal total daily production of saliva is 2 to 3 pints (1,000 to 1,500 cc.).

Constituents of Saliva. Mucin is a complex glycoprotein of high viscosity which gives saliva its stringy consistency, a property that causes food particles to stick together and makes them easier to swallow. Mucin also lubricates the mouth cavity. The *inorganic salts* include chlorides, carbonates, phosphates, and sulfates of sodium, potassium, calcium, and magnesium. Evidence of their presence in saliva is the *tartar* which forms on teeth as a result of precipitation of insoluble calcium salts with associated substances when CO_2 evaporates from carbonates. The *enzymes* include ptyalin, a diastase that converts boiled starch to maltose, and maltase, which converts maltose to dextrose. The *organic compounds* consist of mucin, traces of urea, and other substances. The "miscellaneous cells" are salivary corpuscles (modified leucocytes from lymphoid tissue), and epithelial cells from the oral mucosa.

Reaction of Saliva. The reaction of saliva when exposed to air is normally slightly alkaline (pH 7.2). When loss of CO_2 is prevented, it is slightly acid (pH 6.6).

Functions of Saliva. Saliva performs the following functions: (1) Moistens and lubricates mucous surfaces, making speech and swallowing possible. (2) Moistens and lubricates food, facilitating swallowing. (3) Acts as a solvent whereby food particles go into solution and are thus enabled to stimulate taste buds. (4) Helps food particles to stick together and form a *bolus* so that they can be swallowed as a mass. (5) Initiates the process of digestion through the action of ferments or enzymes. (6) Acts as a cleansing agent for the mouth and a neutralizing agent that tends to counteract tooth decay. (7) Aids in the elimination of foreign substances from the blood.

Structure of the Salivary Glands Proper. The largest of the salivary glands, the *parotids*, weigh 14 to 30 gm. each. They lie anterior and ventral to the ears, partly covering the rami of the mandible.

A portion of each extends forward over the masseter muscle. Each is tightly encased in a sheath which is continuous with the cervical fascia. The superficial layer of this fascia, the parotid fascia, is dense and closely adherent to the gland, being attached to the zygomatic process, the styloid process, and the angle of the mandible, the latter two attachments forming the stylomandibular ligament. The *parotid duct* (*Stenson's duct*) passes anteriorly across the masseter muscle to empty into the vestibule of the mouth opposite the upper 2nd molar tooth. The parotids are pure serous (albuminous) glands. Their secretion is watery and lacks mucus. Each of the *submaxillary* (*submandibular*) *glands* weighs 7 to 10 gm. They lie just within the lower jaw anterior to the angle, occupying a fossa on the inner side of the mandible. The major portion of the submaxillary gland consists of serous alveoli; some mucous alveoli are present. A few *demi-lunes* (crescent-shaped groups of serous cells) are present. A *submaxillary* or *Wharton's duct* extends from the anterior end of each gland and opens into the floor of the mouth on each side of the frenulum. Each weighing about 3 gm., the *sublingual glands* lie in the loose areolar tissue just beneath the floor of the mouth. They consist of several separate lobes or aggregations of tissue and do not possess a capsule. The sublingual gland is a mixed gland. Mucous cells are much more abundant than in the submaxillary gland. Serous cells are in the minority and in general are arranged in the form of a crescent (demi-lunes). The *sublingual ducts* (*ducts of Rivinus*) vary in number from 4 to 20. They open into the floor of the mouth. Some of them may join Wharton's duct.

The Liver and Biliary Apparatus. The liver is a compound tubular gland located in the upper right portion of the abdominal cavity immediately below the diaphragm. It is the largest gland of the body, its weight averaging about 1,500 gm.

Lobes and Surfaces of the Liver. The liver comprises a large right lobe and a smaller left lobe. The right lobe is further subdivided into the right lobe proper, the quadrate lobe, and the caudate lobe (*lobe of Spigelius*).

The *surfaces* of the liver are: right, posterior, and inferior. On the convex *anterior and superior* surfaces is the *umbilical notch*, which separates the right from the left lobe. In this notch is a curved fold of the peritoneum, the *falciform ligament*, which extends superiorly to the diaphragm and the anterior body wall. This ligament is a rudiment of the ventral mesentery. Its free edge, known as the *round ligament* (*ligamentum teres*) represents the occluded umbilical vein. The *inferior surface* is divided by a number of fissures which separate the lobes. The most important of these is the *portal* or *transverse fissure* (*porta hepatis*). This constitutes the *hilum*, a wide cleft about 2 inches long which encloses the portal vein, the hepatic artery, the common bile duct and its divisions, lymphatics, and nerves. All are enclosed in a connective tissue membrane called *Glisson's capsule* (*capsula fibrosa perivascularis*), which continues over the entire surface of the liver except that adjacent to the diaphragm. Adjacent to Glisson's capsule, the peritoneum forms the outermost covering.

Other ligaments which attach to the liver are: the *lesser omentum*, divided into the hepatogastric and hepatoduodenal ligaments; the coronary ligaments; the right and left triangular ligaments; and ligamentum venosum. The last-named is a fibrous cord which represents the *ductus venosus*, an embryonic vessel connecting the umbilical vein with the inferior vena cava.

HISTOLOGIC STRUCTURE OF THE LIVER. The structural and functional unit of the liver is the *lobule*. Each lobule is a cylindrical structure with flattened sides, separated from adjacent lobules by a small amount of connective tissue. At the points of junction between two or three lobules are found the terminal branches of the portal vein, the hepatic artery, and the hepatic ducts.

In the center of each lobule is a *central* or *intralobular vein*. Extending radically from the central vein are anastomosing *cords of liver cells*. Between these cords are blood spaces (*sinusoids*), which communicate with the branches of the portal vein and the hepatic artery and centrally with the central vein.

The *sinusoids* of the liver are irregular, tortuous spaces which differ from capillaries in that they lack a definite wall of continuous endothelial cells but possess instead a lining of phagocytic (Kupffer) cells along with some nonphagocytic cells. Kupffer cells have the power to engulf bacteria and to store vital dyes. *Bile capillaries* arise in the cords of liver cells and pass peripherally to the margin of the lobules, where they enter primary divisions of the interlobular ducts, which lead to larger bile ducts and in turn to the hepatic ducts.

FUNCTIONS OF THE LIVER. The principal functions of the liver are: secretion of bile; formation of blood; metabolic functions; protective functions; and a thermal function.

1. *Secretion of Bile.* The role of bile in the digestion and absorption of food is discussed on page 186.

2. *Formation of Blood (Hemopoietic Function).* Blood-forming functions of the liver include: (*a*) *red-cell formation in the embryo;* (*b*) *storage of the antianemia factor;* (*c*) *production of fibrinogen, prothrombin, and heparin;* (*d*) *regulation of blood volume.*

3. *Metabolic Functions.* Metabolic functions of the liver consist of (*a*) *carbohydrate metabolism* (glycogenesis, or formation and storage of glycogen, and glycogenolysis, or conversion of glycogen to glucose and liberation into the blood stream); (*b*) *fat metabolism* (synthesis of fatty acids from carbohydrates, desaturation of fatty acids, production of ketones as intermediary products in fat metabolism, synthesis and storage of fat, oxidation of fat); (*c*) *protein metabolism* (deamination of amino acids and formation of urea, synthesis of amino acids,

synthesis of hippuric acid and uric acid); (*d*) *mineral metabolism* (storage of iron and copper); (*e*) *vitamin metabolism* (formation of vitamin A, storage of vitamins A, D, and B_{12}.

4. *Protective Functions*. These functions comprise *detoxication* of substances such as *indol and skatol* and the *phagocytic action of Kupffer's cells*.

5. *Thermal Function*. The liver plays a role in the production of body heat.

The Duct System of the Liver. This system transports bile from its place of origin, the liver cells, to the duodenum or the gallbladder. The smallest branches are small *bile capillaries*. These lead to *intralobular ducts* which lead to *interlobular ducts*. The last join others and form still larger ducts which lead to the right and left tributaries of the *hepatic duct*. The hepatic duct unites with the *cystic duct* from the gallbladder to form the *common bile duct*, which enters the duodenum a short distance below the pylorus.

The Gallbladder. The gallbladder is a reservoir for concentrating and storing bile. It is pear-shaped and lies in a fossa in the inferior side of the right lobe of the liver. It is about 3½ to 4 inches in length and has a capacity of about 50 cc. The constricted portion or *neck* is bent and attached closely to the peritoneal covering of the organ. Its expanded portion or *fundus* is directed anteriorly and lies near the end of the 9th costal cartilage. The *cystic duct*, 3 to 4 cm. long, leads from the gallbladder to the hepatic duct, with which it unites to form the common bile duct. It contains a *spiral valve*, a fold which serves to keep the duct open.

Histologic Structure of the Gallbladder. The wall of the gallbladder has four layers:

1. *Mucosa*, the innermost layer, composed of simple columnar epithelium. Goblet cells are lacking. The mucosa is thrown into folds (primary and secondary) which unite to form polygonal pocket-like areas of variable size. Gland-like evaginations may extend into the muscular layer. The mucosa rests on the *tunica propria*, a thin layer of connective tissue.

2. *Muscular layer*, composed of smooth muscles arranged in small bundles with connective tissue between them.

3. *Connective tissue layer*, lying outside the muscular layer.

4. *Serosa*, the outermost or peritoneal layer.

The Common Bile Duct. This duct, about 7 cm. long, extends from the union of the cystic and hepatic ducts to the duodenum. It passes obliquely through the intestinal wall and opens on the *papilla of Vater*, which is located about 8 to 10 cm. from the pylorus. The common bile duct is dilated slightly within the papilla, that portion forming the *ampulla of Vater*. This duct receives the main pancreatic duct just before it terminates. Two sphincter muscles (*sphincters of Boyden* and of *Oddi*) regulate the flow of bile.

The Pancreas. The pancreas is a compound tubuloacinar gland lying below the liver and the stomach, at the level of the 2nd and 3rd lumbar vertebrae. Its larger portion, or *head*, lies adjacent to the middle portion of the duodenum. The remainder (a neck, a body, and a tail) extends transversely to the left, terminating near the spleen.

The pancreas is a finely lobulated, straw-colored organ, averaging 20 to 25 cm. in length and weighing from 65 to 160 gm. It lacks a definite capsule but is enclosed in a thin covering of connective tissue. The pancreas consists of two types of secreting tissue: an *exocrine portion*, which secretes pancreatic juice; and an *endocrine portion*, which secretes hormones. Pancreatic juice is discharged through the pancreatic ducts into the duodenum; pancreatic hormones, of which *insulin* is the most important, are absorbed into the blood stream.

EXOCRINE PORTION OF THE PANCREAS. The *acini*, terminal secreting divisions, are grouped in lobules which are bound together by connective tissue. Some acini are flask-shaped; others are tubular. Each acinus consists of a single row of pyramidal cells surrounding a lumen which is small in the inactive state but. distended when the gland is active. The lobules are separated by interlobular septa. The exocrine portion of the pancreas contains two excretory ducts:

1. The main excretory canal or *pancreatic duct* (*duct of Wirsung*), which passes through the middle of the pancreas from left to right. At about the midpoint it bends sharply downward and continues to its termination in the common bile duct at the *ampulla of Vater*, where its secretion enters the duodenum.

2. The accessory excretory canal (*duct of Santorini*), a tributary of the main duct, which opens into the duodenum about 2½ cm. above the opening of the common bile duct. It drains a portion of the head of the pancreas and usually communicates with the main duct.

Both main and accessory ducts receive branches, the *interlobular ducts*, which in turn receive intralobular ducts, one from each primary lobule. The intralobular ducts receive *intercalated ducts*, one from each tubule or acinus.

There is also a system of anastomosing tubules which connect with both the larger ducts and the islets of Langerhans. They do not, however, carry any secretion.

ENDOCRINE PORTION OF THE PANCREAS. The *islets of Langerhans* comprise the endocrine portion of the pancreas. These small masses of cells scattered throughout the pancreas number 200,000 to 2,000,000. Each islet is a small, irregular structure enclosed in a delicate reticular connective tissue membrane. The islet cells secret *insulin*, a hormone concerned with the metabolism of carbohydrates.

8: THE PHYSIOLOGY OF DIGESTION

Digestion is the process of converting food substances to a state in which they can be absorbed by the lining of the digestive tract. It is accomplished by *mechanical processes,* such as changes in form brought about by the action of the teeth or the muscular movements of the walls of the various portions of the alimentary canal, and by *chemical processes,* such as the changes induced by enzymes produced by digestive glands.

FOODS

A thorough understanding of the physiology of the processes of digestion requires for its foundation a knowledge of the chemical nature of foodstuffs, their classification, and the role of "food accessories" (water, vitamins, inorganic salts, and other substances).

Functions of Foods. Foods are substances taken into the body which serve the following functions:

1. To provide the chemical elements or compounds essential for the *synthesis of protoplasm* (that is, for the building of new tissue or the repair of injured or worn-out tissue). They also provide the materials for growth and those from which secretions of glands are synthesized.

2. To serve as sources of *heat and energy* for metabolic activities and for the maintenance of body temperature.

3. To provide essential substances for *regulation* of cellular or bodily functions.

Classification of Foodstuffs. Foodstuffs are grouped in two general classes: foods proper and food accessories. The main divisions within these classes follow:

Foods Proper (*Organic compounds serving as sources of energy*)

Carbohydrates	Proteins	Fats (Lipids)
monosaccharides	simple proteins	true fats
disaccharides	conjugated proteins	lipoids
polysaccharides	derived proteins	sterols
		hydrocarbons

Food Accessories (*Substances needed for life activities but providing no energy*)

Water	Inorganic salts	Vitamins

Carbohydrates. In this class of foodstuffs are found compounds of carbon, hydrogen, and oxygen, the two last being in the ratio of 2:1.

A carbohydrate molecule usually consists of six or a multiple of six carbon atoms. The three principal kinds are monosaccharides, disaccharides, and polysaccharides.

MONOSACCHARIDES. These are *simple sugars*. Their empirical formula is $C_6H_{12}O_6$. Examples are grape sugar (glucose or dextrose) and fruit sugar (fructose or levulose), and galactose. These sugars are soluble in water and readily absorbed by the mucosa of the digestive tract. In Fehling's or Benedict's solution copper hydroxide is reduced to cuprous oxide with an accompanying color change from blue to orange or brick red; for this reason these solutions are used in testing substances such as urine for presence of sugar. Monosaccharides are readily oxidized in the tissues; consequently, they are readily available sources of energy.

DISACCHARIDES. These are *double sugars*. Upon hydrolysis they yield two molecules of a simple sugar. Their empirical formula is $C_{12}H_{22}O_{11}$. Examples are cane sugar (sucrose), malt sugar (maltose), and milk sugar (lactose). Sucrose is the common form found in the stem of the sugar cane and the root of the sugar beet. Maltose is found in germinating grains and in malt; lactose is found in the milk of all animals. Disaccharides are formed in the hydrolysis of starch.

POLYSACCHARIDES. These are *multiple sugars*, which are insoluble in water. Their empirical formula is $(C_6H_{10}O_5)_n$. Examples are starch (in plant cells), glycogen (animal starch, abundant in liver and muscle cells), and cellulose (in walls of plant cells). They are a common form of storage for carbohydrate.

Fats or Lipids. Fats, too, are compounds of carbon, hydrogen, and oxygen. They are organic esters consisting of a glycerol radical, C_3H_5, combined with a fatty acid such as palmitic, stearic, or oleic acid. They are insoluble in water but readily soluble in ether or alcohol. Fats are classified as follows: (1) *True fats* (esters of a fatty acid and glycerin), of which olein and palmitin are examples. (2) *Lipoids* (fat-like substances including phospholipids or phosphatides), such as lecithin and cephalin. (3) *Sterols* (hydrogenated phenathrene derivatives), such as cholesterol and ergosterol. (4) *Hydrocarbons*.

Proteins. Proteins are compounds containing carbon, hydrogen, nitrogen, and oxygen, and sometimes sulfur and phosphorus. They are of three kinds: (1) *Simple proteins*, which include albumins, globulins, glutelins, prolamines or gliadins, albuminoids and scleroproteins, histones, and protamines. (2) *Conjugated proteins*, whose molecule is combined with a nonprotein group and which includes nucleoproteins, chemoproteins (hemoglobin and hemocyanin), glycoproteins (mucin), lipoproteins, and phosphoproteins (caseinogen and vitellin). (3) *Derived proteins*, produced by the action of acids or enzymes on simple or conjugated proteins. These include: primary derivatives (proteans, metaproteins, coagulated proteins); and secondary derivatives (proteoses, peptones, peptides).

CHEMICAL NATURE OF PROTEINS. The protein molecule is composed of a number of chemical units linked together. These units are *amino acids*, the so-called "building stones" of proteins. Some 25 different amino acids have been identified. Some proteins contain all or most of the amino acids; others, such as gelatin, contain only 14 or 15; while some simple proteins may have only 3 or 4. Protein molecules are extremely complex and have a very high molecular weight. They vary in shape, the *fibrous* proteins having an elongated fiber-like form, the *globular* proteins a more or less compact, globular form. Owing to their structural and chemical properties, proteins constitute the most important component in the structural organization of the protoplasm of cells.

Proteins which enable an animal to grow and to carry on fundamental life activities are *complete proteins;* that is, they contain *all* the essential amino acids. Those which lack some of these essential acids are *incomplete proteins.* Ten of the amino acids are regarded as "essential."

AMINO ACIDS. An amino acid is an organic compound having the basic formula NH_2—R—COOH, the R standing for any aliphatic radical. The simplest amino acid is glycine (amino-acetic acid), which has the formula $H_2N \cdot CH_2 \cdot COOH$. Amino acids are either aliphatic or aromatic. In the following list are seen 21 of the best-known amino acids; the 10 essential ones are marked with asterisks:

Aliphatic amino acids

Glycine	Aspartic acid
Alanine	Glutamic acid
Serine	Hydroxyglutamic acid
*Threonine	*Arginine
*Valine	*Lysine
Norleucine	Cystine
*Leucine	*Methionine
*Isoleucine	

Aromatic amino acids

*Phenylalanine	*Histidine
Tyrosine	Proline
*Tryptophane	Hydroxyproline

Food Accessories. A number of food substances, some organic, others inorganic, do not serve as sources of energy. These, called "food accessories," include water, inorganic salts, and vitamins.

WATER. Water is the most important single compound in the body, comprising about 70 per cent of body weight. (See pages 18–19.)

INORGANIC SALTS. These include the mineral compounds or the ash constituents of the body. The principal minerals of the body and the percentage of total ash in each are as follows: calcium (Ca), 39; phosphorus (P), 22; potassium (K), 5; sulfur (S), 4; chlorine (Cl), 3; sodium (Na), 2; magnesium (Mg), 0.7; iron (Fe), 0.15. The following appear in only minute amounts: iodine (I), manganese (Mn), copper (Cu), nickel (Ni), Fluorine (Fl), zinc (Zn), aluminum (Al), arsenic (As), bromine (Br), silicon (Si), and selenium (Se).

The principal minerals in the body have the following specific roles:

Calcium—essential for development of bone and teeth, coagulation of blood, normal heart action, and normal muscle irritability.

Phosphorus—functions principally with calcium as calcium phosphate, consequently is also essential for development of bone and teeth; phosphorus plays an important role in liberation of energy for muscle contraction and in other bodily processes involving energy transfer.

Potassium—an essential constituent of all cells and of importance in maintenance of normal osmotic pressure and acid-base balance of the body fluids; essential for normal nerve conduction and muscle contractility.

Sulfur—important constituent of all proteins and especially abundant in protein of hair and nails.

Chlorine and *Sodium*—play primary roles in distribution of extracellular fluids and are of primary importance in maintenance of proper acid-base balance in body.

Magnesium—essential component in a number of enzyme systems.

Iron—essential component of blood pigment, hemoglobin, and therefore essential in formation of red blood cells.

Others—*Manganese*, too, is an essential part of certain enzyme systems. *Copper* plays a role in hemoglobin synthesis. *Iodine* is essential in the formation of thyroxin. *Fluorine* is essential for normal bone and tooth structure; it increases resistance of dentine to caries. *Zinc* is an important component in certain enzyme systems, especially the carbonic anhydrase system.

VITAMINS. The term "vitamin" is applied to a number of unrelated substances found in many foods in minute quantities and essential for the normal metabolic processes. All are complex compounds. Most are produced by animal or plant cells; a few have been synthesized.

In the body most vitamins are obtained from ingested organic foods. In some cases they may be synthesized within the tissues (e.g., vitamin D). In others, symbiotic bacteria residing in the intestines are the source.

There are two general classes of vitamins: *fat-soluble vitamins*, which are either soluble in fats or absorbed with them, and *water-soluble vitamins*, which are soluble in, or absorbed with, water. The common fat-soluble vitamins are A, D, and K. The common water-soluble vitamins are B_1, B_2, B_{12}, C, niacin, and folic acid.

The Fat-Soluble Vitamins. The following table provides information about the common fat-soluble vitamins. (IU is the abbreviation for International Units.)

```
┌─────────────────────────────────────────────┐
│                 VITAMIN A                     │
│          (Antixerophthalmic Vitamin)          │
└─────────────────────────────────────────────┘
```

Chemical Nature

An alcohol ($C_{20}H_{20}OH$) formed in the body from precursors, yellow pigments of plants (alpha, beta, and gamma carotene, and cryptoxanthin). It is stored in the liver of vertebrates.

Source

Yellow and dark green vegetables, especially carrots, spinach, sweet potatoes, yellow fruits, egg yolk, butter, cheese, fresh liver and fish oils (cod and halibut liver oil, in particular).

Function

Normal cell growth and development; integrity of epithelial tissues; activity of osteoblasts and odontoblasts; formation of visual purple (*rhodopsin*) which is essential for vision in dim light.

Daily Requirement

5000 IU for average adult; pregnant women need 6000 to 8000 IU. Massive doses, taken over a considerable period, may produce toxic effects.

Effects of Deficiency

Dryness, hardness, and roughening of skin; night blindness or lessened visual acuity in dim light; degenerative changes in epithelia of mucous membranes, with tendency to cornification of stratified squamous epithelia; failure of normal growth and development; increased susceptibility to infections; alterations in glandular secretions.

```
┌─────────────────────────────────────────────┐
│                 VITAMIN D                     │
│            (Antirachitic Vitamin)             │
└─────────────────────────────────────────────┘
```

Chemical Nature

Mixture of D_2 (calciferol, $C_{28}H_{43}OH$) and D_3 (activated dehydrocholesterol). Ergosterol, precursor of calciferol, is transformed to vitamin D by action of ultraviolet rays. In the body, sunlight or ultraviolet irradiations via the skin bring about production of vitamin D from its precursors in the dermis (hence, "sunshine vitamin"). It is stored in the liver.

Source

Fish liver oils, especially cod liver oil, butterfat, egg yolk. Irradiation of foods, particularly milk, is practiced extensively to convert the precursors to the functional vitamin.

Function

Calcium and phosphorus metabolism; promotes their absorption from intestine and maintains their proper

Daily Requirement

Normal adults need no supplementary intake. Infants and children, and women during the latter half of

Vitamin D (Cont.)

Function (Cont.)
concentrations in blood, especially in bone-forming regions. Essential for normal eruption of teeth and in preventing dental caries.

Daily Requirement (Cont.)
pregnancy and in lactation require 400 IU. For elderly persons or persons receiving inadequate exposure to sunlight, a small amount per day is recommended.

Effects of Deficiency or Excess

In children, lack of vitamin D is evidenced by irritability, abnormal tooth and bone development, and malaise. Severe deficiency causes *rickets*. In adults, severe deficiency is manifested by *osteomalacia*, which predominates in women. It is usually accompanied by tetany.

Excessive intake of vitamin D causes mobilization of calcium and phosphorus from hard tissues and their deposition in soft tissues, especially walls of blood vessels. Calcification may occur in other organs, such as the kidneys, lungs, or heart, with possible fatal consequences. This is the only vitamin for which injurious symptoms have been shown to occur from *overdosage*.

Vitamin K
(Antihemorrhagic Vitamin)

Chemical Nature

Occurs naturally in two forms: K_1 ($C_{31}H_{45}O_2$) and K_2 ($C_{41}H_{56}O_2$). The former is a light yellow oil, the latter a yellow crystalline compound. Two synthetic compounds (phthiocol and menadione) possess similar properties. It is not stored in the body.

Source

Abundant in many foods, but especially in leafy green vegetables. Synthesized in the intestines by bacteria.

Function

Formation of prothrombin by the liver; this is a substance necessary for normal clotting of blood. In its absence coagulation time is prolonged. Vitamin K appears to be an essential part of the enzyme system concerned with the synthesis of prothrombin.

Daily Requirement

Not definitely known, but 2 mg. is considered adequate.

Effects of Deficiency

This is uncommon in man because bacteria in the intestine synthesize vitamin K. In infants, deficiency may result from lack

Vitamin K (Cont.)

of prenatal stores or from the time required for bacterial flora to become established in the intestine. In adults, deficiency may result from biliary obstruction because the natural vitamin is not absorbed in the absence of bile. Diarrhea or excessive use of lubricants may cause loss of vitamin K in feces.

The Water-Soluble Vitamins. The following table provides information about the common water-soluble vitamins. The substance originally known as "vitamin B" has been shown to be a complex of many vitamins (12 or more), of which three have been proved to be essential in human nutrition.

Thiamine
Vitamin B$_1$
(Antineuritic, Antiberiberi Vitamin)

Chemical Nature

White crystalline compound with the empiric formula $C_{12}H_{17}N_4OS$ produced synthetically as thiamine hydrochloride. It is stable in a dry state and not rapidly destroyed by heat.

Source

Widely distributed in various animal and plant foods. Dry yeast and wheat germ are its richest natural sources. Occurs in outer layers of seeds and in nuts, legumes, most vegetables, some meats (especially pork, liver, and muscle). Has been synthesized.

Function

Carbohydrate metabolism. Acts as coenzyme of carboxylases in carboxylation of pyruvic acid, an intermediate product in conversion of glucose to carbon dioxide and water. Thus thiamine is essential for liberation of energy and disposal of pyruvic acid.

Daily Requirement

0.5 mg. for each 1000 Cal., or 1.5 to 3 mg. for normal adults, depending on activity and carbohydrate intake. It is not stored to any extent and must be supplied regularly in the diet. Excess is eliminated in urine and through skin.

Effects of Deficiency

Thiamine deficiency is the commonest vitamin lack. It is also one of the easiest to recognize and to correct. When thiamine is deficient, pyruvic and lactic acids accumulate in blood and brain, with marked impairment of nervous, circulatory, digestive, and endocrine functions. Moderate deficiency is manifested by irritability, loss of appetite, muscle tenderness, and fatigue. Pronounced deficiency causes *beriberi*, whose symptoms are neuritis, paralysis, nerve lesions, digestive disorders, cardiac disturbances, and neurasthenia (the *fatigue syndrome*). Symptoms disappear quickly upon administration of thiamine.

Riboflavin
VITAMIN B$_2$
(Vitamin G, Lactoflavin)

Chemical Nature

An orange-yellow crystalline powder ($C_{17}H_{20}N_4O_6$), comparatively stable to heat and air but unstable to light. It is absorbed readily by the small intestine but stored only to a limited extent in the liver and kidney. It is lost in urine and possibly in feces.

Function

Tissue respiration. In combination with phosphoric acid, it is a component of flavoprotein coenzymes which, acting with nicotinamide-containing enzymes, are essential in oxidation reactions in normal metabolism of cells. Riboflavin is essential for normal health, vigor, and resistance to disease. It is necessary for tissue repair.

Source

Milk and milk products, leafy green vegetables, liver, beef, fish, and dry yeast.

Daily Requirement

1.5 to 2.0 mg., depending on activity. For pregnant and lactating women, 2.5 to 3.0 mg. Intake should be increased after tissue injury, for growth of new tissues is dependent on supply of riboflavin.

Effects of Deficiency

Owing to the wide distribution of riboflavin and to its bacterial synthesis in the body, deficiency of this vitamin is not common in man and there is no distinct, general clinical picture. The most common signs are: eye disorders (vascularization of cornea, conjunctivitis, increased lacrimal secretion, photophobia); cracking and splitting of lips at angles (cheilosis); magenta-colored tongue resulting from inflammation (glossitis); seborrheic dermatitis, especially of face and scalp.

Niacinamide
NIACIN (NICOTINIC ACID)
(Pellagra-preventive Factor)

Chemical Nature

Produced in body from niacin (nicotinic acid), a white crystalline substance ($C_6H_5O_2N$). Is unusually stable in contact with heat, air, light, and alkalies.

Source

Same foods that provide riboflavin, plus mushrooms, whole wheat products, poultry.

NIACIN (NICOTINIC ACID, CONT.)

Functions

Essential component of two co-enzymes which act in series with flavoproteins in cellular respiration. Plays an important role in the absorption and metabolism of carbohydrates.

Daily Requirement

12 to 20 mg. for men and 11 to 15 mg. for women; this is approximately 5 mg. per 1000 Cal. Increased amounts with unusual energy expenditure and in stress situations.

Effects of Deficiency

Same as those of pellagra—inflammation of mouth cavity and tongue; gastrointestinal disturbances; bilateral dermatitis (especially of arms, legs, and neck, and submammary regions); and nervous symptoms (insomnia, irritability, neurasthenia). Degeneration of spinal pathways may occur. In severest form may be fatal.

Pteroylglutamic Acid
FOLIC ACID

Chemical Nature

The folic acids include a large and poorly defined group of B complex vitamins, the best-known of which is pteroylglutamic acid (PGA), a substance of bright yellow crystals, slightly soluble in water. Its sodium salts are readily soluble.

Source

Widespread in animal and plant kingdoms, especially abundant in leafy dark-green vegetables, liver, kidney, and yeast. Synthesized by bacteria in the intestine. A synthetic form has been prepared.

Functions

Possibly assists in utilization of thiamine and other purines and pyrimidines in nucleoprotein metabolism. In experimental animals, found essential for normal growth and formation of red blood cells.

Daily Requirement

Not definitely established. A minimum of 0.25 mg. daily is recommended.

Effects of Deficiency

Brings on macrocytic anemia, leucopenia, and hyperplasia of the bone marrow. Importance in human nutrition not well established but has proved effective against *sprue*, a tropical disease frequently fatal, characterized by glossitis, inflammation of digestive tract, loss of appetite, emaciation and marked macrocytic anemia. When used with B_{12}, folic acid has a marked hemopoietic effect; for this reason, it is used in the treatment of *pernicious anemia*. Sulfa drugs, which inhibit bacterial growth, may induce some of the aforementioned symptoms.

Cyanocobalamine
VITAMIN B_{12}
(Anti-Pernicious Anemia Factor)

Chemical Nature

Consists of deep-red, needle-like crystals soluble in water *and* alcohol. Contains cobalt in its molecule. Is stable to heat but inactivated by acids and alkalies.

Source

Animal tissues, especially liver, kidney, muscle, milk and milk products. Is synthesized by certain microorganisms (*e.g.*, *Streptomyces griseus*).

Functions

Exact functions not known, but thought to be involved in synthesis of nucleoproteins and in transformation of carbohydrates to fat.

Daily Requirement

Not definitely established for man; 2 micrograms daily is recommended maintenance allowance.

Effects of Deficiency

In experimental animals a deficiency results in retarded growth and high mortality in offspring. In man pernicious anemia and other macrocytic anemias are thought to be due to deficiencies in both folic acid and B_{12}.

Ascorbic Acid
VITAMIN C
(Antiscorbutic Factor)

Chemical Nature

White crystalline compound ($C_6H_8O_6$). Soluble in water. Stable in air when dry, but in solution is readily oxidized to products lacking in antiscorbutic properties. Light, alkalies, and certain metals (iron and copper) accelerate its oxidation. It is inactivated by prolonged application of heat.

Source

Citrus fruits, other raw fruits, vegetables, greens (especially cabbage and peppers). Synthesized by most plants and by many animals (man, monkey, guinea pig *do not*). Fruits and vegetables lose their vitamin C activity rapidly when stored at room temperature.

Function

Exact mode of action not well understood. Plays a role in metabolism of certain amino acids. Necessary for formation of collagen, a protein forming an essential part of the white fibers of connective tissue and for

Daily Requirement

75 mg. for men, 70 mg. for women. During pregnancy and lactation, 100 to 150 mg. recommended. Growing children need relatively more than do adults. Intake should be increased during convalescence

Vitamin C (Cont.)

forming the organic substance of bone. Maintains integrity of intercellular cement in many tissues, especially capillary walls. Involved in formation and utilization of adrenal cortical hormones.

from fevers, infections, or injuries such as burns and fractures.

Effects of Deficiency

Pronounced deficiency results in *scurvy*. Some symptoms are: redness, swelling, and bleeding of gums, with resultant loss of teeth; subcutaneous hemorrhages due to increased fragility of capillaries; delayed healing of soft tissues and injured bones; edema; secondary anemia; pain and tenderness in extremities. In *subclinical* cases the symptoms are less pronounced but may also include irritability, loss of appetite, and weight loss.

Other Vitamins. In addition to the vitamins already described, a considerable number have been found to play significant roles in the nutrition of laboratory animals. Their importance in human nutrition has not yet been determined. The more important of them are:

Vitamin E (anti-sterility vitamin), a fat-soluble vitamin found in wheat germ and most vegetable oils. In rats it is essential for the development of functional spermatozoa and for the normal intrauterine development of fetuses.

Pyridoxine (vitamin B_6), thought to be an essential factor in normal nutrition, being concerned with the metabolism of proteins and fats. Deficiency results in dermatitis, heart disorders, degenerative changes in nerve tissues, and anemia.

Pantothenic acid, essential in the growth of yeast and in the general well-being of laboratory animals. Deficiencies are manifested by emaciation, dermatitis with loss of and graying of hair, digestive disturbances, structural alterations in heart, kidney, and adrenal tissue, spinal cord lesions, and nerve degeneration.

Inositol, a necessary factor in the diet of laboratory animals, for normal growth and development. In mice, rats, and guinea pigs, deficiency results in retarded growth, loss of hair, dermatitis, and deposition of fat in the liver. Since inositol is present in living tissues in greater quantities than other vitamins, it probably serves as a structural component rather than as a catalyst.

Biotin, deficiency of which in experimental animals results in loss of hair, loss of weight, abnormal gait and posture, and eventually death. In man, experimentally induced deficiency has resulted in dermatitis, pallor, lassitude, insomnia, anorexia, and coronary insufficiency. Biotin is probably involved in protein metabolism.

Choline, which is essential in animal nutrition, plays a role in the synthesis of certain amino acids and serves as the precursor of acetylcholine (important in the transmission of nerve impulses). It is also involved in fat metabolism; it promotes utilization of fatty acids. Deficiency leads to excessive accumulation of fat in the liver and other degenerative changes throughout the body. There is some question as to whether choline should be regarded as a vitamin or as one of the foods proper since, like inositol, it occurs in the body in such large amounts that it may be a structural component as well as a catalytic agent.

Para-aminobenzoic acid (PABA), a growth-promoting factor in chicks and an anti-gray-hair factor in rats and mice. It is an essential growth factor also for certain microorganisms, especially those inhibited by the sulfonamides and related drugs. It is theorized that the sulfa drugs, which are related to PABA, produce their antibacterial effects by replacing this factor.

MOVEMENTS OF THE ALIMENTARY CANAL

The muscles of the lips, jaws, tongue, cheeks, walls of the pharynx, and upper portion of the esophagus are striated; accordingly, the movements of these parts, with the exception of the pharynx and the upper portion of the esophagus, are *voluntary*. Throughout the remainder of the digestive tract, all muscles are of the smooth type and are innervated by the autonomic nervous system; therefore, they are *involuntary* in action. The following description of the movements of the alimentary canal is confined to a consideration of these smooth muscles.

Characteristics of Smooth Muscles of the Alimentary Canal. The smooth muscles of the viscera are generally arranged in two layers: an outer *longitudinal* layer, which upon contraction brings about a shortening of the digestive tube and dilation of its lumen; and an inner *circular* layer, which, upon contraction, decreases the size of the lumen and increases the length of the tube.

Smooth muscles differ functionally from striated muscles in the following respects: (1) They have a much longer latent period (three seconds or more). (2) The threshold stimulus is higher. (3) They are much less excitable. (4) Their tonus does not depend on impulses from the central nervous system; thus, when the stomach or intestines are empty, their cavities are practically obliterated, owing to the muscle tone of the smooth muscles in their walls.

A fifth, and perhaps the most noteworthy, difference between the action of smooth muscles and that of striated muscles is that *the former exhibit slow contraction and relaxation repeated rhythmically at regular intervals.* Such rhythmic activity occurs in the smooth muscles of the arterial walls and even in a loop or section of the intestine removed from the body. This activity is thought to be controlled by a plexus of nerve fibers and cells located between the layers of smooth muscles in the digestive tract. There is also the possibility that this rhythmic activity is an inherent quality of the smooth muscle itself, occurring independently of the nervous system, but evidence supporting this view is not conclusive.

Movements of the Various Portions of the Alimentary Canal. The functions of the various portions of the alimentary canal are accomplished by a variety of movements which are peculiar to the local structure and to the immediate objectives.

MOVEMENTS OF THE MOUTH AND PHARYNX. The first two actions of the digestive tract, performed in the mouth and the pharynx, are *mastication* and *deglutition*.

Mastication. In mastication the lower jaw is raised and lowered, protracted and retracted, and moved laterally. Through combinations of these movements, the particles of food ingested are ground by the teeth into very small particles. The tongue and cheeks act to keep the food between the teeth; for soft foods, the tongue alone may be used to break up the larger particles. During mastication, saliva, a product of the salivary glands, is released into the mouth cavity. It moistens the food, causing soluble materials to go into solution. The mucin in saliva makes the solid particles stick together to form a *bolus*.

Deglutition. In deglutition, the process of *swallowing*, there are three stages. The first is under voluntary control, but after food has entered the pharynx all the successive movements are of an involuntary, reflex nature.

In the *first stage*, food passes from the mouth to the pharynx. The food mass is placed on the dorsal depressed surface of the tongue and the tip of the tongue is raised and placed against the teeth and hard palate. Elevation and backward movement of the tongue then forces the food posteriorly through the isthmus of the fauces into the pharynx.

In the *second stage*, food passes through the pharynx and into the esophagus. The pharynx is the common passageway for food and air. To conduct food to the proper channel (so that it will not enter the air passages), as the food is pushed backward by the tongue, the soft palate and uvula are elevated, closing the *posterior choanae* (openings into the nasal cavity). The larynx is now elevated, causing the epiglottis, which is directed upward, to be directed posteriorly and to serve as a shield that prevents food from entering the laryngeal opening and directs it into the esophagus. Simultaneously, the vocal cords approach each other, closing the glottis. During this stage, all inspiratory and expiratory movements are reflexly inhibited. Fluid substances pass quickly through the pharynx to the esophagus. Semisolid or solid substances are acted on by the constrictor muscles of the pharynx, which press on the bolus, forcing it into the esophagus. Should the respiratory passageways be opened while food is in the pharynx (as sometimes occurs from a cough, sudden laughter, or an attempt to speak), food may enter the larynx or the posterior portion of the nasal cavity.

In the *third stage* of deglutition, food passes through the esophagus and into the stomach. Liquids are expelled by the pharynx and travel to the lowest part of the esophagus without any assistance from the esophagus. Semisolid or solid foods must be forced through this organ by peristaltic contractions of the circular muscle in its wall. Relaxation of the muscles immediately below the bolus, combined with contraction of the muscles directly above it, causes the bolus to be moved downward slowly. As it progresses downward, the muscles of the area just passed contract, and by such successive muscular actions the bolus is propelled toward the stomach. The foregoing process is called *peristalsis*. The cardiac sphincter, at the opening of the stomach, is normally in a state of relaxation when the stomach is empty, but it is contracted when food is present. When the bolus reaches this sphincter, the sphincter relaxes and the food enters the stomach.

Except for the first stage, deglutition is a *reflex act*. The sensory nerve endings of the pharynx are stimulated by the presence of food or saliva and the impulses are transmitted over afferent nerves (trigeminal, glossopharyngeal, and vagus) to the medulla of the brain, in which there is a *deglutition center*. Here motor impulses are initiated which pass over efferent nerves (trigeminal, glossopharyngeal, vagus, spinal accessory, and hypoglossal) and bring about contraction of the muscles of the pharynx and the esophagus. Although the muscles are striated, they are not under voluntary control.

The *time required* for deglutition is variable. Fluids reach the cardiac sphincter in about one second, but they remain above the contracted sphincter for four or five seconds until it relaxes from the peristaltic wave. For most semisolid substances, the time averages six seconds, although it may be longer.

MOVEMENTS OF THE STOMACH. The first food to enter the stomach fills the pyloric end and the peripheral portion of the body. As food continues to enter, it assumes a more central position and is almost completely enclosed by the food that preceded it. In this way the continuance of salivary digestion is facilitated.

The *muscles* of the stomach differ from those of the other parts of the digestive tract in having a third *inner* layer in which the fibers run *obliquely*.

In an empty stomach, the walls are almost in apposition, there being little or no cavity except in the region of the fundus, which may be distended with gas. As food enters and fills the stomach, the muscles relax and the volume of the cavity is adjusted to its contents with little or no increase in intragastric pressure. The muscles in the upper half of the stomach remain in a state of steady tonic contraction and show little movement, but at about the middle of the stomach active peristaltic contractions occur at intervals of 10 to 20 seconds. They pass down the stomach to the pyloric region, about 20 to 30 seconds being required for their passage. The waves increase in strength in the pyloric region; this region serves as a "mixing chamber."

If the food is sufficiently acid and the duodenum is empty, the pyloric sphincter relaxes and a small amount of the semifluid contents, called *chyme*, is passed into the duodenum. The sphincter closes almost immediately and remains closed while the duodenum contains food. Consistency of food is a factor in this action; solid masses moved by peristaltic contractions against the pyloric opening do not bring about the relaxation of the pyloric sphincter, even when the duodenum is empty.

Emotional states such as grief, fear, and anger have an influence on the muscular movements of the stomach. They reflexly inhibit gastric motility and alter glandular secretion.

As to the *length of time food remains* in the stomach, foods *begin* to leave the stomach a few minutes after ingestion. The food consumed in an ordinary meal requires three to five hours to pass through this portion of the digestive system. Water leaves the stomach almost immediately after it has been swallowed. The first of the organic foods to leave are carbohydrates; they are followed by the proteins and their derivatives, and, finally, the fats.

MOVEMENTS OF THE SMALL INTESTINE. Two distinct types of movements occur in the small intestine: rhythmic segmentation and diastalsis (peristalsis).

In *rhythmic segmentation* (a "dividing" motion), the intestine is observed to divide itself into a number of segments by constriction of the circular muscles. After two or three seconds, the muscle fibers in the center of each of these segments contract, dividing the segment into two parts and uniting the halves of adjoining segments. Then the fibers in the center of these segments contract. This rhythmic activity produces a churning movement which thoroughly mixes the intestinal contents with glandular secretions and facilitates absorption by bringing the contents into contact with the villi. It also stimulates the flow of blood and lymph in the vessels in the intestinal wall. Food is *not propelled onward* by this movement.

The *peristaltic wave* (or diastalsis) comes about when the intestines are stimulated by the presence of a mass of food. Circular fibers at or above the food mass contract, while those below, over a considerable distance, relax. This is known as *Starling's law of the intestine*. The wave of contraction and relaxation moves down the small intestine at a rate of one-half inch to one inch per minute.

In addition to the slow peristaltic wave, there may occur at times a "peristaltic rush," in which the wave travels much faster (from one inch to ten inches per second). Such a movement takes place over a much longer portion of the intestine than does the peristaltic wave.

It requires two to four hours for chyme to traverse the length of the small intestine and reach the ileocecal sphincter, which then follows Starling's law and relaxes, permitting food to enter the upper part of the cecum. If the cecum is full, the sphincter remains closed.

MOVEMENTS OF INTESTINAL VILLI. The villi of the intestines are almost constantly in motion—constricting, shortening, elongating, and swaying from side to side. Such movements are probably due to contractions of smooth muscle fibers within each villus. In this manner the intestinal contents which bathe the villi are stirred and the chyle within the lacteals is forced out into the larger lymph vessels.

MOVEMENTS OF THE LARGE INTESTINE. In the large intestine, peristaltic, antiperistaltic, and segmentation movements are either absent or extremely weak or ill-defined. Food enters the cecum and makes its way up the ascending colon; the factors responsible for this movement in man are not clear. A wave starts in the region of the hepatic flexure and proceeds for a considerable distance, moving the contents of the bowel along with it. It is comparable to the peristaltic rush of the small intestine. This wave is frequently initiated by the entrance of food into the stomach; consequently, the desire for a bowel movement is often experienced after breakfast. Mass peristalsis may occur two or three times a day. As a result of this movement, the intestinal contents (at this point called *feces*) is forced into the pelvic or *sigmoid colon*.

Defecation. This is the process of emptying the rectum. It is a reflex act initiated by the presence of feces in the rectum, which is generally empty until just before defecation. Mass peristalsis causes the feces to enter the rectum. When intrarectal pressure reaches 30 to 40 mm. Hg, the *desire* to defecate is initiated; pressure of 40 to 50 mm. Hg initiates the defecation reflex. This results automatically in a bowel movement in an infant (or in an adult suffering from spinal cord injury). In normal children or adults, however, the reflex can be inhibited or assisted voluntarily.

The muscular mechanism involved in activity of the intestines during defecation is as follows: Sensory fibers carry impulses to the lumbosacral region of the spinal cord, and the musculature of the colon and rectum is reflexly stimulated to contract. A strong wave of mass peristaltic contractions takes place in the colon. At the same time, the internal and external anal sphincters are inhibited and relaxed. Contraction of the abdominal wall muscles brings about compression of the abdomen and thus increases the pressure on the lower portion of the colon and the rectum. To keep the abdominal contents from moving upward, the contraction of abdominal muscles is usually preceded by a deep inspiration, and the glottis is kept closed. As a result of these processes, pressure in the rectum is greatly increased, leading to the expulsion of feces.

The levator ani and other muscles of the pelvic floor play an important role in defecation. They support the pelvic floor against increased intra-abdominal pressure. Fibers of the levator ani are inserted into the walls of the anal canal and on contraction tend to enlarge the anal opening and pull the anus over the feces. At the end of the act of defecation, they tend to bring about expulsion of any material that may remain.

The number of bowel movements normally required in one day varies with individuals. Most people have one or more a day; others have bowel movements only every other day; some have even less frequent movements.

Composition of Feces. Feces consists of (1) undigested food such as muscle fibers, starch grains, fat droplets; (2) indigestible materials such as cellulose and mucin; (3) products of fermentation and putrefaction such as skatole and indole; (4) bacteria, both living and dead, which make up about 25 per cent of the feces; (5) inorganic salts, especially compounds of calcium, iron, magnesium, and phosphorus; and (6) bile pigments or their derivatives. The brown color of normal feces is due principally to the presence of *stercobilin*, which is derived from bile.

Foreign substances may appear in feces under pathologic conditions. For example, blood cells may be present in hookworm infestation, in ulceration, or in a late stage of carcinoma. Animal parasites and their eggs or larvae may be found.

Amount of Feces. The amount of feces formed each 24 hours depends on the amount and nature of the food that has been ingested. It is larger on a vegetable diet. The average daily amount of fecal discharge for a person in normal health is about 200 gm.

THE ROLE OF ENZYMES IN DIGESTION

Most of the foods taken into the body are in the form of large complex molecules which, in the form in which ingested, are incapable of being absorbed by the epithelium of the intestinal walls and of being drawn into the blood and lymph. Digestion, which makes the necessary changes, is brought about by enzymes produced by the glands of the digestive system.

Enzymes as Catalysts. An *enzyme* is a catalytic agent produced by a living cell. (A catalyst is a substance which increases the velocity of a chemical reaction.) Catalysts are not reacting agents in the reactions they modify, for they can be recovered unaltered after the reaction has taken place. They are effective in very small quantities and apparently can exert their effects again and again. Catalysts may be either inorganic or organic.

ACTION OF AN INORGANIC CATALYST. If *sucrose* is dissolved in water, the following reaction takes place:

$$C_{12}H_{22}O_{11} + H_2O \rightarrow C_6H_{12}O_6 + C_6H_{12}O_6$$
$$\text{(sucrose)} + \text{(water)} \rightarrow \text{(glucose)} + \text{(fructose)}$$

This reaction (*hydrolysis*) takes place at an extremely slow rate, even though the temperature may be increased to boiling. If, however, a little hydrochloric acid is added, the hydrolysis of sucrose is greatly speeded up. Other acids may produce the same effect; apparently the presence of hydrogen ions is responsible for the effect. In this case, hydrochloric acid serves as the catalyst.

ACTION OF AN ORGANIC CATALYST. *Sucrase* is an enzyme that may be obtained by extraction from the mucosa of the intestine. If a small quantity of sucrase is added to a solution of sucrose, the hydrolysis (as in the case of adding hydrochloric acid) will occur speedily, even at low temperatures. A small quantity will bring about the hydrolysis of a large amount of sucrose.

Characteristics of Enzymes. Enzymes have the following nine characteristics:

(1) They are *organic in origin,* being produced only by living cells.

(2) They are *catalysts,* producing their effects only when the substrate (the substance acted upon) is in solution.

(3) They are *soluble,* being extracted from animal or plant sources by various solvents, such as water, salt solutions, dilute alcohol, and glycerol.

(4) They are *precipitated by alcohol or metallic salts,* such as copper sulfate or mercuric chloride, in this respect resembling proteins.

(5) They *behave as colloids,* and do not diffuse through semipermeable membranes, such as parchment paper and collodion.

(6) They are *responsive to temperature changes,* each enzyme having an optimum temperature of activity. Enzymes are inactivated but not destroyed by freezing (0° C.). Most are destroyed by temperatures of 70° C. All are destroyed by boiling (100° C.). The optimum temperature for most enzyme activity is body temperature (38° to 40° C.).

(7) They are *sensitive to changes in hydrogen-ion concentration.* Each enzyme produces its effects only within a limited pH range. Some act in acid solutions (for example, pepsin, which acts in the stomach at a pH of 1 to 3); others act in an alkaline medium (for

example, the protease of pancreatic juice, which acts in the intestine with a pH of 6.8 to 9.5). Most enzymes produce their effects in solutions having a pH around 7 (neutrality).

(8) They are *specific in their action*. A given enzyme will act on only one type of chemical substance or one very closely related to it. For instance, sucrase acts on the double sugar, sucrose, but it will not act on proteins or fats or even on other double sugars, such as lactose and maltose.

(9) They are *capable of reversing the reactions catalyzed*. Lipase, an enzyme which during digestion hydrolyzes fats to fatty acids and glycerine, can also act in the reverse of this process wherein resynthesis of fat occurs.

Theory of Enzyme Action. The first step in an action in which an enzyme is involved is a union of the enzyme with its substrate. In combination the enzyme has the power to either decompose or synthesize, after which it separates from the substrate and acts on a new molecule. The analogy between this action and the action of a lock and key has given rise to the "lock-and-key" theory of enzyme action. The enzyme (key) fits the configuration of a particular substrate (lock). As a key acts to rearrange the components of the lock in such a way that the parts of the lock either separate or unite, so presumably an enzyme has a molecular configuration which fits into specific types of molecules and by its action can split molecules into smaller ones or cause them to unite.

Chemical Composition of Enzymes. All enzymes show the properties of proteins. But whether the enzymes are themselves proteins or nonprotein substances attached to a protein molecule has not been determined, owing to the difficulty of preparing enzymes in a pure or nearly pure state. Some twenty or more hydrolyzing enzymes have been purified and have been found to be simple proteins. Many enzymes contain a metallic element (Ca, Fe, Zn, Cu, Mg, Mn), and their activity is associated with its presence.

Inactive Form of Enzymes. Some enzymes are secreted in an inactive form and require activation to exert their catalytic effect. The inactive form of an enzyme is called a *zymogen*. For example, when pepsin is obtained from gastric glands it is not proteolytic, but upon reaching the lumen of the stomach it is activated by the hydrochloric acid and becomes actively proteolytic. The precursor of pepsin (that is, its zymogen) is called *pepsinogen*. Similarly, trypsinogen, secreted by the pancreas, is the zymogen of trypsin. Trypsin is activated by enterokinase, a substance present in intestinal juice. Enterokinase may be an enzyme, but its zymogenic character has been questioned.

Classification of Enzymes. There are three important classes of enzymes: (1) *oxidases*, or oxidizing enzymes; (2) *dehydrogenases*, which catalyze oxidation by removing hydrogen; and (3) *hydrolases,* which bring about hydrolysis. All the digestive enzymes are hydrolases; they are classified on the basis of the substrate acted upon, as follows:

Amylases, starch-splitting enzymes (ptyalin and amylopsin);
Disaccharases, which hydrolyze double sugars (sucrase, lactase, maltase);
Lipases, which hydrolyze fats (gastric lipase and steapsin);
Proteases, proteolytic enzymes, which hydrolyze proteins (pepsin, trypsin).

Enzymes may also be classified on the basis of the site at which their effects are produced. Enzymes that normally act within a cell are called *intracellular* enzymes; examples are oxidizing enzymes within tissue cells. Enzymes found in the secretions of digestive glands are examples of *extracellular* enzymes.

Results of Hydrolysis of Various Enzymes. The effects produced by the hydrolases are shown in the following table:

ENZYME	SUBSTANCES HYDROLYZED	RESULTING PRODUCTS
Amylases ptyalin (salivary amylase) amylopsin (pancreatic amylase)	starch	maltose
Disaccharases sucrase lactase maltase	sucrose lactose maltose	glucose and levulose glucose and galactose glucose and galactose
Lipases gastric lipase steapsin	fats in emulsified state when ingested fats which have been emulsified by bile	fatty acids and glycerol
Proteases pepsin trypsin erepsin chymotrypsin	proteins proteins proteins and peptids peptones and peptids	proteoses and peptones proteoses, peptones, poly-peptids, peptids, amino acids amino acids amino acids

CHANGES IN FOODSTUFFS DURING DIGESTION

Through the action of the teeth and the effects of secretions of the digestive glands, the ingested foodstuffs are changed to their absorbable forms.

Changes that Occur in the Mouth. In the oral cavity, food is ground by the teeth and moistened by saliva. The saliva helps it to form a *bolus* (ball) and makes it slippery to permit easy passage through the alimentary canal. Food remains in the mouth for so brief a time that the extent of salivary digestion is limited, but the action of the components of saliva continues in the stomach until the salivary enzymes (which require an alkaline medium) are inactivated by the acidity of the gastric secretions.

Changes that Occur in the Stomach. Gastric juice is the secretion of the gastric glands. It contains hydrochloric acid, which is produced by the parietal cells, and pepsin, produced by the chief cells. In addition, the gastric juice contains mucin, mucin-like proteins, inorganic salts, and the intrinsic factor of the antianemia principle. The amount of hydrochloric acid varies from 0.2 to 0.5 per cent by volume. Gastric juice has a pH of 0.9 to 1.5.

Pepsin hydrolyzes proteins through successive stages into metaproteins, proteoses, and peptones. It also acts on the protein of cow's milk (*caseinogen*), transforming it into casein (paracasein). In the presence of calcium ions, insoluble calcium caseinate is formed. This brings about coagulation (or *curdling*) of milk, a semigelatinous mass being formed. By such action milk is prevented from passing directly to the intestine and is held in the stomach long enough for pepsin to act on its protein constituents. This coagulation of milk has been attributed to an enzyme, *rennin*, but careful studies have shown that rennin is absent from the gastric juice of adults. Pepsin requires the presence of hydrochloric acid for its action.

The action of *gastric lipase* is very limited because only traces of it are present. It acts to some extent on finely emulsified fats such as egg yolk, butter, and cream, hydrolyzing them into fatty acids and glycerol.

Through muscular and enzymatic action, the food in the stomach is reduced to *chyme*, a substance of semiliquid consistency in which all food substances are in solution or in an emulsified state. Chyme is distinctly acid, and the acid acts as a stimulus to bring about relaxation of the pyloric sphincter. This action of the pyloric sphincter permits chyme to be squirted into the intestine following peristaltic waves of the stomach.

The *time required* for gastric digestion of an average meal is three to five hours.

Changes that Occur in the Small Intestine. Three juices are of importance in intestinal digestion. They are the bile, pancreatic juice, and intestinal juice.

BILE. Bile is secreted by the liver at the rate of about 500 cc. a day. It is golden-brown in color and alkaline in reaction. Bile passes from the liver through the hepatic ducts into the common bile duct. It may enter the duodenum or it may pass to the gallbladder, where it is stored. The composition of bile taken by fistula from the bile duct differs from that taken from the gallbladder, as the following table shows:

Constituent	Averages Based on 3 Analyses of Fistula Bile from Liver (Per Cent)	Averages Based on 4 Analyses of Bile from Gallbladder (Per Cent)
Water	97.13	86.00
Bile salts	1.55	8.20
Mucin and pigments	0.49	2.25
Cholesterol	0.12	2.17
Fats, including lecithin	0.06	0.66
Inorganic salts	0.72	0.78

SOURCE: P. H. Mitchell, *A Textbook of General Physiology* (5th ed.; New York: McGraw-Hill Book Company, 1956), p. 537.

BILE SALTS. The principal bile salts are sodium salts of glycocholic and taurocholic acids. They are alkaline and have the property of lowering the surface tension of water to a marked degree. This enables them to emulsify fats, that is, to break the larger fat particles into smaller particles. This permits more effective access of pancreatic lipase to the surfaces of fats and results in a more complete hydrolysis of these substances. Bile salts are also capable of dissolving fatty acids and water-insoluble soaps, which enhance the emulsifying power of bile.

BILE PIGMENTS. These substances give bile its color. They are *bilirubin*, having a reddish color, and *biliverdin*, which is greenish. Bile pigments have their origin in hematin, a derivative of hemoglobin. Liver cells phagocytose red blood cells and bring about their disintegration, in the process, hematin is liberated and oxidized to bilirubin. Further oxidation leads to the formation of biliverdin. In the intestine, bile pigments are converted by bacterial action into *stercobilin*, which is responsible for the brown color of feces.

CHOLESTEROL. Cholesterol ($C_{27}H_{45}OH$), a sterol present in all cells and fluids of the body, is excreted by the liver cells and by the cells lining the gallbladder. In large quantities cholesterol tends to crystallize, forming concretions of varying size known as gallstones.

FUNCTIONS OF BILE. Bile (1) reduces the acidity of chyme in the upper portion of the small intestine; (2) emulsifies fats, ensuring more complete digestion and absorption; (3) increases the solubility of fatty acids, thus aiding in their utilization; (4) serves as a vehicle for excretion of waste substances, such as those resulting from destruction of hemoglobin in the liver; (5) lessens fermentation and putrefaction in the intestine by aiding in more complete utilization of proteins and carbohydrates; (6) favors the absorption of vitamins, especially the fat-soluble vitamins A, D, and K; and (7) stimulates intestinal motility.

PANCREATIC JUICE. The exocrine portion of the pancreas secretes a juice that resembles saliva in its general consistency. It contains proteins, inorganic salts (including carbonates and phosphates which render it alkaline), and a number of enzymes. Among the enzymes secreted are trypsin, chymotrypsin, peptidase, amylopsin, maltase, and steapsin.

Upon entering the intestine, pancreatic juice acts on all classes of foods. Its action is greatly stimulated by the presence of bile. The enzymatic action on the various foods is as follows:

Action of Pancreatic Proteases. It had been generally thought that the pancreas secreted only one proteolytic enzyme, trypsin, but now it is known that two or more enzymes are present. These are *trypsin,* secreted as trypsinogen, and *chymotrypsin,* secreted as chymotrypsinogen. The former is activated by the enterokinase present in intestinal juice, the latter by trypsin. The source of enterokinase is unknown, although the intestinal glands or the pancreas have been suspected. Pancreatic *peptidase* (carboxypeptidase) acts on peptids, hydrolyzing them into amino acids. The foregoing enzymes act on all proteins but are most effective with proteins that are already partly hydrolyzed by pepsin. They complete the hydrolysis of peptones, polypeptids, and peptids to amino acids, the final products of digestion.

Pancreatic Amylases. These amylases—amylopsin and maltase—continue the digestion of starches that is initiated in the mouth by ptyalin. The starches are hydrolyzed to various stages of dextrins, which are then hydrolyzed to maltose. Pancreatic maltase hydrolyzes maltose to simple sugar (glucose).

Pancreatic Lipase. Steapsin is the principal enzyme in the digestion of fats. It acts on fats emulsified by the bile, hydrolyzing them to fatty acids and glycerol, the end-products of fat digestion.

Intestinal Juice. Succus entericus consists of the secretion of the glands in the intestinal mucosa (Brunner's glands and the crypts of Lieberkühn). It contains water, salts, mucus, and the following substances: (1) *enterokinase,* which activates trypsinogen; (2) *inverting enzymes* (maltase, sucrase, lactase), which act on the disaccharides, splitting them into monosaccharides; (3) *peptidases,* which include a number of enzymes formerly believed to be a single enzyme, erepsin, which cannot hydrolyze proteins but acts on proteoses, peptones, and peptids, hydrolyzing them to amino acids; and (4) a *miscellany of enzymes* which have been demonstrated in extracts of intestinal mucosa, among them a group that hydrolyze nucleic acids, liberating phosphoric acid, and traces of lipase and amylases.

Note that the inverting enzymes are involved in the following reactions:

> Maltase hydrolyzes maltose to glucose.
> Sucrase hydrolyzes sucrose to glucose and levulose.
> Lactase hydrolyzes lactose to glucose and galactose.

Changes that Occur in the Large Intestine. By the time food has reached the large intestine, the digestible materials have been acted on by enzymes and their end-products. The functions served by the large intestine are: (1) absorption of water; and (2) elimination of waste products.

ABSORPTION OF WATER. Fluid chyme passing through the ileocecal valve is of about the same consistency as that entering at the pylorus. Although much water with substances in solution is absorbed by the small intestine, an equivalent amount is added in the secretions of the mucosa and the various glands. Feces leaving the rectum are semisolid in consistency, indicating that a very considerable amount of water is absorbed by the large intestine.

ELIMINATION OF WASTE PRODUCTS. In addition to the elimination of feces, the large intestine is the principal organ for the excretion of calcium, magnesium, iron, and phosphates. Foreign substances, such as bismuth and mercury, are also eliminated by this organ. The fluid secreted by the large intestine is thick and alkaline (pH 8.4) and contains much mucus.

Bacterial Action in the Intestines. Large numbers of bacteria are usually consumed along with food. Most of these are destroyed by the sterilizing and digestive action of the acid contents of the stomach, though some acid-resistant bacteria may pass through unaffected.

The contents of the first portion of the small intestine are sterile, or nearly so. The bile has a mild antiseptic action. As the chyme moves downward through the intestines, the floral content increases both in number and in species. It consists principally of bacteria, although yeasts and filamentous fungi may be present; the types of bacteria vary among individuals, but in one individual they remain relatively constant. These organisms live symbiotically, the relationship between them and their host being that of *commensalism*.* Sometimes a *mutualism* may exist in that these organisms, through fermentation, may aid in the digestion of foods or through their synthetic activities produce substances, such as vitamins, which are

---

* *Commensalism* describes an intimate association between the organisms of different species in which neither organism suffers from the association; *mutualism* is an association in which some benefit is derived by both (nourishment, protection, etc.); *parasitism* is an association in which one is harmful to the other, its host.

absorbed by the intestines and utilized by the body. When their activities are harmful, the organisms must be regarded as *parasites*. Included in this group are the pathogenic forms which cause disease (for example, the dysentery, cholera, and typhoid bacilli) and bacteria which cause undesirable fermentations.

The principal changes brought about by bacteria in the intestines are fermentations. Carbohydrates are decomposed, with alcohol and acid products resulting. Indeed, this action helps to account for the increased acidity of chyme as it moves through the intestine. Proteins are acted upon, giving rise to putrefactive products which include amines (histamine, thylamine, thyramine), phenols (skatole, indole, creosole), volatile acids, and various gases (H_2S, H_2, CO_2, and CH_4). These products are responsible for the typical odor of feces. Some of the amines are potentially toxic, but they have little or no effect on the body, for most are eliminated through the feces and, if absorbed, are rendered innocuous through detoxifying action of the liver. If intestinal putrefaction is excessive or the liver cells fail to perform their functions, toxic products of digestion may enter the general circulation and produce a condition known as *autointoxication*. There is, however, some uncertainty as to the extent of this condition.

SECRETION BY DIGESTIVE GLANDS

The initiation and regulation of secretion by digestive glands are accomplished by nervous, humoral, and mechanical factors. In *nervous control*, nerve impulses are initiated through the action of stimuli on receptors (ends of afferent or sensory nerves). This gives rise to impulses which are transmitted to the reflex centers in the brain. From these centers impulses travel to the gland involved and the secretory activity begins. In *humoral control*, hormones or other chemical substances are transmitted to the glands through the blood stream. They are specific in their action and initiate secretion by direct effect on the gland cells. *Mechanical factors* (for example, the presence of food in the stomach or intestines) are believed to play a role in secretion, but the extent of their influence is not well established.

Secretion by Salivary Glands. The salivary glands are entirely under nervous control; severing the nerves leading to a gland causes all of its secretion to stop. Impulses initiating salivary secretion originate in chemoreceptors, pressure receptors, and higher nerve centers.

IMPULSES FROM CHEMORECEPTORS. Food or other substances, such as acetic acid, stimulate chemoreceptors. The impulses give rise to sensations of taste or smell and reflexly initiate gland secretion.

IMPULSES FROM PRESSURE RECEPTORS. These sense organs respond to physical factors such as the presence of food or other substances in the mouth, or to the movement of mouth parts.

IMPULSES FROM HIGHER NERVE CENTERS. Impulses may arise in these centers when the individual sees food, hears the name of a food or the sounds associated with food preparation (the frying of a steak), or thinks of food and situations associated with it. Secretion resulting from such stimuli is called *psychic secretion*. The basis for such action is the conditioned reflex. As in other cases, it depends on previous experience and training which have established conditioned reflex paths.

Secretion of Gastric Juice. The juice of the stomach is secreted in three phases: psychic or cephalic, gastric, and intestinal. The phases are named after the sites of stimulation.

PSYCHIC (CEPHALIC) PHASE. The sight, taste, smell, and memory of activities associated with food-getting usually initiate secretion of gastric juices. Impulses reach the stomach from the reflex center in the medulla by way of the vagus nerve to stimulate the gastric glands.

GASTRIC PHASE. This phase refers to the secretion of gastric juice after food has entered the stomach. Certain foods contain substances called *secretogogues* which incite secretory activity. Among them are meat extractives and peptones (products of incomplete hydrolysis of proteins). It has been suggested that secretogogues act on the cells of the pyloric mucosa, causing the production of a hormone called *gastric secretin* or *gastrin*, which is carried by the blood to the glands of the stomach. Gastric juice contains *histamine*, a powerful gastric stimulant, and some investigators consider gastrin and histamine to be identical substances.

INTESTINAL PHASE. The presence in the duodenum and jejunum of the products of gastric digestion is thought to excite the production of a hormone, *intestinal gastrin*, which is carried by the blood stream to the gastric mucosa, where it stimulates secretion by the glands in that layer.

Secretion of Pancreatic Juice. The secretion of pancreatic juice appears to be principally under chemical control. Acid substances entering the duodenum from the stomach cause the duodenal mucosa to secrete *secretin*, a hormone which is absorbed into the blood stream and carried to the pancreas, where is stimulates secretion. Another hormone, *pancreozymin*, is produced by the duodenal mucosa. Secretin increases the rate of flow and concentration of bicarbonates in pancreatic juice; pancreozymin increases the enzymatic content.

Nervous control plays a minor role in the secretion of pancreatic juice. There is a flow of pancreatic juice a few minutes after ingestion of food. This is the result of a reflex arising from stimulation of receptors in the mouth. Stimulation of the vagus nerve increases the rate of secretion; severing it inhibits secretion. Psychic stimulation may occur to a limited extent.

Secretion of Bile. The secretory activity of liver cells is practically continuous and apparently depends largely on blood supply. It occurs independently of nervous activity, although stimulation of the vagus nerve· increases bile secretion and stimulation of sympathetic nerves inhibits it. The presence of bile or of certain foods in the intestine stimulates secretion by the liver cells. Substances which increase the secretion of bile are called *choleretics;* bile salts and bile acids are the most potent. Among foodstuffs which are effective choleretics are fats or the products of their digestion. Production of bile is also stimulated by *secretin* produced by the intestinal mucosa; the secretin stimulates secretory activity in both the pancreas and the liver.

Discharge of Bile from the Gallbladder. As acid chyme enters the intestine, the tonus of the muscular layer of the gallbladder wall is increased, forcing bile through the relaxed sphincter muscle at the ampulla of Vater. The contraction of the gallbladder is brought about by a hormone, *cholecystokinin,* secreted by the duodenal mucosa. Acids and fats are specific stimuli for the liberation of cholecystokinin.

Secretion of Intestinal Juice. The secretion of intestinal juice (succus enterious) is principally under nervous control. The presence of food or of undigested food residues in the intestine acts as a mechanical stimulus reflexly initiating secretory activity. Inasmuch as this occurs in a denervated intestine, it is assumed that these reflexes are local, involving the nerve plexus (Meissner's plexus) within the intestinal wall. Chemical factors may also be involved. Secretin stimulates the secretion of intestinal juice as well as pancreatic juice and bile. Pancreatic juice locally excites the intestinal glands. In addition, certain substances have been isolated from the intestinal mucosa which act as hormones stimulating secretion by the intestinal glands. The secretion of mucus by the goblet cells of the intestinal epithelium is brought about by the direct stimulation of the goblet cells by mechanical and chemical stimuli.

ABSORPTION BY THE DIGESTIVE SYSTEM

Absorption is the process in which the final products of digestion pass through the intestinal mucosa and are taken into the blood or lymph. It depends on the physical and chemical processes of filtration, diffusion, osmosis, imbibition, and adsorption. In addition to these factors, certain vital activities must be attributed to the epithelial cells of the mucosa to account for absorption which seems contrary to physicochemical principles.

Pathways of Absorption. Absorbed substances, especially amino acids and simple sugars, are picked up by the capillaries of the mucosa. These lead to veins (mesenteric) which lead to the *portal vein,* which enters the liver. After passing through the liver sinusoids, the blood enters the *inferior vena cava* via the hepatic veins. Such is the pathway of absorption into the blood stream. As for absorption into the lymphatic system, absorbed substances, particularly fats, are taken into the lacteals, which are blind lymph capillaries within the villi. The lacteals lead to larger lymph vessels, which, in turn, lead to the main lymph vessel, the *thoracic duct*. This duct empties into the blood stream at the junction of the left subclavian and left innominate veins. The material carried by lymphatic vessels is called *chyle*.

Sites of Absorption. Absorption occurs principally in the small and large intestines. There is little or no absorption of water or of food substances in the stomach, although alcohol, simple sugars, and certain drugs (strychnine and potassium cyanide) may be absorbed to some extent.

Absorption in the Small Intestine. This is the principal organ for the absorption of foods. Digestive processes are carried to completion here, and their final products are taken into the blood or lymph. Proteins are absorbed into the blood as amino acids, carbohydrates as monosaccharides. Fats are absorbed into both the blood and the lymph.

Concerning the *absorption of fats*, there are two views:

1. That fats can be absorbed without hydrolysis, especially if they are in a finely emulsified condition.

2. That all fats *must* be hydrolyzed into fatty acids and glycerol. In the latter instance, the sequence of events is thought to be as follows: The glycerol is readily absorbed by the epithelial cells, but the fatty acids react with the alkali to form *soaps*. Bile readily dissolves the soaps and within the epithelial cells the soaps break down, liberating the fatty acids, which then recombine with glycerol to form neutral fats. These neutral fats then enter the blood directly or indirectly by way of the lymphatic system.

The small intestine also absorbs water, salts, vitamins, and, sometimes, the products of fermentation or putrefaction.

Absorption is facilitated in the small intestine by the presence of (1) *circular folds* of the wall of the intestine, and (2) *villi*, which greatly increase the absorption surface. The *total absorptive surface* of the small intestine is estimated to be about 10 square meters.

METABOLISM OF FOODS

The term *metabolism*, in its general sense, refers to the processes that take place in the utilization of foods after they have been absorbed into the circulatory fluids. Constructive synthetic activities such as the building of protoplasm or of substances within the protoplasm of cells constitute *anabolism*; destructive processes constitute *catabolism*.

General metabolism is the term applied to the sum total of all the chemical reactions taking place in the body. Some of these reactions are *endothermic*; that is, they are accomplished by the taking up of heat. Most reactions, however, are oxidative and are accompanied by the liberation of heat, and thus are called *exothermic*. Metabolism is generally measured and expressed in *calories* of heat given off by the body within a given period of time. For an average adult male, this is 40 calories per square meter of body surface per hour.

Special metabolism refers to the chemical changes, either anabolic or catabolic, which involve a particular type of substance, such as a carbohydrate, a fat, a protein, or a mineral (carbohydrate metabolism, fat metabolism, protein metabolism, calcium metabolism).

General Metabolism. Through the action of chlorophyll, a green pigment, plants are able to utilize the energy of the sun in the manufacture of simple sugars. The primary reaction is:

$$6CO_2 + 6H_2O + Energy \rightarrow C_6H_{12}O_6 + 6O_2$$

In this process, light energy, which is *kinetic* in nature, is changed to *potential* energy and is stored in the molecule of sugar.

Animals, however, are unable to utilize solar energy in this way. Their food (carbohydrates, fats, and proteins) serves as their source of energy. The carbon in foods is oxidized in the tissues of the animal, and energy is liberated. The basic reaction for this is:

$$C_6H_{12}O_6 + 6O_2 \rightarrow 6CO_2 + 6H_2O + Energy$$

The energy liberated is used for the many activities that take place in animal cells, such as contraction, secretion, conduction, and assimilation, and for the maintenance of body temperature.

CALORIC VALUE OF FOODS. When foods are oxidized in the body, heat is produced. The unit of heat measurement is the *calorie*. It is possible to determine the amount of heat produced by foods by burning them in a *calorimeter*. A *small calorie* (cal.) is the amount of heat required to raise 1 gram of water 1° C. A Large Calorie (Cal.) is the amount of heat required to raise 1 kilogram of water 1° C. In studies of metabolism, the Large Calorie is used. In terms of other units of energy, a Calorie equals 426.85 kilogram meters, or 3087.4 foot pounds, or 1000 calories.

The caloric value of the three general classes of foods are as follows: 1 gm. of fat yields 9.3 Cal.; 1 gm. of carbohydrate yields 4.1 Cal.; 1 gm. of protein yields 4.1 Cal. Outside the body, 1 gm. of protein yields 5.3 Cal., but within the body it is not completely oxidized, the nitrogenous part being excreted.

CALORIMETRY. There are two methods of measuring the heat generated by an organism: the direct method and the indirect method.

Direct Calorimetry. In this method the test animal is placed in an apparatus in which the amount of heat liberated can be measured. Because such an apparatus is expensive to build and difficult to operate, indirect calorimetric methods are used in the study of metabolism.

Indirect Calorimetry. By this method, heat production of an animal is calculated from the amount of oxygen produced, the carbon dioxide liberated, or both. The results from indirect calorimetry agree within less than 1 per cent with those from direct calorimetry.

A number of types of apparatus have been developed for use in indirect calorimetry. The type most widely used for clinical purposes in the determination of the human metabolic rate is the *Benedict-Ross closed circuit apparatus.* The heat produced is calculated from the oxygen consumption alone. In the determination of the basal metabolic rate, the subject lies on a couch and breathes through a mouthpiece connected to the apparatus. Pure oxygen contained within the spirometer bell is inspired; carbon dioxide expired passes through a canister of soda lime and is absorbed. As oxygen is consumed, the spirometer bell slowly falls, its movements being recorded on a sheet of paper attached to a slowly revolving drum. The heat production is calculated from the quantity of oxygen used during a six-minute period.

Respiratory Quotient (RQ). This is the ratio of the volume of CO_2 produced and oxygen consumed, expressed as follows:

$$\frac{\text{Volume of } CO_2 \text{ expired}}{\text{Volume of } O_2 \text{ inspired}} = \text{Respiratory quotient}$$

In the oxidation of a carbohydrate, the following reaction takes place:

$$C_6H_{12}O_6 + 6O_2 \rightarrow 6CO_2 + 6H_2O \quad plus \text{ energy}$$

Then,

$$\frac{6 \text{ volumes of } CO_2}{6 \text{ volumes of } O_2} = 1.0 \quad (\text{RQ of a carbohydrate})$$

Similarly, the RQ for a fat is 0.71; for a protein, it is 0.80. For a person on an average mixed diet, it is 0.85. For a person who has fasted for 12 hours, the RQ is 0.82.

TOTAL CALORIC REQUIREMENTS. The total bodily requirement of Calories varies with the activity. In general the requirement each 24 hours for persons engaged in the following activities is:

	Cal.
Lying in bed	1850
Sedentary occupation	2400
Moderate activity	3200
Above average activity	4400
Heavy work	6000 to 8000

For the average person, proteins contribute 10 to 15 per cent of the caloric value, carbohydrates 50 to 70 per cent, and fats 20 to 30 per cent.

Basal Metabolism. The heat production of the body, determined 14 to 18 hours after the last meal, at a room temperature of approximately 20° C., and with the body at complete rest and the subject lying quietly and free from environmental distractions, is called the *basal metabolism* or the *basal metabolic rate* (BMR). It represents the minimum expenditure of energy compatible with life, that is, the energy utilized in all activities involved in vital functions, such as heart beat, respiratory movements, digestive activities (such as glandular secretion and peristaltic contractions), maintenance of body temperature, and maintenance of muscle tonus. For a young adult male, the BMR is:

In terms of Calories	1500 to 1800 Cal. per day
In terms of body weight	1 Cal. per kilogram per hour
In terms of body surface	40 Cal. per sq. meter per hour

Normal Range of BMR. The basal metabolic rate is commonly expressed as the percentage deviation from the normal figure established for individuals of corresponding age and sex. For example, a person with a BMR of +20 would have a rate 20 per cent above normal, while a person with a BMR of −15 would have a rate 15 per cent below normal. Values ±15 per cent of the mean are considered to fall within the normal range; values above or below these variations are regarded as indicative of some abnormal condition.

Factors Influencing Basal Metabolism. The basal metabolism of an individual is influenced by the following factors:

1. *Size of the Individual.* The number of Calories produced in a given unit of time per unit of surface area is fairly constant for the individual. Because a small person has proportionately a much larger surface exposed to the environment and radiates more heat per unit of body weight than does a larger person, the small person must produce more heat to maintain body temperature and as a consequence usually has a higher basal metabolic rate than that of the larger person.

2. *Age.* The basal metabolic rate varies with age. It is lowest in a newborn child; it increases rapidly, reaching its peak between the ages of 5 and 10; it decreases steadily until the age of 20; and, finally, it then decreases slowly until death.

3. *Sex.* Males have a slightly higher (by 6 to 7 per cent) BMR than females.

4. *Weight.* In terms of body weight, thin people have a much higher rate than stout people—at least 50 per cent higher.

5. *External Temperature.* Lowering of the external temperature

greatly increases metabolism, owing to increased muscle tone and increased activity in general.

6. *Internal Temperature.* For each degree Fahrenheit of increase in body temperature, the basal metabolic rate increases about 7 per cent.

7. *Exercise.* Approximately 75 per cent of the energy liberated by muscular activity is in the form of heat. Exercise, or any other form of muscular activity, is therefore the greatest single factor in energy output and has a profound effect on the metabolic rate.

8. *Ingestion of Food.* The ingestion of food brings about an increase in heat production over and above that which can be accounted for by the increased activities of the digestive tract. Proteins especially exhibit this characteristic. For example, if a person ingests 100 Calories of protein, 130 Calories of heat are produced—an increase of 30 per cent. The stimulating effect that food intake has on metabolism is referred to as *specific dynamic action.* All three classes of foods show this specific dynamic effect in the approximate rates of 30 per cent for proteins, 7 per cent for carbohydrates, and 4 per cent for fats.

9. *Chemical Substances.* Caffeine, adrenaline, thyroxine, benzedrine, and dinitrophenol increase the basal metabolic rate. Anesthetics decrease the rate.

10. *Pathologic Conditions.* The metabolic rate is *decreased* in starvation, malnutrition, obesity due to pituitary disorders, hypothyroidism, adrenal cortical insufficiency (Addison' disease), and lipoid nephrosis. It is *increased* in hyperthyroidism, fever, diabetes insipidus, cardiorenal disease, dypsnea, leukemia, and polycythemia.

Metabolism of Specific Foods. The mechanisms of metabolism of the three classes of foods are specific for each class, as described in the following paragraphs.

METABOLISM OF PROTEINS. Proteins form the framework of all protoplasm. All of them contain carbon, hydrogen, oxygen, and nitrogen, and, in addition, usually sulfur and phosphorus. Proteins supply the body with the major portion of the nitrogen, sulfur, and phosphorus used in metabolism.

In the process of digestion, proteins are broken down into proteoses, peptones, polypeptids, and, finally, amino acids. The amino acids are absorbed by the intestinal mucosa and enter the blood of the portal vein, through which they are carried to the liver. Some continue in the blood stream and are carried to all parts of the body, where they are utilized in the cells of the tissues in the synthesis of proteins essential for the building of protoplasm. Wherever new cells are being produced, as in the bone marrow, in the reproductive organs, and in the repair of injured tissues, amino acids are required. Amino acids are also utilized in the formation of glandular secretions, such as enzymes and hormones.

Neither excess amino acids nor excess proteins are stored in the body, except temporarily in the liver. Amino acids that are not used are deaminized. *Deamination* is the process, carried on principally in the liver, in which the incombustible amino (NH_2) group is split off from the combustible acid (COOH) group. Deamination is accomplished by reduction, hydrolysis, or oxidation. Ammonia (NH_3) is produced, which combines with carbon dioxide to form *urea*. Urea thus formed leaves the liver through the blood stream and is excreted by the kidneys. The non-nitrogenous fatty acid remainder may be oxidized in the body or it may be converted into glucose. The glucose in turn may be stored as glycogen or converted into fat and stored in adipose tissue, or it may be oxidized to CO_2 and water.

Urea. This white crystalline substance is soluble in water. It is a diamide of carbonic acid ($NH_2CO \cdot NH_2$). The amount daily excreted averages 20 to 30 gm., depending on the nature of the food consumed. Urea contains the major portion of the nitrogen excreted by the urine. The urea in urine is derived not only from deamination of amino acids from the proteins of food but also from the breakdown of proteins taking place in the various tissues of the body.

Other nitrogenous products derived from catabolism of proteins in the tissues are: uric acid, creatine, creatinine, hippuric acid, and ammonia salts. All are excreted in the urine.

Uric Acid. This crystallizable acid ($C_5H_4N_4O_3$) is a normal constituent of blood and urine. It is practically insoluble in water but soluble in alkaline salts. Uric acid is a product of the metabolism of purines, substances forming a part of the nucleoproteins present in all cells. When uric acid is present in excess in the blood, it may be deposited at joints in the form of urates, causing *gout*. The amount of uric acid daily excreted ranges from 0.1 to 1 gm. *Creatine* ($C_4H_9N_3O_2$) is a compound present in most tissues, especially muscle tissues, in which it is combined with phosphates to form phosphocreatine. It plays an important role in muscle contraction. *Creatinine*, a creatin anhydride ($C_4H_7N_3O$), is present in urine in amounts of 1 to 2 gm. daily. It is derived from creatine. *Hippuric acid,* a crystallizable aminoacetic acid, is synthesized in the kidney and the liver from glycocoll and benzoic acid. This is a detoxication reaction which renders the toxic benzoic acid harmless. Ammonium salts, chiefly salts of inorganic acids, are present to a limited extent in the blood. Most are converted to urea in the liver, but the reverse of this process may occur in the kidney, with the salts being eliminated in the urine.

Nitrogen Balance. In the utilization of proteins, except in those processes which involve synthesis of body proteins, nitrogenous waste products are formed. When proteins are being converted to fats and carbohydrates and when they are being utilized for energy, nitrogenous end-products are produced and eliminated—the greater portion in the urine and small amounts in the feces and sweat. Under normal conditions, the intake and output of nitrogen are equal, and the body is said to be in *nitrogen balance* or *nitrogen equilibrium*. When the intake exceeds the output, as occurs during growth or pregnancy or in convalescence following a wasting disease, *positive* nitrogen balance exists. When the nitrogen intake is less than the output, *negative* nitrogen balance exists; this is seen in malnutrition and in certain disease states, especially wasting diseases.

The amount of protein necessary to maintain nitrogen equilibrium depends not only on nitrogen intake but also on the amount of fats and carbohydrates consumed. In their absence, tissue protein is utilized for energy, with a consequent increase in nitrogen output. Even on a diet consisting exclusively of proteins, the excretion of nitrogen always exceeds the intake. The ingestion of fats and carbohydrates, especially the latter, along with proteins, makes possible a reduced protein intake to meet the needs of the body. In this role these foods serve as *protein sparers*; their presence permits proteins to be used for other purposes.

METABOLISM OF CARBOHYDRATES. Carbohydrates are absorbed by the intestine in the form of monosaccharides, principally *glucose*. Glucose enters the blood of the portal vein, which carries it to the liver. In the liver, excess glucose is resynthesized into *glycogen*, or animal starch, and stored in the liver cells. This process is called *glycogenesis*.

The amount of glucose in the blood remains fairly constant, averaging about 100 mg. per 100 cc. (0.1 per cent). The blood-sugar level is the result of the balance between glucose entering the blood and that leaving it. Glucose *enters* the blood stream (*a*) from the digestive tract by absorption, (*b*) from the tissue fluids, (*c*) from the liver as a result of the breakdown of glycogen to glucose (*glycogenolysis*), and (*d*) artificially by subcutaneous or intravenous injections. Glucose *leaves* the blood stream (*a*) by diffusion into the tissue fluids, (*b*) by conversion to glycogen in the liver and muscle cells, (*c*) by conversion to fat, (*d*) by being oxidized in the tissues, and (*e*) in cases of excess, by renal excretion.

Endocrine and Nervous Control. The formation and utilization of glucose are under the control of endocrine and nervous factors. Endocrine control is effected through hormones of the pancreas, the anterior lobe of the hypophysis, the adrenal gland, the thyroid gland, and the gonads. Hormones of these glands regulate the storage and liberation of glucose by the liver and its utilization by the tissues. Nervous control is effected primarily through nervous regulation of the endocrine glands.

Insulin. The maintenance of normal blood-sugar level is regulated principally by a hormone, *insulin*, secreted by the islets of Langerhans in the pancreas. If the pancreas is removed from an animal experimentally, or if the islets fail to secrete an adequate supply of insulin, the percentage of sugar in the blood rises. If the amount is greater than 0.17 per cent, a condition of excess blood sugar (*hyperglycemia*) exists and the kidneys strive to offset this by excreting sugar in the urine (*glycosuria*). As a result, glycogen stored in the liver becomes depleted and the body converts fats and tissue proteins into glucose.

METABOLISM OF FATS. The fats in animal and plant foods are compounds of higher fatty acids (palmitic, stearic, and oleic acids) combined with glycerol. The combination of a molecule of glycerol with three molecules of one or another of these fatty acids results in the formation of a molecule of *neutral fat*. The three most common neutral fats are *tripalmitin*, *tristearin*, and *triolein*, commonly called *palmitin*, *stearin*, and *olein*. Adipose tissue in animals consists of these three fats in varied amounts, triolein being the most abundant.

In the process of digestion, fats are hydrolyzed to fatty acids and glycerol, in which form they pass into the epithelial cells of the intestinal mucosa, where they are resynthesized into neutral fats, glycerides, and phosphatides, which enter the blood of the portal vein or the lymph. The major portion (70 per cent, on the average) passes into the lymph contained within the lacteals of the villi and thence through lymphatic vessels into the thoracic duct. The thoracic duct opens into the left subclavian vein near its junction with the internal jugular vein, at which point the fat molecules enter the blood stream. The milk-like fluid of the lymphatic vessels draining the intestine is called *chyle*. Following the ingestion of large quantities of fat, a distinct milkiness of blood plasma may be observed, owing to the presence of microscopic fat particles, or *chylomicrons*. A marked rise in blood lipids (fats) is called *lipemia*.

In the body, fats are (*a*) stored in adipose tissue or incorporated in cells as constituent fats of tissues, (*b*) stored and metabolized in the liver, (*c*) oxidized to CO_2 and H_2O with release of energy, (*d*) converted to carbohydrates, or (*e*) excreted in the secretions of certain glands (mammary and sebaceous) or in the feces.

The liver plays an important role in fat metabolism. It contains an average of 3 to 5 per cent of fat made up principally of phospholipids and glycerides. In pathologic conditions, the percentage of fat may increase greatly, resulting in fatty degeneration of the liver. In the oxidation of fatty acids, which occurs chiefly in the liver, the fatty acid is first desaturated. Then the long chain of carbon atoms comprising the fatty acid molecule loses these carbon atoms two at a time. This gives rise to ketone bodies, which are eventually oxidized in the tissues or excreted in the urine.

Sterols. Sterols are secondary alcohols closely related to the fats. They occur in plant and animal tissues. The most important in the human body is *cholesterol*, which was first discovered in gallstones. Cholesterol is present in nearly all parts of the body, but it is most abundant in the suprarenal glands and in the brain, especially the white matter. It also occurs in the bile, the blood, sheaths of nerve fibers, and the skin, particularly in sebum secreted by oil glands. Closely related to it chemically are such substances as cholic acid, the sex hormones, and vitamin D. The last-named is formed in the skin through the action of ultraviolet rays on a sterol closely related to cholesterol. Another sterol, *ergosterol,* found in plant cells (especially yeasts), acquires antirachitic properties when exposed to ultraviolet irradiation.

Phospholipids. These phosphorus compounds, also known as *phosphatides,* are commonly present in animal and plant cells. Belonging to this group are: lecithin, cephalin, and sphingocephalin.

Lecithin is a complex compound composed of glycerol and fatty acids with one fatty acid replaced by a phosphoric acid-nitrogenous base complex. The nitrogenous substance *choline* forms its base. *Cephalin* is a substance similar to lecithin but having aminoethanol as its base. *Sphingocephalin* possesses two bases (choline and sphingosine) with one fatty acid radical but no glycerol.

All three of these substances are widely distributed throughout the body; it is thought that one or more of them may be present in all cells. In general, for a particular organ in a given species, the amount of phospholipids remains fairly constant, even under conditions of starvation. This would indicate that they are basic constituents of cells, probably forming an important part of their structural make-up. They form an integral part of the plasma membrane and in that position play an important role in cell permeability.

REGULATION OF BODY TEMPERATURE

Because body temperature depends in large part on the oxidative processes that take place in the metabolism of food substances, the subject of its regulation is discussed here.

With respect to body temperature, animals are divided into two classes: warm-blooded, or homoiothermal, and cold-blooded, or poikilothermal.

Homeothermal animals include the birds and mammals. In this group the body temperature remains constant irrespective of environmental temperature. It is determined by the relationship between heat produced and heat lost. Heat is produced by oxidative processes. Heat loss depends on various physical, rather than chemical, factors.

Poikilothermal animals include the fishes, amphibians, and reptiles.

In this group the body temperature is variable, changing with the temperature of the environment. When the body temperature of a cold-blooded animal falls, metabolic processes are slowed down and body activities become sluggish. In warm-blooded animals the metabolic processes continue at a fairly constant rate all of the time.

Heat Production. All the oxidative processes that occur in the body tissues result in the production of heat. Because the muscles constitute the bulk of the body (50 per cent of weight of soft tissues and 40 per cent of total body weight in males, 36 per cent of total body weight in females), most of the heat produced comes from muscular activity. Another source of heat is the liver. A small amount of heat comes from the ingestion of hot foods and drinks.

Heat Loss. Heat is lost from the body through the following channels: skin, lungs, and urinary and digestive excretions.

HEAT LOSS THROUGH THE SKIN. Approximately 85 per cent of body heat is lost through the skin, by the processes of (1) *convection,* when air in contact with the body has a lower temperature (the skin being reheated and the heat removed by air currents); (2) *conduction,* when the body is in contact with a cooler object (heat being lost to that object); (3) *radiation,* in the giving off of heat waves; and (4) *evaporation,* the vaporization of water as in sweat, about 0.6 Cal. being required for each gram of water vaporized at 37° C.

HEAT LOSS IN RESPIRATION. Heat is lost in the warm air which is expired by the lungs. It is also lost in the process of warming inspired air, which is usually below body temperature.

HEAT LOSS THROUGH URINARY AND DIGESTIVE EXCRETIONS. These excretions (urine and feces) are at body temperature when they are passing from the body. This accounts for a small loss of heat.

Heat is also lost when foods are taken into the body which are below body temperature.

DAILY HEAT LOSS

Process	Cal.	Per Cent
Radiation, convection, conduction	2100	70.0
Evaporation from the skin	500	16.9
Vaporization of water from the lungs	300	9.1
Warming of inspired air	80	2.5
Excretion of urine and feces	50	1.5
	3030	

Temperature Control. The balance between heat production and heat loss is maintained primarily through the activity of the nervous system. There are numerous reflex centers in the spinal cord and the lower portions of the brain which are concerned with the production and loss of heat, principally the latter. They regulate activities such as sweating, vasoconstriction, vasodilation, muscle tonus, and shivering.

The most important heat-regulating centers are located in the *hypothalamus*, a portion of the diencephalon. These centers are subject to two influences: nerve impulses from the skin and other parts of the body; and the temperature of the blood flowing near the centers. The hypothalamus acts in two ways. A nerve center located in its anterior portion controls the mechanism involved in heat loss and thus prevents overheating of the body; another center located in the posterior portion regulates heat production and thus prevents chilling of the body.

The hypothalamus acts in the nature of a thermostat. When heat production is increased in the body or outside temperature is increased, activities are brought about reflexly which increase the heat loss. This is accomplished to a large extent through the circulatory system. Flow of blood to the skin is accelerated, and this is accompanied by dilation of blood vessels and increased activity of sweat glands, as a result of which heat is lost from the body surface. The rate of respiration tends to increase, and muscular activity is reduced. When outside temperatures are low, peripheral vessels are constricted, and the consequent reduced activity of sweat glands conserves heat. Simultaneously, heat production is increased through muscular activity, sometimes involuntarily, as in shivering, and the metabolic rate is generally increased.

The *normal temperature of the body* is 98.6° F. (37° C.). Temperature readings are taken by mouth, under the arm, or within the rectum. Rectal temperature is usually about 1° higher than by mouth, axillary temperature about 1° lower. The body temperature may show variations of 0.5° to 1° F. in the course of 24 hours. It is lowest at 5 A.M., highest in the late afternoon or early evening.

Role of Endocrine Glands in Heat Regulation. Two endocrine glands play a role in heat production and heat loss, namely, the thyroid and the adrenal glands. As the thyroid regulates basal metabolism, hyperthyroidism, by increasing the basal metabolic rate, increases heat production. Conversely, either hypothyroidism or surgical removal of the thyroid gland reduces heat production and reduces body temperature. The adrenal medulla, through its hormone epinephrine (adrenalin), stimulates oxidations in the tissues, with a resulting increase in heat production. At the same time, its vasoconstrictor effect on the blood vessels of the skin reduces heat loss. The adrenal cortical hormones also play a role in temperature regulation, for in their absence animals do not resist cold well.

Two other endocrine glands are concerned in temperature regulation: the hypophysis and the ovaries. Anterior hypophyseal insufficiency results in a reduced metabolic rate and a decrease in resistance to cold. Through its effects on the activities of the thyroid and adrenal glands, it exerts a continuous indirect action on heat production.

In women, body temperature fluctuates during the menstrual cycle. It remains normal during the first portion of the cycle, then drops suddenly about 1° at the time of ovulation. Then it rises to about 1° above normal, where it remains during the second half of the cycle, returning to normal at menstruation. The exact mechanism of this temperature change is not known.

Fever (Pyrexia). In this condition, the body temperature remains above normal for a protracted period. The highest temperature compatible with life is about 108° F. Functionally, fever is due to disorder of the mechanisms involved in heat elimination, particularly the blood volume, vasodilation, and sweat secretion. The heat-producing mechanisms of the body are usually not accelerated in fever. The causes of fever include: (1) *infection by organisms*, as in typhoid fever, yellow fever, septicemia, viral conditions; (2) *trauma*, as in surgical fever when tissues are injured; (3) *brain injury* involving the heat-regulating center (neurogenic fever); (4) *dehydration*, in which there is reduction in the water content of the blood, as following injections of hypertonic solutions of glucose and salt into the blood stream and in the use of strong cathartics; and (5) *effects of drugs*, such as ergotoxine, dinitrophenol, adrenalin, thyroxin, or foreign proteases.

Body Heat Disturbances. Conditions in which the thermal balance of the body is upset are: heat cramps, heat exhaustion or prostration, and heat stroke.

Heat Cramps. In heat cramps, one encounters muscle spasms, pains, dilated pupils, and a weak pulse. The condition is common among those who work in regions of high temperatures. The fundamental cause is dehydration and reduction in blood chlorides through the elimination of the salts in excessive sweating.

Heat Exhaustion or Prostration. In heat exhaustion, excessive, long-continued demands upon the body mechanisms regulating heat loss may result in pronounced weakness, dizziness, nausea, and sometimes collapse (prostration). Body temperature usually rises to about 101° F.

Heat Stroke. In heat stroke, including "sunstroke," the body temperature rises markedly, the skin becomes dry, and there are muscular cramps, dizziness, thirst, nausea, and headache. Often, there is loss of consciousness. The heat-regulating center in the hypothalamus is usually unable to cope effectively with the sudden increase in heat production.

PRACTICAL CONSIDERATIONS

Hunger. When the body has been deprived of food for some time, the sensation of *hunger* is experienced. Hunger is an unpleasant sensation accompanied by dull or acute pains (referred to the epigastric region) and an overwhelming desire to eat. It is distinguished from *appetite* in that the latter is a sensation based on previous experience of ingesting foods which are pleasing to the taste and which provide one with the sensation of well-being. The pains which accompany hunger ("hunger pangs") are due primarily to strong peristaltic contractions which occur in the stomach. However, in prolonged fasting, after the first few days there is a gradual decline in hunger pains, although strong gastric contractions persist.

Vomiting. Vomiting (or *emesis*) is the ejection of the stomach contents through the mouth. It is a reflex act controlled by a vomiting center in the medulla. Vomiting is usually preceded by a feeling of nausea, at which time the tonus of stomach decreases and the upper part dilates. The expulsion of the stomach contents is brought about as follows: A deep inspiration occurs and the diaphragm descends. The soft palate rises and closes the nasopharyngeal opening, and the glottis closes. Vigorous contractions of the abdominal muscles force the abdominal organs upward against the diaphragm, which, in turn, compresses the stomach. The food is expelled through the relaxed cardia and esophagus. It should be noted that in the act of vomiting the musculature of the stomach is passive and plays no essential part in the action.

CONTROL OF VOMITING. Vomiting is under nervous control effected through a vomiting center located in the medulla oblongata. It may occur as a result of a number of disorders, or it may be induced to rid the digestive tract of harmful substances. The vomiting center may respond to (1) afferent impulses from the isthmus of the fauces, pharynx, stomach, intestines, or other parts of the body; (2) impulses from higher cerebral centers; or (3) chemical substances in the blood stream.

FACTORS INDUCING VOMITING. Some of the conditions which induce vomiting are: (1) mechanical stimulation of the fauces or pharynx; (2) inflammation or mechanical disturbances of the digestive tract, as in enteritis, appendicitis, intestinal obstruction, and strangulated hernia; (3) disturbances in other abdominal organs, such as the kidney, bladder, uterus, and gallbladder; (4) the presence of certain foods, food products, or drugs in the stomach (these substances include tartar emetic, mustard, ipecac, mercuric chloride, and zinc and copper sulfates, which are referred to as *emetics*). Emetics may act reflexly, stimulating nerve endings in the digestive tract, or, if injected intravenously, they may cause vomiting by acting directly on the vomiting center in the medulla.

Vomiting may be initiated by impulses from the higher cerebral centers. Excessive fatigue, severe pain, hysterical states, emotional reactions (as may follow the witnessing of a "nauseating" scene), or psychogenic factors may bring about vomiting. The excitability of the vomiting center varies in different individuals and in the same individual under varying conditions. Blood supply has an influence on the center. A sudden increase in intracranial pressure may bring on a forceful, "projectile" type of vomiting. A reduced oxygen supply, as in anemia or following hemorrhage, may reduce the threshold of the center and induce vomiting.

The exact cause of *morning sickness* of early pregnancy is unknown, but it is thought that carbohydrate starvation and dehydration accompanied by ketosis are factors. The nausea and vomiting that accompany *seasickness* or other forms of motion sickness result from stimulation of the sensory receptors in the ear which induce vomiting reflexly through the vomiting center.

A serious consequence of vomiting is excessive loss of chlorides, which may bring on *alkalosis*.

Diarrhea. The condition in which there are abnormal frequency of bowel movement and increased liquidity of the fecal discharge is known as *diarrhea*. It is characterized by abnormally rapid passage of food through the small intestine, which interferes seriously with the digestive processes and reduces the amount of food absorbed.

Diarrhea is symptomatic of many diseases. It may be caused by: (1) enteric infections, such as bacillary and amebic dysentery, cholera, and typhoid and paratyphoid fevers; (2) food poisoning; (3) food sensitivities; (4) poisons, such as mercury and arsenic; (5) avitaminosis, such as pellagra; (6) toxic or septic states accompanying a number of diseases, or in emotional states such as fear or grief.

Constipation. In constipation, bowel movements occur infrequently or with difficulty, and the feces are retained within the rectum. The effects vary in different persons, but general symptoms are: headache, a feeling of depression, sluggishness, and general malaise. These effects are due to the mechanical pressure of the foods on the walls of the colon and not to the absorption of toxic products (autointoxication), as was once supposed.

Among the causes of constipation are: (1) gross mechanical obstructions, such as tumors, adhesions, strictures, and developmental anomalies; (2) poor toilet habits, that is, failure to evacuate the bowel in response to the sensations aroused by a full rectum; (3) poor muscle tone of the intestine ("atonic constipation"), which may result from debilitating disease, senility, or obesity; (4) excessive muscle tone ("spastic constipation"), in which the muscles are hypertonic and remain contracted, often the result of emotional or nervous tension; (5) improper diet, especially one lacking in bulk or roughage or containing too little water; (6) excessive use of cathartics ("cathartic constipation"); (7) lesions of the digestive tract, especially in the colon and rectum, such as inflammatory conditions (appendicitis), hemorrhoids, and cancer.

Methods of Inducing Bowel Movements. Various measures are employed to bring about the elimination of the indigestible contents of the digestive tract. These include the use of purgatives, lubricants, and enemas.

PURGATIVES. Mild purgatives are called *laxatives* or *aperients*. Stronger purgatives are usually called *cathartics*. Common laxatives include: *bulk laxatives* (e.g., bran and agar-agar), which act by increasing the bulk of the intestine and thus mechanically stimulate muscular activity (peristalsis); *irritant laxatives* (e.g., castor oil, senna, cascara, and croton oil), containing a chemical substance which stimulates intestinal contraction; and *saline laxatives* (e.g., Epsom salt, or magnesium sulfate, and citrate of magnesia), which increase the osmotic pressure within the lumen of the intestine, causing water to enter with resultant increase in the fluidity of the bowel contents.

LUBRICANTS. Normally, the intestinal passage requires no artificial lubricant because the mucus secreted by epithelial cells of its wall provides adequate natural lubrication. It may, however, be desirable to soften the fecal mass to facilitate defecation. Any agent used for this purpose should not be amenable to enzymatic action but should pass through the digestive tract more or less unchanged. *Mineral oil* is such a substance. Continuous use of a lubricant is undesirable, however, for the presence of excessive oils in the intestine interferes with the action of enzymes on food substances and with normal absorptive processes. In the presence of mineral oils, fat-soluble vitamins (A, D, and K) may be inadequately absorbed.

ENEMAS. Injection of a liquid through the anal opening serves (1) to make the contents of the colon more fluid and (2) to stimulate activity in the muscles of the colon by distention of its walls.

Nutrient enemas are occasionally employed when food cannot be taken by mouth. Because no enzymes are produced by glands of the large intestine, food thus injected must be *predigested*. Water is readily absorbed by the large intestine; accordingly, *thirst enemas* are regarded as effective.

Malnutrition. Malnutrition is the condition caused by an inadequacy of one or more of the essential components of one's diet: calories, proteins (including certain essential amino acids), certain fatty acids, vitamins, and minerals. It may result from: inadequate ingestion of foods, ingestion of foods lacking in essential constituents, defective absorption by the intestine, or defective metabolism within the tissues. The effects of malnutrition are:

1. Reduction in body weight. If the malnutrition is mild, the loss is principally from adipose tissue, but if it is continued (as in fasting), loss of protein occurs with breakdown of essential body tissues and, ultimately, emaciation.

2. Reduction in the basal metabolic rate, with resultant lower body temperatures and reduced blood pressure.

3. Increased susceptibility to fatigue, accompanied by mental apathy and disinclination for physical exertion.

4. Tendency of organs to become displaced, owing to loss of the fat which normally supports them.

5. Reduction in blood proteins, resulting in edema (swelling from accumulation of fluids).

6. Increased susceptibility to infectious diseases, especially tuberculosis.

Obesity. Obesity is the state in which an abnormal amount of fat has accumulated in the adipose tissues of the body. It is either endogenous or exogenous. *Endogenous obesity* results from disordered metabolism due to malfunctioning of the hypothalamus or one of the endocrine glands (hypophysis, gonads, adrenals, thyroid). *Exogenous obesity* (simple obesity) arises from overeating, with the food intake far in excess of the demands of the body for growth, repair, and energy. Obesity has the following deleterious effects:

1. It decreases efficiency in the performance of work; the greater load interferes with muscular movements.

2. It places a greater burden on the circulatory system (through its heavier demand in the performance of work), with accompanying hypertrophy of the heart.

3. It interferes with the release of body heat; subcutaneous fat acts as insulation.

4. For a variety of reasons, the obese person is especially susceptible to infectious diseases (pneumonia, nephritis), to gallstone formation, and to such degenerative diseases as atherosclerosis and hypertension.

DISORDERS AND DISEASES OF THE DIGESTIVE SYSTEM

The digestive system is prey to a wide range of disorders and diseases which may be classified as developmental anomalies and endogenous and exogenous conditions.

Developmental Anomalies. The following developmental anomalies are commonly seen in various portions of the alimentary canal:

ANOMALIES OF THE MOUTH AND PHARYNX. *Harelip*, in which the median nasal processes of the embryo fail to unite; the condition may be unilateral or bilateral, and may involve the fleshy lip, the bony maxilla, or both. *Cleft pal-*

ate, in which the lateral palatine processes fail to unite, and which may involve the hard or soft palate, or both, and is often associated with harelip. *Tongue-tiedness*, or reduced mobility of the tongue, owing to an abnormally short frenulum.

ANOMALIES OF THE ESOPHAGUS. *Double esophagus* has been seen. Or the esophagus may be *absent* (abnormal development of the communication with the trachea).

ANOMALIES OF THE STOMACH. The stomach may be *transposed* to the right side. There may be *atresia* (closure) or *stenosis* (narrowing) of the esophageal opening. Also seen is *hour-glass stomach*, in which a constriction divides the stomach into two compartments.

Endogenous and Exogenous Conditions. The following are the commonest disorders and diseases that arise from malfunction, circulatory disturbances, invasions of microorganisms, and infestations. In addition, there are the *neoplasms* (new growths), which occur as either benign or malignant tumors, including various forms of carcinoma (cancer).

CONDITIONS OF THE MOUTH AND PHARYNX. *Caries*, decay of teeth, involving destruction of the enamel and dentine; frequently an opening is made into the pulp cavity which permits infectious organisms to gain access to the alveolus, with resulting abscesses. *Mumps*, a virus disease involving the salivary glands, especially the parotids, which may involve other glands of the body (for example, the testes). *Gingivitis*, inflammation of the gums. *Pyorrhea*, inflammation of the dental periosteum accompanied by formation of pus; necrosis of the alveoli may concur, with loss of teeth. *Gum boil*, a superficial abscess of the alveolus. *Tonsillitis*, inflammation of the palatine tonsils. "*Adenoids*," or hypertrophy of the pharyngeal tonsil.

CONDITIONS OF THE ESOPHAGUS. *Cancer* of the esophagus is common, the regions most frequently involved being the upper and lower portions, especially the area where the stratified epithelium of the esophagus undergoes transition to the simple columnar epithelium of the stomach. *Obstruction* may occur if foreign bodies lodge in constricted portions, especially the region where the bronchus crosses and the esophagus passes through the diaphragm. *Diverticula* (blind pockets), which result from excessive pressure from within or excessive pull or traction from surrounding tissues.

CONDITIONS OF THE STOMACH. *Ulcers*, which are usually found near the pyloric end and along the lesser curvature. *Stricture* or *stenosis* of the pyloric opening, which results in dilation of the stomach. *Diverticula* are also found in the stomach.

CONDITIONS OF THE INTESTINES. *Enteritis*, inflammation of the intestinal tract, a common ailment; it usually results from bacterial or viral infections. *Various infectious diseases*, in which the small intestine is primarily involved, such as typhoid fever, cholera, and amebic dysentery. *Infestations by animal parasites*, such as the tapeworms and the thread worms.

Tapeworms (Cestodes) include *Taenia saginata*, *Taenia solium*, and *Diphyllobothrium latum*, which are acquired by ingesting (respectively) beef, pork, and fish, containing the larval forms of these worms. *Thread worms* (Nematodes) include the Ascaris (eel worm, found in horses and swine), hookworm, and pinworm. The *hookworm (Necator)* is acquired through the skin, especially between the toes; the larvae pass via the lymphatics to the blood stream, thence through the heart to the lungs, from which they are coughed up and swallowed and thus pass to the intestines, where they attach themselves to the villi. The *pinworms* or *seatworms* (*Enterobius* or *Oxyurus*), residing in the large intestine, are common in children; they also frequent the rectum, causing severe itching about the anus. The *whipworm* (*Trichurus trichiura*), about 2 inches long, having a slender anterior portion, inhabits the large intestine; its presence may cause diarrhea, vomiting, or nervous disturbances.

Other disorders of the intestines include: *Appendicitis*, inflammation of the vermiform appendix, rupture of which may permit infectious organisms to gain access to the peritoneal cavity, giving rise to *peritonitis*. *Colitis*, inflammation of the colon, frequently accompanied by excessive secretion of mucus ("mucous colitis"); it may be psychogenic in origin ("irritable colon"). *Intussusception*, a condition in which a portion of the intestine slips over an adjacent region. *Hemorrhoids*, or "piles," excessive dilation of the veins in the wall of the rectum; they are "external" when visible outside the anal sphincter, they are "internal" when within the anal sphincter.

CONDITIONS OF THE LIVER AND GALLBLADDER. *Jaundice* (*icterus*), in which bile pigments are deposited in the skin and mucous membranes, giving the subject the yellowish skin coloration characteristic of this condition. Jaundice may result from (1) obstruction of bile passageways with resultant absorption of bile into the blood; (2) increased destruction of red blood cells by the spleen (hemolytic jaundice); or (3) toxic or infectious conditions in which liver tissue is damaged. *Cirrhosis*, a chronic progressive disease of the liver characterized by an increase in the amount of connective tissue and a decrease in the parenchymal tissue. *Cholecystitis*, an inflammation of the gallbladder. *Cholelithiasis*, a condition in which biliary concretions or *gallstones* are present in the gallbladder or the bile ducts.

CONDITIONS OF THE PANCREAS. *Diabetes*, a pancreatic disorder involving the endocrine tissues of the organ; the primary cause is failure of the islets of Langerhans to secrete insulin, which is essential for the metabolism of sugar. *Pancreatitis*, inflammation of the pancreas. *Malignant tumors* are also seen in the pancreas.

9: THE BODY FLUIDS

The *principal body fluids* (found in all body regions) are: *blood* (fluid within heart and in vessels of circulatory system); *tissue fluid* (occupies intercellular spaces); and *lymph* (fluid within lymph vessels and lymphatic organs, such as lymph nodes, tonsils, thymus, spleen). Other fluids more specifically located and performing distinct functions are: *cerebrospinal* (fills spaces within and surrounding brain and spinal cord); *synovial* (fills cavities of articulations); *aqueous humor* (in anterior and posterior chambers of eye); *endolymph* (fills membranous labyrinth of ear); and *perilymph* (within bony labyrinth of ear).

THE BLOOD

The blood fills the heart and the blood vessels. It is pumped by rhythmic contractions of the heart into the larger arteries, from these into smaller arteries and arterioles, and eventually into the capillaries of all tissues. It passes through capillaries into small vessels (venules), which empty into larger veins that return blood to the heart. The blood is constantly in circulation.

Functions of Blood. Blood is the chief medium of transportation within the body. Its principal functions are: (1) To transport *materials to cells*. Among these are nutrient substances, water, oxygen, hormones, and other substances required for metabolic or secretory activity. (2) To transport *materials from cells*. These include food substances that have been absorbed by cells in the walls of the intestines, waste products (carbon dioxide, lactic acid, urea), and hormones from glands of internal secretion. (3) To transport *phagocytes and antibodies*. These are defensive cells and immunogenic substances, important in the body's defenses against disease. (4) To transport *excess internal heat to lungs and body surfaces*. This is important in regulation of body temperature.

Functions of blood may also be listed as: (1) *Respiratory*—carrying oxygen from lungs to tissues, carbon dioxide from tissues to lungs. (2) *Nutritive*—carrying food substances (glucose, amino acids, fats) from intestines or storage "depots" to tissues. (3) *Excretory*—carrying waste products (urea, lactic acid, creatinine) from cells to organs of excretion. (4) *Protective*—carrying defensive cells and antibodies throughout the body to resist disease. (5) *Regulatory*—(*a*) carrying hormones and other chemical substances that regulate functioning of

211

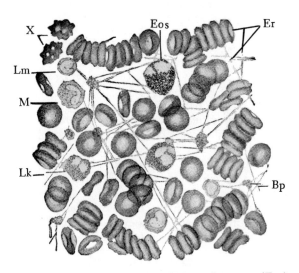

Fig. 9-1. Human blood. (Bp) platelets. (Er) erythrocytes. (Eos) eosoniphil leucocyte. (Lk) neutrophil leucocyte. (Lm) lymphocyte. (M) monocyte. (X) crenated erythrocytes. (Reprinted with permission of W. B. Saunders Company from Maximow and Bloom, *A Textbook of Histology*, 6th ed., 1952.)

many organs; (*b*) carrying excess internal heat to lungs and body surfaces, through which it is lost, and thus regulating body temperature; (*c*) maintaining water balance and constant internal environment for tissue cells.

Origin of Blood. In the embryo, blood develops from mesenchyme (derived from mesoderm). Subsequently, red and white cells develop as follows: 4th week, wall of yolk sac; 5th week, body mesenchyme and blood vessels; 6th week, liver; 7th to 13th weeks, spleen, thymus, lymph nodes; 13th week on, red bone marrow, lymph nodes.

General Characteristics of Blood. In systemic arteries, it is *bright red*; in systemic veins, it is *brownish red* or *purple*. Its *specific gravity* ranges from 1.050 to 1.060 (specific gravity of plasma is 1.027). Its *viscosity* is about five to six times that of water. As to *quantity*, blood constitutes 5 to 7 per cent, or $\frac{1}{15}$, of body weight. For a person weighing 150 pounds, this would amount to 5 to 6 liters (9 to 11 pints). When the body is at rest, blood is distributed about as follows; one-fourth in heart, lung vessels, and large blood vessels; one-fourth in vessels of liver; one-fourth in vessels of striated muscles; one-fourth in vessels of remaining organs.

Composition of Blood. Blood consists of *plasma* (fluid portion) and *formed elements* (corpuscles and platelets) suspended in the plasma. Corpuscles comprise red blood cells and white blood cells.

BLOOD CONSTITUENTS

PLASMA (about 55 per cent of blood by volume) consisting of the fluid portion

Water (91 to 92 per cent)

Proteins (8 to 9 per cent)
- serum albumin
- serum fibrinogen
- serum globulin

Inorganic salts (0.9 per cent)
- chlorides
- carbonates
- bicarbonates
- sulfates
- phosphates
- iodides

of
- sodium
- potassium
- calcium
- magnesium
- iron

Organic substances other than proteins

Nitrogenous substances
- ammonium salts
- urea
- uric acid
- creatine
- creatinine
- amino acids
- xanthine
- hypoxanthine

Non-nitrogenous substances
- glucose (0.1 per cent)
- neutral fats
- phospholipids
- cholesterol

Gases in solution
- oxygen
- carbon dioxide
- nitrogen
- gases from the intestines

Miscellaneous substances
- hormones
- antibodies (immune substances)
- enzymes (lipase, catalase, *et al.*)

FORMED ELEMENTS (about 45 per cent of blood by volume) consisting of corpuscles and platelets

Erythrocytes, or red blood cells (RBC)

Leucocytes, or white blood cells (WBC)

Granulocytes
- neutrophils
- eosinophils
- basophils

Agranulocytes
- lymphocytes
- monocytes

Thrombocytes (blood platelets)

THE FORMED ELEMENTS OF THE BLOOD

It should be noted that blood contains three types of formed elements: erythrocytes, leucocytes, and thrombocytes.

Erythrocytes. Red blood cells (RBC'c) are nonnucleated biconcave discs, circular in general form but possessing a dumbbell shape when seen from the side. In freshly drawn blood they tend to adhere to each other with their flat surfaces together, forming *rouleaux*, each of which resembles a stack of coins. Lacking a nucleus, they do not fully qualify as cells. *Size:* The average mean diameter is 7.7 microns; the average mean thickness is 1.9 microns. Red blood cells may show considerable variation in size within an individual. They are slightly larger in venous blood than in arterial blood, owing to osmotic changes. *Surface area:* A single RBC has a surface area of 120 sq. microns. The total surface area of all the RBC's in the body is about 4900 sq. yds. *Volume:* The volume of a single red blood cell is .85 cu. microns.

NUMBER OF ERYTHROCYTES. The red blood cell *count,* or number of erythrocytes in the body, is expressed by *volume*. In males, there are generally about 5,000,000 RBC's per cu. mm.; in females, about 4,500,000 per cu. mm. The *total* of RBC's in the average-sized person is, roughly, thirty-five trillion.

Variations in the number of RBC's occur under certain conditions: (1) *With age.* At birth the erythrocyte count (averaging over 6,000,000 per cu. mm.) is much higher than later in life. (2) *With time of day.* The count is lower during sleep, higher during activity. (3) *With altitude.* Persons living at altitudes of 10,000 feet or more above sea level have red blood cell counts as much as 30 per cent above normal. A temporary ascent to high altitudes causes a discharge of immature RBC's from bone marrow into the blood stream. (4) *With muscular exercise or an increase in environmental temperature.* An increase in red blood cells occurs under such conditions. This is the result of release of concentrated blood from the spleen, which accompanies increased activity.

STRUCTURE OF ERYTHROCYTES. A nucleus is lacking in mature red blood cells. The *body* of the cell consists of a sponge-like *stroma* which contains a respiratory pigment, *hemoglobin*. Hemoglobin comprises 60 to 80 per cent of the total solids of the cell; the remaining solids include other proteins (0.5 to 1.0 per cent), phospholipids, such as lecithin and cephalin (0.4 per cent), cholesterol (0.3 per cent), inorganic salts, urea, amino acids, and creatine. The cell membrane consists of proteins in combination with lipid substances. It possesses a high degree of selective permeability, being relatively impermeable to sodium and calcium ions but readily permeable to potassium ions.

Red blood cells are so flexible and elastic that they can pass through the extremely small capillaries.

HEMOGLOBIN. This is the most important constituent of the red blood cell. It is a conjugated protein consisting of a colored iron-containing portion (*hematin*) and a simple protein (*globin*). Hemoglobin has the ability to unite readily with oxygen, a process called *oxygenation*, in which an unstable compound, *oxyhemoglobin*, is formed. In so doing, it acquires a bright red color—the color characteristic of arterial blood. This occurs in the passage of the blood through the lungs, where the oxygen tension is high.

Human blood contains approximately 15 gm. of hemoglobin per 100 cc. of blood: 16 gm. for males, 14 gm. for females. The total amount of hemoglobin present in the body averages 1 kilogram. The oxygen-carrying capacity of one gram of hemoglobin is 1.34 cc. The amount of hemoglobin present can be determined with a *hemoglobinometer*, an apparatus by which the color of a sample of blood is compared with known standards.

FUNCTION OF ERYTHROCYTES. The primary function of the erythrocytes is to carry oxygen to the tissues. This is accomplished through the ability of the iron-containing hemoglobin to combine readily with oxygen in the formation of oxyhemoglobin. Hemoglobin also plays an important role in the transportation of carbon dioxide from the tissues, a part of the carbon dioxide (8 to 10 per cent) combining directly with the hemoglobin to form *carbohemoglobin*. The hemoglobin also serves in an indirect way in carbon dioxide carriage.

ORIGIN OF ERYTHROCYTES. In the adult, red blood cell formation (*erythropoiesis*) takes place in the red bone marrow, principally in the vertebrae, ribs, sternum, diploë of cranial bones, and proximal ends of the humerus and femur. The red cells arise from stem cells (*proerythroblasts*), which are cells of variable size possessing a nucleus and lacking hemoglobin. These by mitosis give rise to *erythroblasts*, which gradually acquire hemoglobin. In successive development, the hemoglobin content increases and the cells become smaller, reaching a stage called *normoblast*. Normoblasts multiply but eventually reach a stage at which degenerative changes occur in their nuclei and the nuclei are extruded from the cell, sometimes entire but usually in fragments. At this stage, they are *young erythrocytes*, the cytoplasm of which contains a delicate reticular structure giving them the name of *reticulocytes*. The reticulocytes lose their reticular pattern before the cells enter circulation as *mature erythrocytes*.

LIFE HISTORY OF ERYTHROCYTES. Lacking a nucleus, red blood cells can live only a limited time. Estimates of the amount of bile pigment excreted daily indicate that in a normal adult approximately 20,000,000 red blood cells are destroyed every minute. Bile pigments are formed from the disintegration products of hemoglobin. The daily loss of hemoglobin averages about 20 grams. The total number of red blood cells and the hemoglobin content of the blood at any one time is dependent upon the balance between blood cell formation in the bone marrow and blood cell destruction.

The life span of a red blood cell is not definitely known, but various studies, including some making use of radioactive isotopes, indicate that it is approximately 120 days. Blood cells are lost by the processes of hemolysis and fragmentation, which occur throughout the circulatory system, and phagocytosis of whole cells and cell fragments, which takes place in the cells of the reticuloendothelial tissues, especially those in the spleen, the liver, and bone marrow.

In the blood-destroying organs, the hemoglobin breaks down into an iron-free portion (*globin*) and an iron-bearing portion (*hematin*). The latter is decomposed into bilirubin and an iron compound. Both are carried to the liver, where the bilirubin is excreted in the bile as one of the bile pigments, while the iron, if not needed for the formation of new red blood cells, is stored.

Leucocytes. Leucocytes or white blood cells (WBC) are found in the blood and lymph and, to a limited extent, in the tissues and tissue fluids. They differ from red blood cells in the following respects: they possess a nucleus, lack hemoglobin, have the power of active ameboid movement, are usually larger in size, and are much less numerous. They average about 6,000 per cu. mm., with a normal range of 5,000 to 10,000 per cu. mm.

CLASSES OF LEUCOCYTES. White blood cells are of two general classes, granulocytes and agranulocytes. Granulocytes are subdivided into neutrophils, eosinophils, and basophils; agranulocytes into lymphocytes and monocytes.

Granulocytes. Also called *polymorphonuclear leucocytes,* these white blood cells are characterized by the presence of specific types of granules in their cytoplasm. The nucleus is usually constricted into a varying number of lobes (hence the term "polymorphonuclear"). On the basis of the staining reaction of the granules, there are three types of granulocytes: (1) *Neutrophils*, averaging 9 to 12 microns in diameter. The nucleus usually possesses 3 to 5 lobes. The cytoplasm is filled with fine granules which stain with neutral dyes. With Wright's stain they stain a light purple. They are the most numerous of the WBC's, comprising 65 to 75 per cent of the total. They are highly phagocytic (see page 218). (2) *Eosinophils*, averaging 9 to 12 microns in diameter. They usually possess a bilobed nucleus. The cytoplasmic granules, large and coarse, stain with a bright red dye, eosin (an acid dye). They are relatively few in number, making up only 2 to 5 per cent of the white cell count. (3) *Basophils*, averaging about

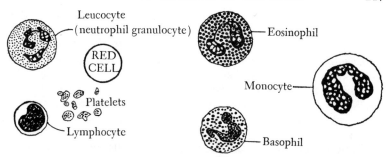

Fig. 9-2. Common varieties of white blood cells and platelets.

Fig. 9-3. The less common varieties of white blood cells in man.

(Figs. 9-2 and 9-3 reprinted with permission of the University of Chicago Press from Carlson and Johnson, *The Machinery of the Body*, 4th ed., 1953.)

10 microns in diameter. The nucleus is large and indistinctly lobed. The granules are irregular in shape and stain with basic stains, taking on a *purplish blue* color when stained with Wright's stain. Basophils comprise only 0.5 per cent of the leucocyte count.

Agranulocytes. These relatively undifferentiated cells lack granules in their cytoplasm. They can reproduce by mitosis, a mode of multiplication occurring principally in the lymphatic organs and in the connective tissues. They are ameboid and readily migrate through the tissues or through capillary walls. On the basis of cell size and structure, agranulocytes are of two types: (1) *Lymphocytes*, which are spherical cells, may average about 8 microns in diameter (small lymphocytes) or may reach a size of 12 microns in diameter (large lymphocytes). The nucleus is large and usually possesses a slight indentation; it occupies a major portion of the cell. The cytoplasm is homogeneous and stains a pale blue with the usual blood stains. Small lymphocytes constitute 20 to 25 per cent of the white cell count. Large lymphocytes are similar to small lymphocytes excepting in size; they are numerous in children, but in adults they occur in insignificant numbers. (2) *Monocytes*, also called *large mononuclear leucocytes*, average 12 to 15 microns in diameter. The nucleus is large and horseshoe-shaped, usually indented on one side. The cytoplasm stains grayish-blue with Wright's stain. Monocytes constitute about 3 to 8 per cent of the white cell count.

FUNCTIONS OF LEUCOCYTES. All leucocytes, but especially the neutrophils, exhibit the property of ameboid movement; that is, they are able to protrude cytoplasmic projections (pseudopodia) into which the protoplasm of the cell flows, thus bringing about changes in the shape and position of the cell. As a consequence, they are not confined within blood or lymph vessels, but are found widely distributed in the tissues, particularly the connective tissues. Leucocytes are constantly migrating through the capillary walls to the tissues (*diapedesis*), and from the tissues they may re-enter the blood stream.

Inflammation. Leucocytes are especially numerous in tissues where inflammatory processes are in progress. Inflammation results from the reaction of tissues to injury. It is characterized by local heat, redness, swelling, pain, and, usually, altered functioning. The migration of leucocytes through the walls of blood vessels into inflamed tissue can be readily observed. It is pronounced in tissues that are infected with pyogenic (pus-forming) bacteria. Leucocytes are attracted to points of injury by chemical substances that are probably derived from injured tissue cells. This response of blood cells to chemical susbtances is termed *chemotaxis*.

Phagocytosis. This is the process, exhibited by all classes of leucocytes except the eosinophils, of engulfing substances of a particulate nature, especially bacteria. It is very pronounced in the neutrophils. The ability of leucocytes to ingest (*phagein*—Gr., to eat) constitutes one of the body's primary defenses against invasion by infectious organisms. In certain diseases, the number of neutrophils may increase markedly, a condition known as *leucocytosis*, in which WBC counts may reach 30,000 to 50,000 or more per cu. mm. Leucocytes produce powerful proteolytic enzymes which may either act within the cell to digest phagocytosed substances or be discharged and act extracellularly on the surrounding tissue.

The specific functions of the eosinophils and the basophils are not definitely known; they are ameboid, but exhibit little or no propensity for phagocytosis. They do, however, increase in number in certain conditions, such as bronchial asthma and some infestations with animal parasites (e.g., trichinosis). Basophils increase in number in Hodgkin's disease, certain virus infections (smallpox and chickenpox), and chronic sinus infection.

The functions of the nongranular leucocytes are not completely understood. The larger lymphocytes and the monocytes both exhibit phagocytosis. The smaller lymphocytes possess marked motility, and it is thought that they play an important role in the repair processes taking place in injured tissue. In tissue cultures, lymphocytes have been observed to undergo radical morphologic changes and to assume a form remarkably similar to that of the fibroblasts of connective tissue. It is believed that they function in the formation of scar tissue (to replace injured tissue) and in the localization of foreign bodies, such as invading bacteria, tumor cells, grafted tissue, and the like. There is considerable evidence that lymphocytes are the source of antibodies and immunogenic substances.

Origin, Length of Life, and Fate of Leucocytes. Granular leucocytes originate in the red bone marrow. Lymphocytes are formed in lymphoid tissue, especially in the lymph nodes. The germinal centers of lymph nodes are the areas primarily involved in the production and development of lymphocytes. The seat of monocyte formation is not definitely known. Under certain conditions, other organs, such as the liver and the spleen, may be sources of leucocytes.

The length of life of granular leucocytes is not known. For lymphocytes it is estimated to be 12 days.

Disintegrating leucocytes are destroyed in the same manner as are red blood cells. In addition, some are lost by migration into the lumen of the intestine.

Thrombocytes or Blood Platelets. These are small, colorless bodies found in the circulating blood. They are nonnucleated bodies, thought to originate from large cells called *megakaryocytes*, which are found in bone marrow. They vary in size, their diameter averaging 3 microns or less. Their number is difficult to determine, but it is estimated to be 250,000 to 400,000 per cu. mm.

In the process of *coagulation*, thrombocytes disintegrate, liberating a *thromboplastic* (clot-forming) substance, probably *cephalin*. This substance initiates a series of reactions that results in clotting. Also, by adhering to small leaks in capillaries and small vessels, thrombocytes tend to seal the leaks and thus help to close injured vessels.

BLOOD CLOTTING AND HEMORRHAGE

Within the blood vessels, circulating blood is of fluid consistency. If, however, it ceases to circulate or escapes from a blood vessel, it soon loses its fluidity, and sets into a jelly-like mass. It is then said to have *clotted* or *coagulated*. A *clot* consists of a mass of tangled strands of *fibrin* in which are enmeshed red and white blood cells. If the clot stands for a time, it undergoes shrinkage, in the course of which a clear, straw-colored fluid is exuded; this fluid is called *blood serum*. It is similar to plasma except that it is lacking in fibrinogen.

Coagulation. Not all the details of the mechanism of blood clotting are precisely known, but the process is generally believed to be somewhat as described here.

Essential Substances. Four substances seem to be essential for clotting of blood:

1. *Prothrombin:* a substance present in circulating blood, which is capable of being converted to *thrombin.*

2. *Thromboplastin:* a substance liberated from injured tissues, from disintegrating platelets, and possibly from leucocytes.

3. *Calcium:* in free ionic form.

4. *Fibrinogen:* a protein present in the plasma.

Steps in Coagulation. The steps in coagulation are, generally:

(1) *Thromboplastin* is liberated from injured tissue cells and disintegrating platelets; a small amount may be present in the plasma. (2) *Prothrombin* is acted on by the thromboplastin, and in the presence of calcium ions is converted into *thrombin*. (3) *Thrombin*, reacting with soluble fibrinogen, converts the latter into insoluble *fibrin*, the basis of the blood clot. Summarized in brief, the reactions are:

prothrombin + Calcium (Ca^{++}) ions + thromboplastin $\rightarrow$ thrombin

thrombin + fibrinogen $\rightarrow$ fibrin

Blood does not normally clot in blood vessels because prothrombin is maintained in an inactive state by the presence of an inhibitor, *antiprothrombin*.

Bleeding time is the time required for the blood to clot sufficiently to close a small opening made by pricking the skin. For the average individual, this is about two and one-half minutes. Reduction in the number of blood platelets or the amount of fibrinogen present *increases* the bleeding time.

Coagulation time is the time required for the blood to clot when removed from the body. For the average individual, this is usually five to six minutes.

VITAMIN K AND COAGULATION. Vitamin K, the "coagulation vitamin," plays a vital role in the clotting of blood. It is found in greenleaf foods and is produced by certain bacteria. In case of the absence (or a reduced supply) of vitamin K, the liver fails to produce the necessary prothrombin and the blood fails to clot or clots very slowly. Absorption of this vitamin depends on the presence of bile; consequently, cases of obstructive jaundice are usually accompanied by delayed clotting of the blood. Deficiency of this vitamin in foods is of little significance in man, as it is produced by bacteria in the intestine. In newborn infants, however, the prothrombin level may fall during the first few days, giving rise to hemorrhagic attacks.

METHODS FOR HASTENING COAGULATION. (1) *Application of heat.* Cloths moistened with a hot physiological salt solution are effective. (2) *Application of styptics or hemostatics.* These are substances such as alum, ferric chloride, zinc chloride, and silver nitrate. They act (*a*) through their astringent action, constricting the walls of the blood vessels, and (*b*) by precipitating plasma proteins, thus interfering with the flow of blood. (3) *Provision of a rough surface,* such as sterile gauze or cotton. (4) *Injection of tissue extracts* which contain thromboplastic substances. (5) *Injection of epinephrine,* whether into the blood stream or liberated naturally as the result of emotional excitement or muscular exercise, which brings about more rapid clotting of blood.

METHODS FOR DELAYING COAGULATION. Several substances, known

as *anticoagulants*, act to delay blood clotting. They are: *sodium and potassium oxalate*, which act by precipitating calcium; *fluorides and citrates*, which form soluble compounds with calcium, thus suppressing its ionization; *hirudin*, a substance secreted by buccal glands of the medicinal leech (*Hirudo*); *heparin*, a substance formed in the liver and present in blood; and *dicoumarin*, a substance isolated from spoiled sweet clover, which reduces the prothrombin content of the blood. In collecting blood for experimental, analytical, or transfusion purposes, one can retard coagulation by preventing contact of the blood with foreign substances or injured tissues, by cooling it, collecting it in a receptacle in which the surfaces have been treated with a nonwetting agent such as paraffin or silicone, or by adding anticoagulants.

INTRAVASCULAR COAGULATION. Clots sometimes form within the blood vessels. They usually result from damage to the endothelial lining of a vessel, as from bacterial infection following injury. They also occur in conditions such as arteriosclerosis or varicose veins. A clot which remains attached at the point where it is formed is called a *thrombus*. A thrombus may occlude a vessel and deprive tissues of their blood supply. If a small vessel is involved, tissues may obtain their blood supply from adjacent anastomosing vessels; if the vessel is large, the blood supply may cease, leading to *necrosis* (death) of tissue.

If a thrombus breaks loose and moves along with the blood stream, it becomes an *embolus*. Emboli may pass freely through the larger vessels and the heart, but they tend to lodge in the smaller arteries, obstructing the flow of blood. If the vessel is one supplying a vital organ, such as the lungs, heart, or brain, death may ensue (e.g., as a result of pulmonary or coronary embolism).

Intravascular clots tend to be slowly resorbed and to disappear.

Hemorrhage. The normal milieu of whole blood is the circulatory system—the closed system of arteries, veins, and capillaries—and the heart. Hemorrhage is the *abnormal* escape of blood from this system. An *external* hemorrhage occurs when a vessel is punctured and blood escapes from the body; an *internal* hemorrhage is one in which the blood escapes from a vessel and accumulates in surrounding tissues, in the cavity of a visceral organ, or in a body cavity.

EFFECTS OF HEMORRHAGE. Some of the effects of severe hemorrhage are: (1) oxygen lack, owing to reduction in the number of RBC's; (2) fall in blood pressure, owing to decrease in blood volume; (3) increase in heart rate; (4) reduction of the force of the heart beat.

REACTIONS OF THE BODY TO LOSS OF BLOOD. Loss of blood through hemorrhage gives rise to the following reactions by the body at large: (1) The *clotting mechanism* is brought into action, and the walls of the injured vessel contract to close the opening. (2) Reflex *vasocon-*

striction on an extensive scale occurs, especially in the blood vessels leading to organs that are not essential to life (skin and muscles, for example). This reduces the capacity of the circulatory system and tends to restore normal blood pressure to facilitate functioning of the vital organs. (3) Restoration of *blood volume* is accomplished temporarily by (*a*) contraction of the spleen, which forces into circulation the blood stored by that organ and (*b*) withdrawal of fluid from the tissues. The latter accounts for the great thirst that usually follows severe hemorrhage. (4) Replacement of *plasma proteins* and *red blood cells*. The time required for this depends on the amount of blood lost, the diet, responsiveness of the liver and bone marrow, and other factors. In a normal healthy subject who has lost a pint of blood, normal conditions are restored within six to eight weeks.

REGULATION OF COMPOSITION OF THE BLOOD

One of the striking features of blood is its constancy of composition. It is continuously receiving and giving up materials to cells, yet fluctuations in its physical nature and its chemical composition are confined to extremely narrow limits. This tendency of the organ-systems and tissues of the body to maintain a balanced state is called *homeostasis*.

Reaction of Blood. The acidity or alkalinity of blood depends on the concentration of hydrogen (H^+) ions and hydroxyl (OH^-) ions. Normally, the blood is slightly alkaline, having a pH between 7.3 and 7.45. Acids (carbonic, lactic, hydrochloric) are being constantly produced in the body during metabolic processes, yet the blood reaction remains relatively constant. This is accomplished by a number of mechanisms, the more important being: (1) elimination of CO_2 by the lungs, (2) elimination of acid substances by the kidney, and (3) action of buffers in the blood.

Buffers are chemical substances in blood which prevent a change in pH when acids or bases are added. A *buffer system* consists of a weak acid and a salt of that acid (for example, carbonic acid and sodium bicarbonate). Buffer action may be illustrated as follows: If hydrochloric acid is added to the blood, it reacts with sodium bicarbonate to form sodium chloride and carbonic acid, thus—

$$HCl + NaHCO_3 \rightarrow NaCl + H_2CO_3$$

In the foregoing reaction, the strong acid (HCl) has been replaced by a weak acid (carbonic acid), which, being volatile, is easily disposed of through the loss of CO_2 from the lungs. The bicarbonate has thus served as an *alkali reserve*, and its presence has prevented a change in the pH of the blood when the strong acid has been added. The principal buffers of the blood are sodium bicarbonate, disodium phosphate, and the plasma proteins.

Effect of Respiration. Respiration is so regulated that the tension of carbon dioxide in the blood is maintained at a constant level. With increased production of CO_2, breathing is increased. When the amount of CO_2 is reduced, as in forced ventilation or by the addition of bases to the blood, the rate of respiration decreases. The ratio of CO_2 to plasma bicarbonate remains fairly constant, at 1:20.

Hydrogen-Ion Concentration (pH). The pH range which is compatible with life lies between 6.8 and 7.8. Fixed acids are not normally present in the blood, but in certain pathologic states, such as diabetes and nephritis, they appear. The presence of fixed acids depletes the alkali reserves, and *acidosis* develops. However, since the pH rarely falls below 7.0, the term "acidosis" does not imply a true acidity of the blood, a condition which occurs only under extreme pathologic conditions. *Alkalosis* means increased accumulation of alkali reserves, a condition which may occur as a result of the ingestion of excessive amounts of alkalis or the loss of HCl in prolonged vomiting. The development of acidosis or alkalosis in which the pH of the blood remains unchanged is referred to as being "compensated"; if the pH increases or decreases, the state is referred to as being "uncompensated."

TISSUE FLUID

Tissue fluid lies outside the blood circulatory system. It occupies the spaces in the various tissues (such as the spaces between cells and between the fibers of connective tissues). It is the ' middleman" of the body, serving as the intermediary by which substances in the blood stream are transmitted to the cells.

Tissue fluid is formed from the blood as the result of *hydrostatic blood pressure*, which tends to force the plasma through the thin endothelial cells of the capillary walls or through the spaces between these cells. The chief process of its formation is *filtration*. Tissue fluid resembles blood plasma but is lacking in red blood cells. It contains all the blood proteins, but they are present in slightly different concentrations from those in the blood. Another factor in the formation of tissue fluid is *osmotic pressure*. Salts, glucose, and other crystalloids in blood plasma exert little osmotic pressure within capillaries, since they diffuse readily through their walls. However, the osmotic pressure exerted by proteins acts to draw water from the tissues into the capillaries. At the arterial end of a capillary, the force of filtration exceeds that of osmosis, and the flow is outward into the tissues. As the blood passes along the capillary, the concentration of plasma proteins rises, increasing osmotic pressure. At the same time, blood pressure decreases; consequently, at the venous end of the capillary, osmotic pressure exceeds hydrostatic pressure and fluid is drawn from tissues into capillaries. Resorption of tissue fluid into the blood stream ensues.

LYMPH

Outside the capillaries, the tissue fluid bathes the cells of the tissues. It is collected into a network of extremely fine vessels (the *lymph capillaries*) or into small spaces (*lacteals*) in the villi of the intestines. The foregoing converge into larger *lymph vessels*, which conduct the fluid away from the periphery. The fluid within these lymph vessels (or lymphatics) is called *lymph*. Lymphatics are more permeable than are capillaries; in fact, their distal ends are regarded as being open, thus permitting ready access to the lymph or colloidal substances and particulate matter which may get into the tissue spaces. All lymph vessels lead eventually to the *right lymphatic* and *thoracic ducts*, which empty into the right and left subclavian veins respectively, where the lymph re-enters the blood stream.

Lymph is a clear, viscid fluid resembling blood plasma in its concentration of salts and some other substances. The same blood proteins are present, but in variable concentrations. Red cells are lacking, but white cells, especially lymphocytes, are numerous.

The *flow* of lymph is brought about by *differences of pressure* at the two ends of the lymphatic system. Pressure in the main lymph ducts is low; accordingly, lymph tends to flow from the peripheral vessels centrally to the main lymph ducts. Supplementary factors that aid in movement of the lymph are: (1) contraction of skeletal muscles, (2) respiratory movements, and (3) contraction of smooth muscles in the villi of intestines. *Valves* in lymphatic vessels prevent back flow of the lymph.

PRACTICAL CONSIDERATIONS

Enumeration of Blood Cells (Blood Count). The apparatus used to determine the number of red and white blood cells is called a *hemocytometer*. This comprises (1) a *counting chamber*, a glass slide marked with cross-rulings; (2) a *cover glass*; and (3) two *pipettes*, one containing in its bulb a red bead, the other a white bead. The former is used for counting RBC's, the latter for counting WBC's.

For the *red cell count*, blood is drawn into the pipette with the red bead up to the 0.5 mark; then it is diluted by drawing in physiologic saline solution or Hayem's solution until the mixture reaches the 101 mark, which gives a dilution of 1:200. The pipette is shaken vigorously to bring about a thorough mixing of the blood and the saline or Hayem's solution. Then a drop of this diluted blood is placed on the counting chamber and allowed to run under the cover glass. The cross-rulings on the slide and the space between the cover glass and the slide are so constructed that each small space contains 1/4000 cu. mm. The erythrocytes within the area of 80 small spaces are counted. The resultant number multiplied by 10,000 gives the total number of red cells per cu. mm. (4000 divided by 80, multiplied by 200 equals 10,000).

For the *white cell count*, the pipette with the white bead is used. Again, blood is drawn up to the 0.5 mark. Tuerk's solution (1 per cent glacial acetic acid, to which a tinge of gentian violet or methyl green has been added) is used as the diluting agent. The acid hemolyzes the red cells while the white cells are stained slightly. Diluting fluid is drawn up to the 11 mark, giving a dilution of 1:20. Cells are counted in the 16 large spaces seen in the four corners of the ruled area on the slide, and the average number in a corner is determined. The cubic content of a large space is 25/4000 cu. mm. Therefore the WBC count (per cu. mm.) is the average number in a corner area multiplied by 200. (4000 divided by 16 × 25, multiplied by 20, equals 200.)

In some instances, a *differential* count is required in order to determine the numbers and percentages of the various kinds of leucocytes. The conditions that alter the numbers of various types of leucocytes are: (1) *leucocytosis* (increase in the number of WBC's, principally neutrophils; it occurs in infections caused by pyogenic organisms and in pneumonia, whooping cough, and other infectious diseases); (2) *eosinophilia* (increase in the number of eosinophils associated with allergic conditions, such as asthma, anaphylactic shock, and certain skin diseases; also with infestations by animal parasites, such as *Ascaris*, *Trichinella*, or hookworm); (3) *lymphocytosis* (increase in the number of lymphocytes, occurring in chronic, inflammatory states following acute infections); (4) *leukemia* (see discussion on page 228); and (5) *leucopenia* (reduction in the number of leucocytes, occurring in typhoid fever, tuberculosis, and influenza; it also results from the effects of certain poisons, such as benzol, aminopyrine and its compounds, and other toxic substances).

Blood Transfusion. Transfusion is the injection of whole blood or some of its constituents into the blood stream. Conditions which may necessitate transfusion are: (1) loss of blood after hemorrhage, (2) reduction of blood volume in circulation which occurs in shock, (3) decrease in red blood cells or plasma proteins, (4) deficiency in blood coagulating factors, and (5) need to replace blood in certain hemorrhagic diseases. The substances which may be injected into the blood stream by transfusion are: whole blood; blood plasma, or serum; colloidal solutions; and solutions of crystalloids.

TRANSFUSION OF WHOLE BLOOD. The most desirable fluid for transfusion is whole blood, but there are several dangers involved in its use: (1) possible transmission of infectious diseases, such as malaria or syphilis; (2) possibility that blood of donor may contain foreign proteins to which recipient is allergic; (3) possible incompatibility of donor's blood with that of recipient.

Compatibility. The normal blood plasma of one subject may contain substances which would cause *agglutination* (clumping together) of the blood cells of the other subject. Such bloods are said to be "incompatible," and if they are mixed fatal effects may ensue. Human blood is classified in four groups, namely, O, A, B, and AB (formerly designated I, II, III, and IV). The reactions of these groups are shown in the following table:

Cells of Donor Groups	Reaction to Serum of Recipient Groups			
	O	A	B	AB
O	−	−	−	−
A	+	−	−	−
B	+	+	−	−
AB	+	+	+	−

+ agglutination   − nonagglutination

A person whose blood falls into Group O is said to be a *universal donor*; the cells of Group O blood are not usually agglutinated by the serum of any other group. Group O individuals whose agglutinins are of high titer may be dangerous in transfusion, and their use should therefore be avoided—as should the term "universal donor." A person whose blood falls into Group AB is called a *universal recipient*, for the serum of this blood type does not agglutinate the blood cells of any other group. Among individuals of the white race, the groups are distributed roughly as follows: Group O, 43 per cent; Group A, 40 per cent; Group B, 13 per cent; Group AB, 4 per cent. The proportions in the various groups vary in different races. In races of the Far East, the proportion in Group A decreases and that in Group B increases; among American Indians, Group O is the predominant group.

The Rh Factor. The blood of most persons (about 85 per cent of the total) contains a substance called the Rh factor (*Rh* is short for the Rhesus monkey, on which relevant experiments have been conducted), which acts as an agglutinogen. When blood of such individuals (Rh positive) is transfused into the blood of one lacking in it (Rh negative), the blood of the recipient develops an anti-Rh agglutinin within about two weeks following the transfusion. If a subsequent transfusion is performed, a hemolytic reaction occurs, owing to the presence of this agglutinin.

In pregnant women such a reaction may take place after a single transfusion. This is believed to be due to the development of Rh agglutinin in the mother's blood as a result of a previous transfusion or the presence in the fetus' blood of an Rh positive factor inherited from the father. In infants a blood disorder, *erythroblastosis fetalis* (hemolytic disease of the new-born), may occur. This is due to the development in Rh-negative mothers of the anti-Rh agglutinin, which passes through the placenta to the fetus, causing the destruction of the red cells of the fetus (which is usually Rh positive). Unless proper treatment is instituted immediately, this disease is likely to be fatal.

TRANSFUSION OF PLASMA. This method has the advantage over other techniques in that the blood products of many donors can be pooled and transfused indiscriminately. The liquid plasma can be kept under refrigeration indefinitely, or the plasma can be frozen or dried; transportation and storage difficulties are thus reduced to a minimum.

TRANSFUSION OF SOLUTIONS OF COLLOIDS. Efforts have been made to substitute a suitable transfusion medium similar to blood or plasma. Among the substances that have been employed are: gum acacia, isinglass, gelatin, and other protein compounds. Their utilization is still limited.

TRANSFUSION OF CRYSTALLOIDS. Solutions of glucose or of physiologic saline solution are sometimes injected for conditions that involve dehydration of tissues. Their effects are usually transitory, for the fluid passes quickly through capillary walls into the tissues.

Edema. Ordinarily, the rate of formation of tissue fluid and lymph and the rate at which lymph re-enters the blood stream either through resorption in the capillaries or by way of the lymph ducts is approximately equal. But if there is a disturbance in the balance between these two processes whereby the formation of tissue fluid increases, it will tend to accumulate in the tissue spaces, giving rise to swelling or *edema*. When this condition is generalized over the body, it is called *anasarca* or *dropsy*. When it is localized in the abdominal cavity, it is called *ascites*.

There are many factors which may play a role in the causation of edema. Some of the principal ones are: (1) *Venous obstruction*, as by a thrombus or neoplasm. Such increases capillary pressure and effective filtration pressure. (2) *Cardiac disease*. The edema of congestive heart failure due to pronounced edema in the extremities is attributed to increased venous pressure and increased permeability of capillary walls. (3) *Renal disease*. In nephritis and nephrosis, there is a reduction in plasma proteins with a resultant decrease in osmotic pressure of the blood. This results in an increased effective filtration pressure. (4) *Nutritional factors*. Edema may result from faulty metabolism, as in hypothyroidism or diabetes, or it may result from malnutrition (for example, if the diet is deficient in vitamins or proteins). (5) *Lymphatic obstruction*. Interference in the drainage of lymph from any portion of the body will result in edema in the part involved. It may be caused by parasites as in filariasis (elephantiasis), tumors, or mechanical obstruction. (6) *Inflammatory conditions*. The edema accompanying inflammation results primarily from increased permeability of the capillaries due to the presence of toxic substances and increased capillary pressure resulting from increased blood flow to inflamed tissues.

DISORDERS AND DISEASES OF THE BODY FLUIDS

Common diseases involving the formation and composition of the body fluids are: anemia, hemophilia, and leukemia.

Anemia. In this condition there is reduction in the number of red blood cells, or a reduction in the amount of hemoglobin, or both. Anemia may result from (1) blood loss or (2) defective red-cell formation. Blood loss may result from *hemorrhage* (either acute, as from an injury, or chronic, as in hookworm infestation); or it may result from destruction of RBC's (*hemolysis*) within the blood stream, as occurs in lead or arsenic poisoning or from the effects of the infectious organisms of malaria or scarlet fever.

The group of diseases known as "the anemias" is broken down into the following types, which are designated according to the nature of defective red-cell formation which occurs: (1) *Nutritional anemia* results from deficiency in the diet of a substance essential to the manufacture of RBC's (iron, copper, cobalt) as well as proteins with their essential amino acids, and certain vitamins, especially B_{12} and folic acid (pteroyglutamic acid). (2) *Aplastic anemia* results from the failure of red bone marrow to produce red blood cells. This may be due to the effect of poisons such as benzol, radium salts, excessive irradiation, toxic products of disease, or disease involving the bone marrow. (3) *Pernicious anemia* results from lack of the *anti-anemic principle*, which is essential for the formation of hemoglobin. This principle is stored in the liver. It is formed by the interaction of two substances: (a) an *extrinsic* factor found in certain foods such as beef muscle, and (b) an *intrinsic* factor secreted by cells in the pyloric region of the stomach and present in gastric juice. The anemia results from the failure of the body to produce, store, or utilize this factor.

Hemophilia. This is the condition in which the blood fails to clot within the normal time. Persons so afflicted are known as "bleeders." They may bleed excessively from minor injuries, such as tooth extraction or even a small cut. Large black-and-blue spots appear under the skin from even light blows. The cause of hemophilia is not known but is believed to be the failure of the blood platelets to disintegrate and liberate thromboplastin.

Hemophilia is hereditary and is due to a sex-linked factor; that is, the gene (hereditary determiner) is carried in the X chromosome. If a male "bleeder" mates with a normal female, none of the offspring will manifest the condition. However, the normal daughters, called "carriers," may transmit the predisposing gene to some of their children, but the condition will develop only in the sons, never in the daughters. As a consequence, hemophilia is almost entirely restricted to males; at the present time, there are records of only three authentic cases of hemophilia in females.

Leukemia. This term is applied to the condition in which the number of white blood cells increases far beyond physiologic limits; it may exceed 1,000,-000 per cu. mm. Leukemia is also characterized by a reduction in the number of red blood cells, hyperplasia of the spleen and the lymphatic tissue, and changes in the structure of the bone marrow. It may be chronic or acute. It is classified on the basis of the type of white cells that predominate: *myeloid* leukemia, with granulocytes predominating; *lymphatic* leukemia, with lymphocytes predominating. In some cases, immature blood cells appear in the blood in large numbers. The disease is usually fatal; its cause is unknown.

Diseases presenting a similar picture to leukemia are *lymphosarcoma* and *Hodgkin's Disease*. *Lymphosarcoma* is a malignant tumor of the lymphoid tissue, with enlargement of all lymphatic organs due to increase and retention of lymphoid cells. Lymphoid tissue of throat and intestine is usually also affected, and sometimes the spleen. *Hodgkin's Disease* is characterized by chronic inflammation of the lymph nodes with frequent enlargement of the spleen. In *lymphosarcoma*, cells are almost all lymphocytes. In *Hodgkin's Disease*, they are extremely varied.

Purpura. This is a hemorrhagic disease in which blood seeps from the capillaries of the skin and the mucous membranes. In the skin it results in the formation of dark purplish areas. Purpura is due to abnormality in the structure of the capillary walls and to an insufficient number of blood platelets. Excessive destruction of platelets by the spleen is apparently a primary causative factor.

10: THE CIRCULATORY SYSTEM

The circulatory system comprises all structures concerned with transportation of body fluids from one region of the body to another. It has two main divisions: a blood-vascular system and a lymphatic system. Structures comprising the *blood-vascular system* are: the *heart*, which by contraction forces blood through the blood vessels; *arteries* (which conduct blood from the heart to tissues) with their smaller branches called *arterioles*; *veins* (which conduct blood from tissues toward the heart) with their smaller branches called *venules*; and *capillaries*, extremely small vessels which connect arteries and veins. Structures comprising the *lymphatic system* are: *lymph capillaries*, minute vessels within tissues (in intestinal villi, they are called *lacteals*); *lymph vessels* (an elaborate system of vessels which carry lymph from the tissues); and *main lymph ducts* (the *right lymphatic* and *left thoracic ducts* which carry lymph from lymph vessels to the blood stream). The two main lymph ducts empty into the right and left subclavian veins, respectively, near their junctions with the internal jugular veins, to form the innominate (brachiocephalic) veins.

THE HEART

The heart, a hollow muscular organ, lies between the lungs in the lower median portion of the thoracic cavity, or middle mediastinum. It is about the size of a man's fist, averaging 12 cm. in length, 9 cm. in width, and 6 cm. in thickness. It weighs about 300 gm. in the male, 250 gm. in the female. Its shape is roughly that of an inverted cone. From the superior portion, the "base," emerge the vessels that enter and leave this organ. The inferior, rounded portion, or "apex," points downward slightly anteriorly and to the left.

Pericardium. The heart is enclosed in a double-walled fibroserous sac, the pericardium. The inner layer (*visceral pericardium*) closely invests the heart and constitutes the outermost layer of the heart wall. The outer layer (*parietal pericardium*) consists of fibrous connective tissue lined with mesothelium. The space between these two layers contains a serous fluid (*pericardial fluid*) which provides smooth surfaces for easy movement of the heart during its expansion and contraction.

Wall of the Heart. The wall is composed of three layers: (1) *epicardium* (the visceral pericardium already mentioned) composed of

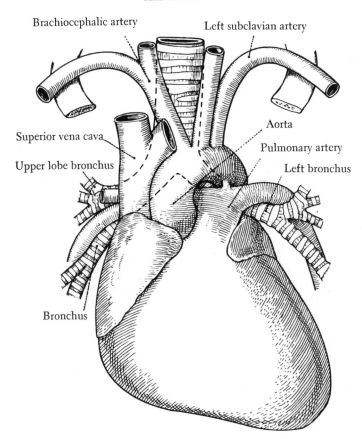

Fig. 10-1. The heart, anterior view. (Reprinted with permission of St. Martin's Press and The Macmillan Company Ltd. from Hamilton, *Textbook of Human Anatomy*, 1956.)

mesothelium and elastic fibers, constituting the outermost layer; (2) *myocardium*, a thick middle layer of cardiac muscle fibers grouped together into bands which tend to run obliquely, this layer being much thicker in the ventricles than in the atria and thickest in the left ventricle; and (3) *endocardium*, the innermost layer, made up of endothelium and a thin layer of underlying connective tissue. The endocardium lines the heart cavities and covers the valves; it is continuous with the endothelium of blood vessels entering and leaving the heart.

Chambers of the Heart. The heart has four compartments or *chambers*: the left and right *atria* and the left and right *ventricles*. *Externally*, an atrioventricular groove separates the atria from the ventricles;

anterior and posterior interventricular grooves separate the ventricles. *Internally*, the atria are separated by the interatrial septum, the two ventricles by the interventricular septum.

Sometimes the term "auricle" is used more or less synonymously with atrium. Strictly speaking, however, *auricles* are limited portions of the atria, forming small ear-like diverticula which project externally.

RIGHT ATRIUM. This chamber constitutes the right superior portion of the heart. It is thin-walled, and into it empty the veins which bring blood from all body tissues except the lungs. These vessels, which enter on the posterior surface, are: *superior vena cava*, bringing blood from upper body regions; *inferior vena cava*, bringing blood from lower body regions; and *coronary sinus*, bringing blood from the heart wall.

On the interatrial septum is an oval depression, the *fossa ovalis*, which marks the position of the foramen ovale, an opening which connects the right and left atria in the fetal heart. Between the right atrium and the right ventricle is the *right atrioventricular opening*, through which blood passes from the right atrium to the right ventricle. It is guarded by the right atrioventricular or *tricuspid valve*.

LEFT ATRIUM. This chamber constitutes the left superior portion of the heart. It is slightly smaller than the right atrium, and its walls are thicker. It receives the four *pulmonary veins*, which bring blood from the lungs. It opens inferiorly into the left ventricle by means of the *left atrioventricular opening*, which is guarded by the left atrioventricular or *bicuspid valve* (the *mitral valve*).

RIGHT VENTRICLE. This chamber constitutes the right inferior portion of the apex of the heart. Leading from its superior surface and directed upward to the left is the *pulmonary artery*, which carries blood to the lungs. Its opening is guarded by three *semilunar valves*. The wall of the right ventricle is thicker than that of the right atrium but has only one-third the thickness of the left ventricle.

The two ventricles are separated by the *interventricular septum*.

LEFT VENTRICLE. This chamber constitutes the left inferior portion of the apex of the heart. Its walls are very thick, for by its contractions the blood is forced through the aorta to all parts of the body except the lungs. From its superior surface the aorta arises, its opening being guarded by three *semilunar* (*aortic*) *valves*.

The inner layers of the walls of both ventricles present irregular surfaces. Muscular ridges (*trabeculae carnae*) and the *papillary muscles*, to which the *chordae tendineae* are attached, project inwardly. The chordae tendineae are fibrous cords attached to the free edges of the bicuspid and tricuspid valves.

Valves of the Heart. Two types of valves are found in the heart: atrioventricular and semilunar.

The *atrioventricular valves* are thin, leaf-like structures or *cusps* located at the atrioventricular openings. The bases of these leaflets form a ring about the opening, so that blood readily passes between them. Their free edges project inferiorly into the ventricular cavities, and from these edges of the valves the chordae tendineae extend to the papillary muscles.

The *right atrioventricular* or *tricuspid valve* consists of three *cusps*; the *left atrioventricular valve* (*mitral valve*) has two cusps.

Upon contraction of the atria, blood readily flows through the openings between the leaflets, spreading them apart. When the ventricles contract, blood is forced upward against the outer surfaces of the valves, causing them to approximate each other, thus closing the opening and preventing return of the blood to the atria.

The *semilunar valves* are pocket-like structures which surround the openings to the aorta and to the pulmonary artery. They are arranged in sets of three. On contraction of the ventricles, the blood is forced through the opening between the valves, forcing them against the walls of the vessels and permitting blood to enter the arteries. On cessation of ventricular contraction, back pressure (resulting from peripheral resistance and the elasticity of the stretched arterial walls) tends to force the blood back into the heart, but this is prevented by the valvular action which closes the openings. The *pulmonary semilunar valves* are located at the point where the pulmonary artery makes its exit from the right ventricle; the *aortic semilunar valves* are located at the point where the aorta makes its exit from the left ventricle.

Conductile Tissue of the Heart. In the heart there is a special *impulse-conducting system* which is concerned with coordination of the beat of the various parts of the heart. It consists of a continuous tract of atypical muscle fibers called *Purkinje fibers,* which lie just beneath the endocardium. These fibers originate in the wall of the right atrium near the entrance of the superior vena cava. This region develops from the sinus venosus of the embryo; it is called the *sinuatrial* or *S–A node.* From this node a plexus of fibers pass through the walls of the right atrium. In a region near the opening of the coronary sinus is found the *atrioventricular* or *A–V node.* From this node a bundle, the *atrioventricular bundle* or *bundle of His,* extends a short distance, then divides into two trunks which pass downward on each side of the interventricular septum. From these trunks branches extend throughout the musculature of the ventricles.

By the medium of the Purkinje fibers, impulses are conducted which regulate the beat of the heart.

STRUCTURE OF BLOOD VESSELS

The blood vessels comprise arteries (and their arterioles), veins (and their venules), capillaries, and sinusoids.

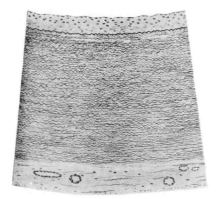

Fig. 10-2. Section through wall of large artery. Note vasa vasorum in the tunica adventitia. (Redrawn from Sobotta.)

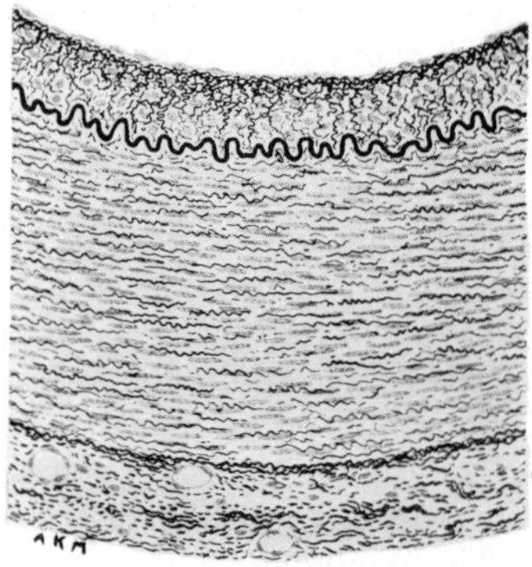

Fig. 10-3. A transverse section through wall of medium-sized artery. (A) tunica intima. (B) tunica media. (C) tunica externa.

(Figures reprinted with permission of St. Martin's Press and The Macmillan Company Ltd. from Hamilton, *Textbook of Human Anatomy,* 1956.)

Arteries. An artery is an elastic muscular tube which conducts blood from the heart.

LAYERS OF WALL OF ARTERY. The wall of an artery has three layers:

1. *Tunica intima* or *interna,* consisting of an inner layer of endothelium resting on the internal elastic membrane of fibro-elastic tissue. This layer forms the lining of the artery.

2. *Tunica media,* the middle and thickest layer, consisting of smooth muscle cells, elastic and collagenous fibers, and thin reticular fibers.

3. *Tunica adventitia,* the outermost coat, consisting of elastic and collagenous fibers which pass into the adjoining connective tissues without a sharp line of demarcation.

TYPES OF ARTERIES. There are three types of arteries:

1. *Elastic arteries.* These arteries are large in caliber and include the aorta, innominate, subclavian, part of the common carotid, and the pulmonary. Elastic fibers predominate in their tunica media. Arteries of this type are called *conducting* arteries.

2. *Muscular Arteries.* These are *continuations* of the elastic arteries and similar to them in structure, except that muscular fibers predominate in their tunica media. These are the principal *distributing* arteries.

3. *Arterioles.* These are very small terminal branches of the muscular arteries which lead to the capillaries. They average 0.3 mm. or less in diameter and are barely visible to the unaided eye.

Arteries and their accompanying veins are generally located on the flexor sides of limbs, thus being protected against injury or excessive stretch resulting from movement of the limbs. Veins and lymph vessels are usually placed less deeply than the arteries.

Veins. A vein is a vessel that conducts blood away from the tissues and toward the heart. Veins increase progressively in size from the tissues to the heart, their course in general paralleling that of arteries. In structure, veins resemble arteries, except that their walls are thinner and less elastic. In microscopic sections their walls are usually collapsed and their lumen is irregular in shape, whereas arteries are usually circular or ovoid in form and their lumen is much smaller, with the tunica intima presenting a corrugated appearance. Veins possess the same three layers that are found in arteries, but their boundaries are usually indistinct. The tunica media contains much less muscular and elastic tissue.

Many veins, especially those of the extremities, contain valves, thin semilunar-shaped flaps of connective tissue which form pocket-like structures. They are attached to the inner surface of the walls of the vessel with their free edges directed toward the direction of blood flow. They are usually arranged in pairs. Such valves prevent a back flow of the blood.

Capillaries. These minute vessels form the terminations of arterioles. Leading to the venules, they form complicated anastomosing networks of vessels in the tissues. The wall of a capillary consists of a single layer of squamous epithelial cells; this endothelium is a continuation of that lining the arteries and veins. Capillaries average about 8 microns in diameter, a lumen which is barely large enough for corpuscles to pass through in single file. It is through the capillary walls that the exchange of substances between the blood and the tissues takes place. The fluid portion of the blood that reaches the tissues passes through the protoplasm of the thin endothelial cells. Leucocytes can pass between the endothelial cells by means of their ameboid movement.

Blood flows slowly through the capillaries. This is due to (1) their very narrow diameter and (2) their greater cross-section area as compared with the artery which supplies them.

Sinusoids. These are minute blood vessels found in certain organs, such as the liver, spleen, adrenal glands, and bone marrow. They differ from capillaries in that their diameter is generally larger and more variable, and their walls, instead of being formed by a continuous layer of endothelium as in capillaries, are formed by irregularly placed phagocytic and nonphagocytic cells. (The phagocytic cells possess the ability to store vital dyes and to phagocytose bacteria.) Furthermore, sinusoids lack a layer of connective tissue, which usually surrounds capillaries; consequently, they lie in closer proximity to the cells of the organs in which they are found. In certain of the blood-forming organs of the body, such as the spleen and bone marrow, the walls of the sinusoids have openings through which cells can enter or leave the blood stream.

CONNECTIONS BETWEEN ARTERIES AND VEINS

In general, the blood passes from an artery to a vein through a single set of capillaries in the tissues. However, there are a number of exceptions to this general plan, some of which are listed below:

1. From an artery directly to a vein (as in the sole or the palm). Such a connection is called an *arteriovenous anastomosis.*

2. From an artery through capillaries to an arteriole and then through a second capillary net to a vein (as in the kidney).

3. From an artery through capillaries to a vein and then through a network of sinusoids to a vein (as in the portal circulation through the liver).

4. From an artery through capillaries to sinusoids and then to a vein (as in the adrenal gland).

5. From an artery through spaces to a sinus and then to veins (as in the placenta of a gravid uterus).

GENERAL PLAN OF CIRCULATION

Blood coming from the body tissues enters the right atrium through the venae cavae. Contraction of the right atrium forces blood past the tricuspid valve into the right ventricle. From this point begin the two subdivisions of the blood-vascular circulatory system: the pulmonary and systemic circulations. As the terms imply, the former serves the lungs, the latter the various "systems" of the body.

Pulmonary Circulation. Contraction of the right ventricle forces blood past the semilunar valves into the pulmonary artery, which carries it to the lungs. In passing through the capillaries of the lungs, the blood is oxygenated and carbon dioxide is given off. Pulmonary veins carry the blood back to the left atrium of the heart.

Systemic Circulation. Contraction of the left atrium forces blood past the bicuspid valve into the left ventricle. Contraction of the left ventricle forces blood past the semilunar valves into the aorta. From the aorta, blood is carried to capillaries of all tissues by arteries and arterioles. From the tissues, capillaries lead to venules, which, in turn, lead to veins, which empty into the superior and inferior venae cavae. The venae cavae empty into the right atrium.

It can be seen from the foregoing that the blood makes a double circuit in its travels, since following pulmonary circulation it re-enters the heart at the left atrium, where it began its course throughout the body as the systematic circulation.

STRUCTURE OF THE BLOOD–VASCULAR SYSTEM

The structure of the pulmonary division of the blood-vascular system is simple compared with that of the systemic division. The former involves comparatively few vessels and connective tissues.

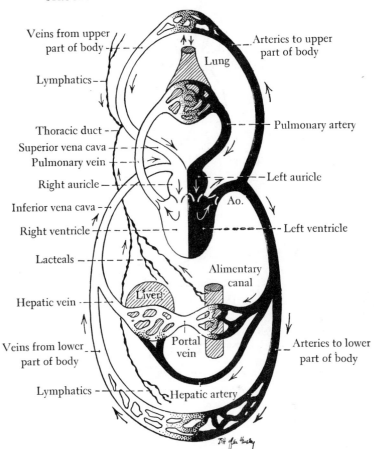

Fig. 10-4. Blood circulation. Arrows show direction of flow. Two arrows above lung show interchange of air. (Reprinted with permission of C. V. Mosby Company from McClendon, *Physiological Chemistry*.)

Pulmonary Circulatory Structures

The pulmonary artery emerges from the superior surface of the right ventricle, passes diagonally upward to the left, and crosses the root of the aorta. It divides into *right* and *left pulmonary arteries*, branches of which enter the right and left lungs, respectively. At its bifurcation a short connective-tissue structure, the *ligamentum arteriosum*, connects with the aortic arch. This cord represents the vestige of an artery, the *ductus arteriosus*, that was functional in the fetus. *Pulmonary veins* are four in number, two from each lung. They carry oxygenated blood from the lungs to the left atrium.

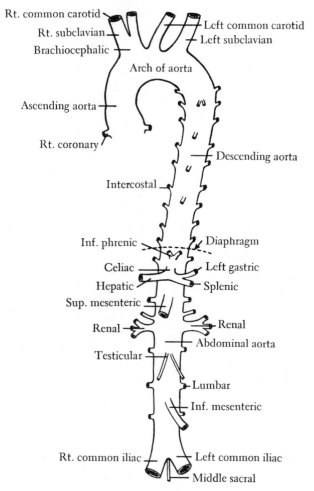

Fig. 10-5. Aorta and branches. (Reprinted with permission of C. V. Mosby Company and the author from Francis, *Introduction to Human Anatomy*, 2nd ed. 1954.)

Systemic Circulatory Structures

The systemic division of the blood-vascular system consists of the aorta (with its numerous branches) and four principal veins (with their branches).

Systemic Arteries. The main arterial trunk carrying blood from the heart to the tissues is the *aorta*. It emerges from the superior surface of the left ventricle, passes upward under the pulmonary artery as the *ascending aorta,* turns to the left as the *aortic arch,* then turns downward as the *descending aorta.* The descending aorta, lying close to the bodies of the vertebrae, passes downward through the diaphragm and continues to the level of the fourth lumbar vertebra, where it terminates by dividing into the two common iliac arteries. The portion of the aorta above the diaphragm is the *thoracic aorta;* that below is the *abdominal aorta.* The principal branches of the various portions of the aorta are as follows:

Ascending aorta   Coronary

Arch of the aorta
- Brachiocephalic (Innominate) { Right common carotid / Right subclavian }
- Left common carotid
- Left subclavian

Thoracic aorta

Visceral branches	*Parietal branches*
Bronchial	Intercostal
Esophageal	Subcostal
Pericardial	Superior phrenic
Mediastinal	

Abdominal aorta

Visceral branches	*Parietal branches*
Celiac	Inferior phrenic
Superior mesenteric	Lumbar
Testicular or ovarian	
Middle suprarenal	
Renal	
Inferior mesenteric	

Terminal branches

Middle sacral
Common iliac { Ext. iliac / Hypogastric (Int. iliac) }

ASCENDING AORTA. The branches of the ascending aorta are the *left* and *right coronary arteries,* which arise close to the origin of the aorta, their openings being in the pockets of the aortic valves. They supply the heart. (See Fig. 10-6.)

ARCH OF THE AORTA. The branches of the aortic arch are the innominate, left common carotid, and left subclavian arteries.

Innominate (Brachiocephalic) Artery. This is the first branch of the aortic arch. It passes superiorly and diagonally to the right, crossing the trachea in its course. As it passes out of the thorax, it divides into two branches: the right common carotid and the right subclavian.

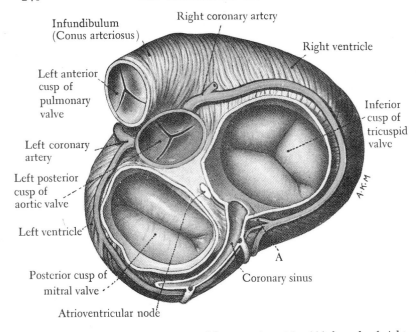

Fig. 10-6. Base of ventricles, exposed by removing atria. (A) branch of right coronary artery to atrio-ventricular node. (Reprinted with permission of St. Martin's Press and The Macmillan Company Ltd. from Hamilton, *Textbook of Human Anatomy*, 1956.)

The *right common carotid artery* passes superiorly alongside the trachea to about the level of the 3rd cervical vertebra, where it divides into the following branches: the *external carotid*, which continues upward giving off branches supplying muscles, glands, skin, and other structures of the face and scalp, then passes in front of the ear as the *superficial temporal artery*; and the *internal carotid*, which continues upward in the neck and enters the cranial cavity through the carotid foramen, terminating at the *circle of Willis*. At the bifurcation of the external and internal carotid arteries, there is a slight dilation, the *carotid sinus*. Closely associated with the sinus is the *carotid body*. These last two structures, about 5 mm. in length, contain the endings of sensory nerves (presso- and chemoreceptors) which play an important role in the regulation of circulation and respiration.

The *circle of Willis* consists of an anastomosing group of blood vessels located at the base of the brain. It surrounds the optic chiasm and the hypophysis and is formed of the following vessels: posteriorly, the proximal portions of the *posterior cerebral arteries*; laterally, the *posterior communicating, internal carotid*, and the proximal portions

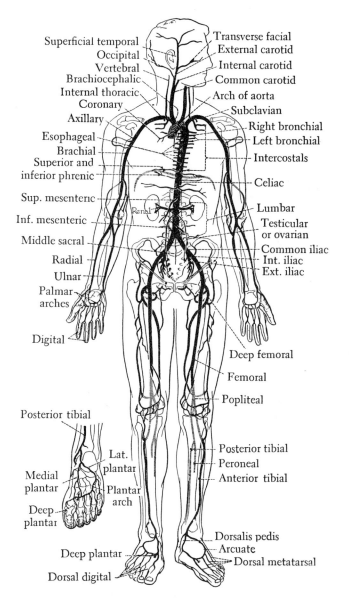

Superficial temporal
Occipital
Vertebral
Brachiocephalic
Internal thoracic
Coronary
Axillary
Esophageal
Brachial
Superior and
inferior phrenic
Sup. mesenteric
Inf. mesenteric
Middle sacral
Radial
Ulnar
Palmar
arches
Digital
Posterior tibial
Medial
plantar
Deep
plantar
Deep plantar
Dorsal digital
Lat.
plantar
Plantar
arch
Renal

Transverse facial
External carotid
Internal carotid
Common carotid
Arch of aorta
Subclavian
Right bronchial
Left bronchial
Intercostals
Celiac
Lumbar
Testicular
or ovarian
Common iliac
Int. iliac
Ext. iliac
Deep femoral
Femoral
Popliteal
Posterior tibial
Peroneal
Anterior tibial
Dorsalis pedis
Arcuate
Dorsal metatarsal

Fig. 10-7. General view of arterial system. (Reprinted with permission of
W. B. Saunders Company from Millard, King, and Showers, *Human Anatomy
and Physiology,* 4th ed., 1956.)

of the *anterior cerebral arteries;* anteriorly, the *anterior communicating arteries.* From this circle arteries extend into the meninges and the brain tissue. The *circle of Willis* receives its blood from the internal carotid and basilar arteries.

The *right subclavian artery* passes laterally to the arm. Two branches of it are the *vertebral* and *internal mammary (thoracica interna) arteries.* In the region of the axilla, it becomes the *axillary artery,* which continues into the arm. Other branches supply the region of the shoulder, axilla, and upper part of the thorax. In the arm, the right axillary continues as the *brachial artery,* which, in the region of the elbow, divides into the *ulnar* and *radial arteries.* These continue into the distal portion of the arm, giving off branches to the wrist and hand. In the hand, the ulnar and radial arteries are connected by the *deep* and *superficial palmar arches,* branches of which supply the digits. The *vertebral artery* arises from the subclavian near its origin. It passes upward through the neck, through the foramina in the transverse processes of the cervical vertebrae. At the 1st cervical vertebra it passes around the atlas and enters the cranial cavity through the foramen magnum. Within the skull, it unites with its mate from the opposite side to form the *basilar artery,* which joins the *circle of Willis* at the base of the brain.

Left Common Carotid Artery. The second branch of the arch of the aorta, the left common carotid, arises close to the innominate. It passes up the left side of the neck, following a course and possessing branches similar to those of the right common carotid.

Left Subclavian Artery. This artery arises from the aortic arch close to the left common carotid. It passes upward and out of the thorax, where it turns abruptly to the left to supply the left arm. It possesses the same branches as does the right subclavian.

THORACIC AORTA. The branches of the thoracic portion of the descending aorta supply either the internal organs or the body wall.

Visceral branches. These branches of the thoracic aorta include the *bronchial* (one right and two left), *esophageal* (four or five), *pericardial* (two or three), and *mediastinal arteries,* which supply the bronchi and lungs, esophagus, pericardium, and mediastinum, respectively.

Parietal Branches. Intercostal arteries (nine pairs) pass laterally and supply the thoracic wall, carrying blood to the chest muscles, the vertebrae, the pleurae, and the meninges of the spinal cord. *Subcostal arteries* (one pair) pass to the body wall. *Superior phrenic arteries* (one pair) supply the upper surface of the diaphragm.

ABDOMINAL AORTA. This portion of the aorta has many branches; it serves the entire lower region of the body. Its branches consist of three groups: visceral, parietal, and terminal. The branches of each group, listed in the order in which they arise, are as follows:

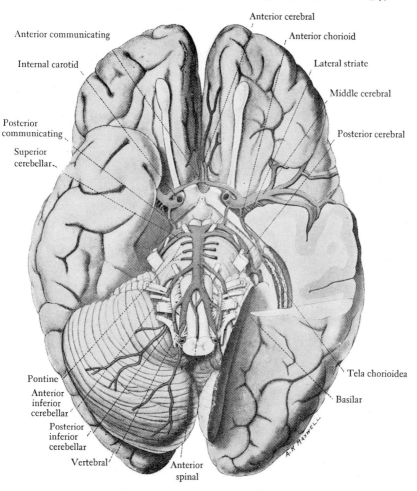

Fig. 10-8. Arteries at base of brain. Part of left cerebellar hemisphere removed. (Reprinted with permission of St. Martin's Press and The Macmillan Company Ltd. from Hamilton, *Textbook of Human Anatomy*, 1956.)

Visceral Branches of the Abdominal Aorta. These arteries supply the internal organs of the abdominal cavity. They include the following arteries: (1) The *celiac artery* is a very short artery emerging from the aorta a short distance below the diaphragm. It divides into three branches: the *left gastric*, or *coronary*, which supplies a portion of the stomach and the lower end of the esophagus; the *hepatic*, which supplies the liver, gallbladder, and portions of the stomach and duodenum; and the *splenic*, which supplies the spleen and portions of the

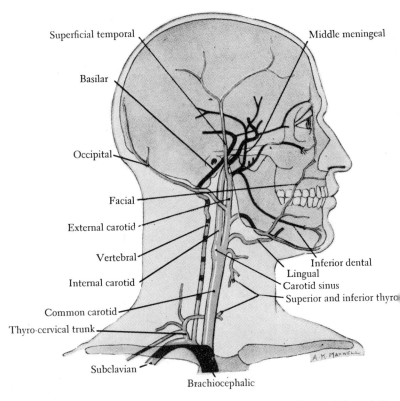

Fig. 10-9. Main arteries of head and neck. (Reprinted with permission of St. Martin's Press and The Macmillan Company Ltd. from Hamilton, *Textbook of Human Anatomy*, 1956.)

stomach and pancreas. (2) The *superior mesenteric artery* arises immediately below the celiac. It supplies the major portion of the small intestine and the first portion of the large intestine. It has many branches: inferior pancreatico-duodenal, twelve or more intestinal arteries, the right and middle colic arteries, and the ileocecal artery. (3) The *middle suprarenal arteries* supply the suprarenal glands. (4) The *renal arteries* supply the kidney. (5) The *internal testicular arteries* in the male and the *ovarian arteries* in the female arise just below the renal arteries. They lead to the testes and ovaries, respectively. (6) The *inferior mesenteric* artery supplies the large intestine. Branches are: the left colic, sigmoid, and superior rectal.

Parietal Branches of the Abdominal Aorta. These arteries supply the structures of the body wall in the lower portion of the trunk. They include the following arteries: (1) The *inferior phrenic arteries* sup-

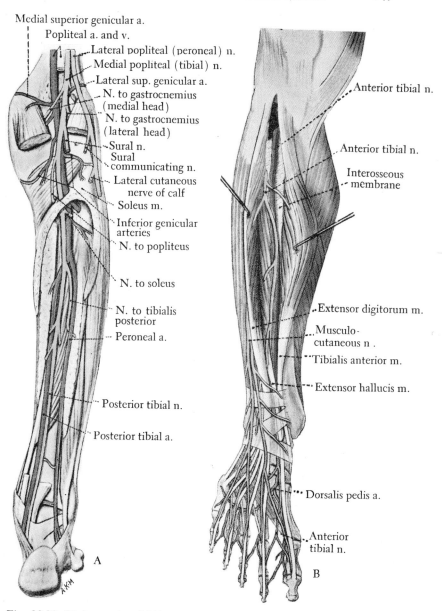

Medial superior genicular a.

Popliteal a. and v.

Lateral popliteal (peroneal) n.

Medial popliteal (tibial) n.

Lateral sup. genicular a.

N. to gastrocnemius (medial head)

N. to gastrocnemius (lateral head)

Sural n.

Sural communicating n.

Lateral cutaneous nerve of calf

Soleus m.

Inferior genicular arteries

N. to popliteus

N. to soleus

N. to tibialis posterior

Peroneal a.

Posterior tibial n.

Posterior tibial a.

A

Anterior tibial n.

Anterior tibial n.

Interosseous membrane

Extensor digitorum m.

Musculo-cutaneous n.

Tibialis anterior m.

Extensor hallucis m.

Dorsalis pedis a.

Anterior tibial n.

B

Fig. 10-10. Main arteries of (A) posterior aspects of knee and leg and (B) anterior aspects of leg and foot. (Reprinted with permission of St. Martin's Press and The Macmillan Company Ltd. from Hamilton, *Textbook of Human Anatomy*, 1956.)

ply the lower surface of the diaphragm. Branches also pass to the adrenal gland. (2) The *lumbar arteries* (four pairs) pass to the body wall, where they supply the muscles, skin, vertebrae, and the spinal cord and its meninges.

Terminal Branches of the Abdominal Aorta. These branches supply portions of the pelvis and the entire lower extremities. They include the following arteries: (1) The *middle sacral artery* arises near the point of bifurcation of the abdominal aorta. It supplies the sacrum and the coccyx. (2) *Common iliac arteries* arise from the bifurcation of the abdominal aorta. Each continues a short distance and then divides into two branches: the *hypogastric* (*internal iliac*) and the *external iliac arteries*. The hypogastric passes into the pelvic cavity, where it divides into an *anterior* and a *posterior* branch. These supply the muscles of the pelvic wall, bladder, reproductive organs (including external genitalia and uterus), and structures on the medial side of the thigh. The *external iliac* passes from its origin (the common iliac) under the inguinal ligament, where it leaves the pelvic cavity as the femoral artery. (3) The *femoral artery*, a continuation of the external iliac, passes through the thigh, lying medial and posterior to the femur. It gives off several branches, the largest being the *profunda femoris*. Above the popliteal fossa (the space directly posterior to the knee joint), the femoral artery becomes the popliteal artery. The *popliteal artery* passes through the popliteal fossa and into the lower leg. Just below the knee, the *anterior tibial artery* branches off from it and passes downward to the ankle joint, where it continues as the *dorsalis pedis artery*. The main portion of the popliteal artery continues to the foot as the *posterior tibial artery*; in the foot, this divides into the *medial* and *lateral plantar arteries*. (4) The *peroneal artery*, a large branch of the posterior tibial, arises just below the border of the popliteus muscles and passes along posterior and lateral sides of the leg to the foot, where it divides into small branches.

Systemic Veins. These are the veins that conduct blood from the tissues to the heart. The principal systemic veins are: (1) the *coronary sinus*, (2) the *superior vena cava*, and (3) the *inferior vena cava*, and their branches; and (4) the *portal vein*, which drains the abdominal viscera. The last-named vein differs from the others in that the blood it carries from the tissues passes through a second capillary network (sinusoids) in the liver before it enters the inferior vena cava.

Venous channels may be classified as: (1) *superficial veins*, which lie in the superficial fascia directly beneath the skin; (2) *deep veins*, which accompany the more deeply located arteries; and (3) *venous sinuses*, channels lacking in valves and devoid of a muscular layer in their walls. The last-named, which are found only in the cranial cavity, are spaces in the dura mater lined with endothelium; the larger of

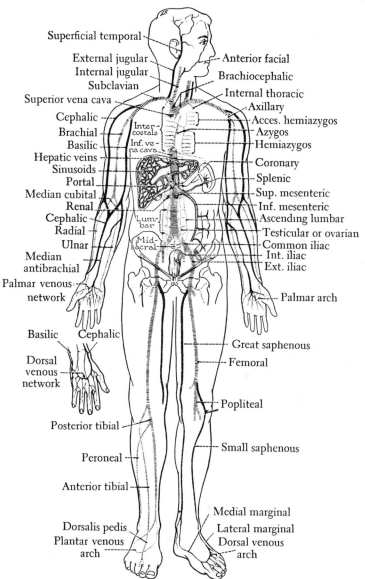

Fig. 10-11. General view of venous system. Deep veins are cut across. Labels of superficial veins are underlined. (Reprinted with permission of W. B. Saunders Company from Millard, King, and Showers, *Human Anatomy and Physiology*, 4th ed., 1956.)

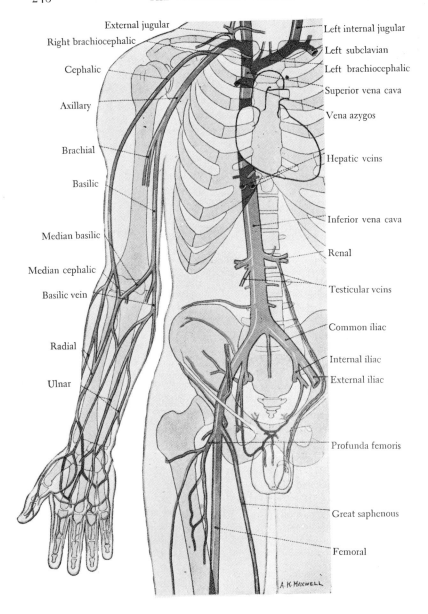

Fig. 10-12. Venae cavae, veins of upper limb, and proximal venous channels of lower limb. (Reprinted with permission of St. Martin's Press and The Macmillan Company Ltd. from Hamilton, *Textbook of Human Anatomy*, 1956.)

these venous sinuses lie in grooves on the inner surfaces of the cranial bones.

CORONARY SINUS AND ITS BRANCHES. The *coronary sinus* is a short vein lying on the posterior side of the heart. Its opening into the right atrium, guarded by an incomplete valve, is situated near the opening of the inferior vena cava. It receives most of the blood from heart tissues through one of the following vessels: the *great, small,* and *middle cardiac veins;* the *posterior vein;* and the *oblique vein.*

Cardiac veins which do not empty into the coronary sinus are: *anterior cardiac veins,* three or four in number, which empty into the right atrium; and *veins of Thesbius,* the smallest cardiac veins. Most of the latter empty into the atria, a few into the ventricles.

SUPERIOR VENA CAVA AND ITS BRANCHES. This vessel is a large venous trunk which returns blood to the heart from the head, neck, upper extremities, and thorax. It is formed by the union of the right and left innominate veins. It opens into the superior posterior surface of the right atrium at about the level of the 3rd costal cartilage.

Veins of the Head and Neck. The principal veins draining the head and neck are the external and internal jugular veins. The *external jugular vein* drains the external portions of the head, including most of the scalp and face. It arises at the angle of the mandible by the union of the *posterior facial* and *posterior auricular veins.* It passes downward through the neck, receiving some branches and terminating at its junction with the subclavian vein. The *internal jugular vein* is the principal vein of the neck. It arises at the jugular foramen, where it is continuous with the sigmoid portion of the transverse sinus. It passes down the side of the neck in close proximity to the internal and common carotid arteries. At the level of the sternum, it unites with the subclavian vein, to form the *innominate (brachiocephalic) vein.* The internal jugular vein receives blood from nearly all parts of the head and neck. Among the branches it receives are: *common facial vein,* from the face; *lingual vein,* from the tongue; *pharyngeal;* and *thyroid* (superior and middle) *veins.* Through the *transverse sinus* the internal jugular vein receives most of the blood from the brain.

SINUSES OF THE CRANIAL CAVITY. These sinuses are venous channels which lie in the dura mater. They receive blood from the brain through the *cerebral* and *cerebellar veins,* from the diploë of the cranial bones through the *diploic veins,* and from the sinuses and external portions of the skull through the *emissary veins.*

Superior Sagittal Sinus. This sinus lies in the midsagittal plane, commencing at the foramen caecum and lying in the convex portion of the falx cerebri. It terminates posteriorly, internal to the posterior occipital protuberance.

Inferior Sagittal Sinus. This sinus lies along the inferior margin of

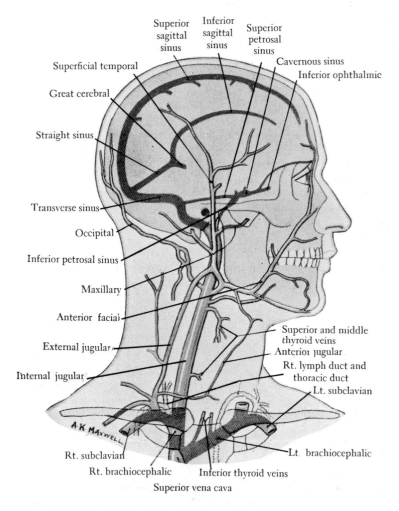

Fig. 10-13. Diagram of venous drainage of head and neck, outlining the superior vena cava and its branches. (Reprinted with permission of St. Martin's Press and The Macmillan Company Ltd. from Hamilton, *Textbook of Human Anatomy*, 1956.)

the falx cerebri. It unites with the great cerebral vein to form the *straight sinus*.

Straight Sinus. This sinus lies along the line of junction of the falx cerebri and the tentorium cerebelli. It empties into the left transverse sinus.

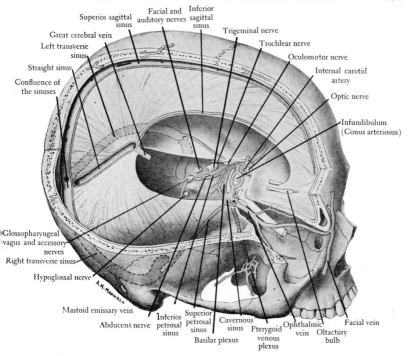

Fig. 10-14. Sinuses of cranial cavity. In this diagram some of the emissary veins are also shown. (Reprinted with permission of St. Martin's Press and The Macmillan Company Ltd. from Hamilton, *Textbook of Human Anatomy*, 1956.)

Occipital Sinus. This sinus lies in the midline, inferior to the confluence of the sinuses, into which it empties. It arises near the foramen magnum. The occipital is the smallest of the sinuses.

Transverse Sinuses. These are large sinuses arising at the internal occipital protuberance. Each passes laterally, then curves anteriorly and downward as the sigmoid portion to pass through the jugular foramen, where it is continuous with the internal jugular vein. Each transverse sinus receives several veins from the base of the brain and the skull.

Confluence of the Sinuses. This is a dilated region located at a point where the superior sagittal, occipital, and transverse sinuses converge.

Several smaller sinuses of the cranial cavity, constituting the anterior-inferior group, include:

Cavernous Sinuses. These lie lateral to the body of the sphenoid bone, posterior to the supraorbital fissure, through which each receives blood from the orbit via the *superior ophthalmic vein.* The two cavernous sinuses are connected with each other by the *intercavernous sinuses:* the *anterior intercavernous sinus,* which passes anterior to the hypophysis; and the *posterior intercavernous sinus,* which passes behind the hypophysis. These two vessels, together with the cavernous sinuses, form the *circular sinus.* Laterally each cavernous sinus receives a small *sphenoparietal sinus.*

The cavernous sinuses communicate with the transverse sinuses by means of the *superior petrosal sinus* and with the *internal jugular vein* through the *inferior petrosal sinus.* A basilar plexus lies over the basilar portion of the occipital bone and connects the two inferior petrosal sinuses.

Veins of the Upper Extremity. The *right* and *left subclavian veins* drain the upper extremities, each terminating at its junction with the internal jugular vein to form the innominate vein. Near its termination each subclavian receives the external jugular. At its angle of union with the internal jugular, the left subclavian receives the *left thoracic duct* (the principal lymph duct) and the right subclavian receives the *right lymphatic duct.* Each subclavian vein is formed by the union of the cephalic and axillary veins.

The *cephalic vein* originates dorsally on the radial side (thumb side) of the hand. It passes upward along the radial side of the arm, turning anteriorly and then passing along the antero-lateral surface of the elbow and continuing laterally to the biceps brachii, and finally to its junction with the axillary vein, where the two form the subclavian vein. Near the elbow, the cephalic vein communicates with the basilic vein by means of a branch, the *median cubital vein.*

The *axillary vein* is a continuation of the subclavian vein. It is formed by the union of the brachial (deep) vein, and the basilic (superficial) vein. The *brachial vein* lies alongside the brachial artery. It originates at the elbow from the union of the *radial* and *ulnar veins.* The *basilic vein* originates near the wrist from the union of the dorsal veins of the hands. It passes up the ulnar side of the forearm on the posterior surface, then swings anteriorly in the region of the elbow, and continues along the medial side of the biceps brachii to its termination at the point where it joins with the brachial vein.

The deep veins and the superficial veins are listed as follows:

Deep Veins	Superficial Veins
subclavian	cephalic
axillary	basilic
brachial	
ulnar	
radial	

Veins of the Thorax. Two large veins, the *left* and *right brachiocephalic* (innominate) are formed by union of the internal jugular and subclavian veins, which return blood from the head, neck, and upper extremities. The left is the larger of the two.

Each brachiocephalic vein receives the *deep cervical, vertebral, internal mammary,* and *inferior thyroid veins.* In addition, the left brachiocephalic receives the *left superior intercostal vein* and veins from the thymus, trachea, esophagus, and pericardium.

The *azygos vein* is a large vein originating in the abdomen from a vessel, the *ascending lumbar vein.* It passes through the diaphragm and continues upward along the *right* side of the vertebral column to the level of the 4th thoracic vertebra, where it turns forward to enter the superior vena cava. It receives the *right subcostal,* several *right intercostal,* the *right superior intercostal, hemiazygos,* and *accessory hemiazygos veins,* and *bronchial veins* from the lungs.

The *hemiazygos vein* has a course comparable to that of the azygos, excepting that it lies to the *left* of the vertebral column. It receives the *left subcostal vein* and veins from the esophagus, mediastinum, and lungs. It empties into the azygos vein.

INFERIOR VENA CAVA AND ITS BRANCHES. This is the venous trunk which receives most of the blood from the regions of the body below the level of the diaphragm. It is the largest vein in the body. The inferior vena cava is formed by the union of the two *common iliac veins* at about the level of the 4th lumbar vertebra. It passes upward to the right of and alongside the aorta, passes through the diaphragm, and enters the right atrium. The inferior vena cava receives blood from the following veins: *inferior phrenic* (from the diaphragm), *hepatic* (from the liver), *right suprarenal* (from the adrenal gland),· *renal* (from the kidneys), *right spermatic* or *ovarian* (from the right testis or right ovary), *lumbar* (from the body wall), and *common iliac* (from the pelvic region), and the veins of the lower extremities.

Inferior Phrenic Veins. These two small veins, *left* and *right,* drain the diaphragm. The left often has two branches, one connecting with the left renal or suprarenal, from which it may receive blood.

Hepatic Veins. These consist of two groups (upper and lower) which enter the vena cava just below the diaphragm. They receive blood from the *sublobular veins* of the liver. Blood received by the liver from the hepatic artery and the portal vein is returned by the hepatic veins to the inferior cava.

Suprarenal Veins. These drain the adrenal glands. The *right* empties into the inferior vena cava, the *left* into the left renal vein.

Renal Veins. These thick but short veins lie anterior to the renal arteries. They receive blood from the kidneys. The *left* also receives blood from the *left spermatic* (or *ovarian*), *left inferior phrenic,* and *left suprarenal veins.* It opens into the vena cava at a higher level than does the right renal vein.

Testicular and *Ovarian Veins*. In the male, testicular veins originate from branches in the testes and epididymides which unite to form a convoluted structure, the *plexus pampiniformis,* which constitutes the main bulk of the spermatic cord. Three or four vessels from this plexus pass through the inguinal canal and unite to form the *testicular vein,* which on the right side enters the inferior vena cava near the renal vein, and on the left side extends into the left renal vein. In the female, ovarian veins, similar in their terminations to the testicular (spermatic) veins, receive blood from the ovaries, uterine tubes, and uterus. During pregnancy they become much enlarged.

Lumbar Veins. Four pairs of lumbar veins lead from the abdominal wall to the inferior vena cava. They collect blood from the skin and muscles, the vertebrae, and the meninges of the spinal cord. They are connected by a longitudinal vein, the *ascending lumbar,* which passes upward and connects with the azygos and hemiazygos veins, on the right and left sides, respectively.

Common Iliac Veins. These are the two large veins that unite to form the inferior vena cava. Each is formed by a union of the *external iliac* and the *hypogastric (internal iliac) veins.* Each also receives the *iliolumbar* and *lateral sacral veins.*

The *external iliac vein,* which continues into the leg as the *femoral vein,* receives the following branches: the *inferior epigastric* (from the anterior body wall) and the *deep circumflex iliac* (from muscles and skin of the abdomen).

The *hypogastric (internal iliac) vein* receives the following branches: (1) Veins having their origin outside the pelvis, among them the *superior gluteal veins* (from the buttocks), *inferior gluteal veins* (from the upper part of the posterior portion of the thigh), *internal pudendal veins* (from the genitalia), and *obturator* (from the upper median region of the thigh). (2) Veins having their origin in venous plexuses of the pelvic viscera, among them the *middle hemorrhoidal (rectal)* (from the bladder, prostate gland, and seminal vesicles), *vesical* (from the lower part of the bladder and the prostate gland), and *uterine* and *vaginal veins.* (3) Veins that originate in front of the sacrum, including the *lateral sacral veins.*

VEINS OF THE LOWER EXTREMITY. Both superficial and deep veins are found in the lower extremity.

The principal *superficial* veins of the leg are: (1) The *great saphenous vein,* lying on the anterior and medial surfaces of the leg. It originates at the dorsum of the foot and extends the entire length of the leg, terminating just inside the fossa ovalis at the femoral vein. It is the longest single vein in the body. The great saphenous vein drains the foot and superficial portions of the leg. (2) The *small saphenous vein* lies on the posterior side of the lower leg. It originates

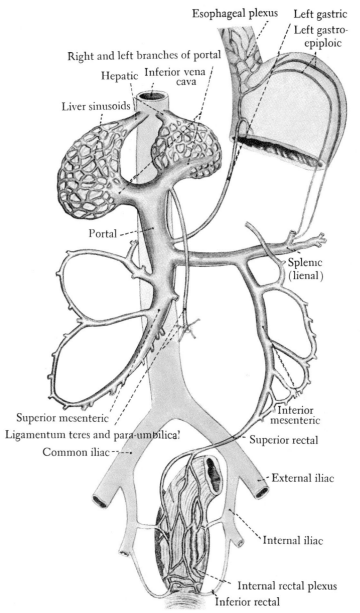

Esophageal plexus

Left gastric

Left gastro-epiploic

Right and left branches of portal

Hepatic

Inferior vena cava

Liver sinusoids

Portal

Splenic (lienal)

Interior mesenteric

Superior mesenteric

Ligamentum teres and para-umbilical

Superior rectal

Common iliac

External iliac

Internal iliac

Internal rectal plexus

Inferior rectal

Fig. 10-15. Portal circulation. (Reprinted with permission of St. Martin's Press and The Macmillan Company Ltd. from Hamilton, *Textbook of Human Anatomy*, 1956.)

posterior to the lateral malleolus, passes upward to the popliteal space (fossa) behind the knee, where it divides into two branches, one opening into the popliteal vein, the other into the deep femoral vein. It drains the lateral and dorsal portions of the foot and the posterior portion of the lower leg.

The principal *deep* veins of the leg are: (1) *Posterior tibial vein*, which arises behind the medial malleolus by a junction of the *medial* and *lateral plantar veins* of the foot. (2) *Anterior tibial vein*, arising as a continuation of the *vena comitantes* and the *dorsalis pedis* of the foot. (3) *Popliteal vein*, arising at the lower border of the popliteus muscles by a union of the posterior and anterior tibial veins. It passes upward through the popliteal fossa a short distance where, together with other femoral vessels, it passes through an aponeurotic opening in the adductor magnus muscle. At this point it becomes the femoral vein. It receives several small tributaries, including the *small saphenous vein*. (4) *Femoral vein* (a direct continuation of the popliteal vein), which continues through the proximal two-thirds of the thigh, lying close to the femoral artery. It receives the *great saphenous, deep femoral*, and *profunda femoris* veins. It passes under the inguinal ligament through the femoral ring, where it continues in the pelvic cavity as the *external iliac vein.*

THE PORTAL SYSTEM. The portal system includes the veins which receive blood from that portion of the alimentary canal lying in the abdominal cavity (with the exception of the lower part of the rectum), from the spleen, and from the gallbladder. Blood from these organs is conducted by the *portal vein* to the liver. In the liver the vein divides into two trunks which in turn subdivide into small capillary-like vessels called *sinusoids*. These sinusoids bring the blood into intimate contact with the liver cells. From the sinusoids, blood enters the *central veins* of the lobules of the liver, which, in turn, lead to *sublobular veins*. These unite into larger vessels and, finally empty into *hepatic veins*, which conduct blood to the inferior vena cava.

In the portal system, blood passes through two *capillary nets*: (1) the capillaries of the intestines, spleen, pancreas, and gallbladder, and (2) the sinusoids of the liver

The *branches* of the portal vein are: *superior mesenteric*, which drains blood from the small intestine, cecum, and ascending and transverse colon, passing upward under the head of the pancreas, where it unites with the *inferior mesenteric* and *splenic veins*, to form the portal vein; *splenic* (*lineal*) (drains the spleen, pancreas, and part of the stomach), *coronary* (drains the stomach and lower portion of the esophagus), *pyloric* (drains the pyloric region of the stomach), *cystic* (drains the gallbladder), and the *para-umbilical veins* (drain the body wall in the region of the umbilicus).

SYSTEMIC CIRCUITS

In the systemic circulation, blood leaves the heart through the aorta, passes through arteries to the capillaries of the tissues, then through veins to the venae cavae or the coronary sinus to re-enter the heart. Within this general pattern, however, the blood may follow any of several courses in completing the circuit. Among the principal possibilities are:

1. Circuit through the heart (coronary circuit).
2. Circuit through the upper extremity.
3. Circuit through the neck and head.
4. Circuit through the thorax.
5. Circuit through the digestive organs (including the liver).
6. Circuit through the pelvis and lower extremity.
7. Circuit through the kidneys (renal circuit).

1. *Circuit through the Heart (Coronary Circuit)*

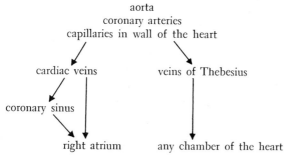

aorta
coronary arteries
capillaries in wall of the heart

cardiac veins   veins of Thebesius

coronary sinus

right atrium   any chamber of the heart

2. *Circuit through the Upper Extremity*

ascending aorta
arch of aorta
brachiocephalic (innominate) artery
subclavian artery
axillary artery
brachial artery
smaller arteries and arterioles
capillaries of the tissues
venules and smaller veins
basilic or cephalic vein
axillary vein
subclavian vein
brachiocephalic (innominate) vein
superior vena cava
right atrium

SYSTEMIC CIRCUITS (Cont.)

3. *Circuit through the Neck and Head*

ascending aorta
arch of aorta
brachiocephalic artery

subclavian artery   right common carotid artery

vertebral artery   internal carotid artery   external carotid artery

basilar artery

circle of Willis

small arteries and arterioles   small arteries and arterioles

to   to

capillaries of the cranial cavity   capillaries of external portions of the head

venous sinuses   external jugular vein

internal jugular vein   subclavian vein

brachiocephalic vein
superior vena cava
right atrium

4. *Circuit through the Thorax*

ascending aorta
arch of the aorta
thoracic aorta

bronchial artery   intercostal artery

small arteries and   small arteries and arterioles
arterioles within lung   of thoracic wall

capillaries of bronchi   capillaries of muscles,
                                      vertebrae and ribs

bronchial veins   intercostal veins
azygos or brachiocephalic vein   azygos or sup. intercostal veins
superior vena cava   superior vena cava
right atrium   right atrium

SYSTEMIC CIRCUITS (Cont.)

5. *Circuit through Digestive Organs, including Liver*

ascending aorta
aortic arch
thoracic aorta
abdominal aorta

celiac artery   superior mesenteric   inferior mesenteric
                              artery   artery

hepatic   splenic   left gastric
artery   artery   artery

through smaller arteries and
arterioles to capillaries of

liver   spleen   stomach   upper intestine   lower intestine
             pancreas

through smaller venules
and veins to

splenic   coronary   superior mesenteric   inferior mesenteric
vein   vein   vein   vein

portal vein

sinusoids of liver

small veins within liver

hepatic veins

inferior vena cava

right atrium

6. *Circuit through the Kidney (Renal Circuit)*

ascending aorta
aortic arch
thoracic aorta
abdominal aorta
renal artery
smaller arteries and arterioles within the kidney

SYSTEMIC CIRCUITS (Cont.)

6. Circuit through the Kidney (Cont.)

afferent artery to glomerulus
efferent artery from glomerulus
capillary plexus about renal tubules
venules and smaller veins within kidney
renal vein
inferior vena cava
right atrium

7. Circuit through the Lower Extremity

ascending aorta
aortic arch
thoracic aorta
abdominal aorta
common iliac artery

external iliac artery   hypogastric (internal iliac) artery

femoral artery

popliteal   posterior tibial
artery   artery

smaller arteries and arterioles   smaller arteries and arterioles

capillaries of the tissues   capillaries of the tissues

great and small   popliteal
saphenous veins   vein

femoral vein

external iliac vein   hypogastric (internal iliac) vein

common iliac vein
inferior vena cava
right atrium

The foregoing circuits describe the course normally followed by the blood. If, however, blood vessels become obstructed or are ligated, a *collateral circulation* may be established by means of anastomoses or interconnections between the vessels.

FETAL CIRCULATION

The human fetus lives under conditions radically different from those of postnatal life. Developing within the uterus of the mother, it secures its oxygen and food through an organ called the *placenta*. In the placenta the blood of the mother is brought into close contact with the fetal blood vessels, so that an interchange of substances can occur between fetal blood and maternal blood. Oxygen and nutritive substances are received by diffusion into the fetal blood, and waste products are given up. The fetus is connected to the placenta by the *umbilical cord*, which contains two *umbilical arteries* and one *umbilical vein*.

In the fetus the lungs and the digestive tract are nonfunctional; consequently, their blood supply is limited. The lungs are collapsed and little blood goes to them because of an arrangement whereby most of the blood by-passes the lungs. This consists of (1) an opening, the *foramen ovale* in the interatrial septum of the heart, by which the blood in the right atrium can pass directly to the left atrium, and (2) a vessel, the *ductus arteriosus*, which connects the pulmonary artery directly with the aorta.

The fetal heart begins to beat early in fetal life (about the fourth week). Blood circulates through the fetus in much the same manner as in the adult, with the exception of structures mentioned in the preceding paragraph and the placental circulation. Blood reaches the placenta through the *umbilical arteries* which are branches of the *hypogastric* or *internal iliac arteries*. In the placenta, blood passes through the capillaries of the villi, then returns to the fetus by way of the *umbilical vein*, which enters the fetus at the umbilicus. Most of the blood passes directly to the inferior vena cava by way of the *ductus venosus*; the remainder passes indirectly by way of the liver through the sinusoids and the hepatic veins.

Changes in Circulation at Birth. At birth, with the first inspiration the lungs become expanded and begin functioning. Placental circulation ceases, and the connection with the placenta is severed by the cutting of the umbilical cord. Correlated with these major changes, the following circulatory changes take place:

1. The ductus arteriosus closes, its closure being brought about by the contraction of the smooth muscles in its wall and the gradual growth of tissue of the intima. Its complete occlusion occurs normally about six to eight weeks after birth, after which it persists as a fibrous cord, the *ligamentum arteriosum*.

2. The foramen ovale closes, its position being indicated later by a depression, the *fossa ovalis*, located on the interatrial septum.

3. The umbilical vein atrophies and becomes a fibrous cord which

persists as the round ligament of the liver, namely, the *ligamentum teres*.

4. The ductus venosus atrophies and is transformed into the fibrous *ligamentum venosum*, which is superficially embedded in the wall of the liver.

5. The umbilical arteries atrophy and become the *lateral umbilical ligaments*, two fibrous cords from the bladder to the umbilicus.

These changes usually take place gradually, sometimes requiring several days (5 to 10) or even a few months for completion. Occasionally, the obliteration of an embryonic structure may not be completed for years, or it may not occur at all. For example, the foramen ovale may fail to close. This is not of physiological significance, for the existence of a valve-like structure prevents back flow of blood into the right atrium. However, if the ductus arteriosus fails to close, a circulatory imbalance results, and this causes unoxygenated blood to pass through the foramen ovale from the right to the left atrium. In such cases, the major portion of the blood fails to pass through the lungs, proper oxygenation fails to occur, and the infant becomes cyanotic, the so-called "blue baby." A similar result may occur from incomplete development of the interventricular septum.

THE LYMPHATIC SYSTEM

The lymphatic system is that part of the circulatory system which conveys lymph from its source, the body tissues, to the point where it re-enters the blood stream. The structures of the lymphatic system are of two kinds: those which are concerned with the conduction of lymph, and those which are composed principally of lymphatic tissue but serve another specific function. The former comprise lymph capillaries, lymph vessels, and lymph ducts. The latter include the lymph nodes, spleen, tonsils, and thymus, collectively called lymph organs.

Circulation of Lymph. As already stated, the chief function of the lymphatic system is to return to the blood stream the fluid which has been filtered out of the blood capillaries. This fluid is the *tissue fluid*, which carries to the tissues the materials which the tissue cells utilize, and to which the cells give up waste products. When this fluid enters the lymph capillaries, it is referred to as *lymph*. The lymph passes through the lymph vessels and the main lymph ducts to re-enter the blood stream.

The lymphatic system has no pumping mechanism, as exists in the blood-vascular system. The flow of lymph is brought about by the following factors:

1. Difference in pressure between (a) lymph vessels originating in the tissues and (b) venous pressure at points where the main thoracic ducts empty into the subclavian veins. The pressure at the capillary

end of lymph vessels is higher than that at the venous end. Valves at the openings of the main lymphatic ducts prevent blood from entering the lymph system.

2. Pressure resulting from the continuous formation of lymph, which is the result of effective filtration pressure (the difference between hydrostatic pressure and osmotic pressure in the capillaries). This forces tissue fluid onward to the lymphatic capillaries. As lymph originates from tissue fluid, which comes from blood, pressure within the capillaries is partly responsible for lymph pressure. Accordingly, the heart beat is the prime, though indirect, cause of the movement of lymph.

3. Intestinal movements (movements of the villi and peristaltic contractions). Each villus contains smooth muscle fibers which by contraction force chyle from the lacteals into the lymphatic vessels. *Chyle* is the material filling the lymphatic vessels of the intestines; it consists of lymph and absorbed food products.

4. Rhythmical, peristaltic contraction of smooth muscles fibers in segments of lymph vessels between valves.

5. Muscular activity. Contraction or passive massage of skeletal muscles tends to propel the lymph onward in the lymphatic vessels. Lymph vessels lying between muscles are compressed, and the lymph is forced onward. Back flow is prevented by the presence of valves in the larger vessels.

6. Respiratory movements. Expansion of the lungs upon inspiration exerts a pressure on lymph in the main thoracic ducts, forcing lymph onward in these vessels. It also increases negative intrathoracic pressure which produces an aspiratory effect acting to suck lymph from the smaller lymph vessels into the larger vessels. Descent of the diaphragm also compresses the abdominal contents, exerting a pressure on all abdominal vassels; this causes lymph to flow into the main thoracic duct from the abdominal lymphatics.

Lymphatic Vessels. The vessels conducting lymph include lymph capillaries, lymph vessels, and the main lymph ducts.

Lymph Capillaries. The lymph capillaries lie in the connective tissue spaces of most organs and tissues. They are thin-walled vessels, usually slightly larger in diameter than the blood capillaries. Lymph capillaries originate as blind tubes, are extensively branched, and anastomose freely. Their diameter is not uniform, as is that of blood capillaries; they tend to be constricted at some points and dilated at others. Lymph capillaries are located among blood capillaries but are independent of them. They are extremely numerous in tissues underlying surface membranes, such as the skin and the mucous membranes of the respiratory and digestive tracts, less numerous in organs such as muscles. They are entirely absent in deeply located tissues, such as

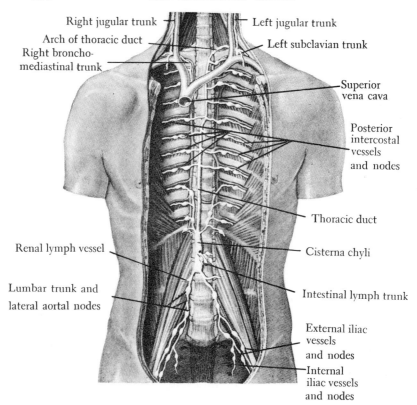

Right jugular trunk

Left jugular trunk

Arch of thoracic duct

Left subclavian trunk

Right broncho-
mediastinal trunk

Superior
vena cava

Posterior
intercostal
vessels
and nodes

Thoracic duct

Renal lymph vessel

Cisterna chyli

Lumbar trunk and
lateral aortal nodes

Intestinal lymph trunk

External iliac
vessels
and nodes

Internal
iliac vessels
and nodes

Fig. 10-16. Thoracic duct. (Reprinted with permission of St. Martin's Press and The Macmillan Company Ltd. from Hamilton, *Textbook of Human Anatomy*, 1956.)

those of the central nervous system and the bone marrow. The wall of a lymph capillary consists of a single layer of endothelial cells. Lymph capillaries in the villi of the intestines are called *lacteals*.

LYMPH VESSELS. Lymph vessels are larger vessels which collect lymph from capillaries. Their walls are thin and transparent; lymph can ordinarily be seen within them. They tend to lie in the subcutaneous or the connective tissue. The principal lymph vessels follow the course of arteries and veins. They form two sets of vessels: a superficial set and a deep set. The *superficial* lymph vessels lie near the surface and in general follow the course of the superficial veins; the *deep vessels* are more remote from the surface, being found deeply located in the extremities, under the mucous membranes of the digestive, respiratory, and urogenital systems, and directly beneath the serous membranes of the thoracic and abdominal cavities. The deep lymph vessels in general follow the course of the deep veins. They are more numerous than the veins, they anastomose freely, and their trunks tend to remain uniform in diameter.

Most lymph vessels have *valves*. These occur in pairs and are placed with their free edges toward the direction of the flow of the lymph. The vessels tend to become distended just above each valve, so that they present a "beaded" appearance. By contraction, smooth muscle fibers in the distended portions aid in the flow of lymph.

MAIN LYMPH DUCTS. The main lymph ducts include the *thoracic duct* and the *right lymphatic duct*.

The *thoracic duct* is the principal lymph duct, conveying lymph from all parts of the body except the right side of the head, neck, and thorax and the right upper extremity. It arises in the abdomen at a dilated portion (the *cisterna chyli*) which lies to the right of the aorta, just anterior to the body of the second lumbar vertebra. This cisterna receives lymph from the vessels draining the lower limbs, the pelvic region, and the abdominal organs. The thoracic duct passes upward through the diaphragm into the thorax, continuing alongside the aorta and the esophagus. It passes posterior to the innominate vein and enters the neck, where it turns to the left and enters the *left subclavian vein* near its junction with the left internal jugular vein. Just before its termination, the thoracic duct receives the principal lymph vessels from the left side of the head, the left upper extremity, and the left side of the thorax.

The *right lymphatic duct*, a short duct, empties into the *right subclavian vein* at its junction with the right internal jugular vein. It receives lymph from the right side of the head, the right upper extremity, and the right side of the thorax.

Lymph Nodes. Lymph nodes are small ovoid or bean-shaped bodies found at intervals in the course of the lymphatic vessels. Each node consists of a mass of lymphatic tissue enclosed in a fibrous connective tissue *capsule*. On one side of the node is a depression, the *hilus*, at which point blood vessels enter and leave and efferent lymph vessels make their exit. Extending inward from the capsule are septa or *trabeculae* which divide the node into compartments. The outer compact region of the node constitutes the *cortex*; the inner more diffuse portion, the *medulla*. In the cortical region can be seen masses of densely packed cells consisting mostly of lymphocytes. These are the *cortical* or *primary lymph nodules*. In the center of each nodule is a lighter staining area called *germinal center*. In these areas lymphocytes are formed. The tissue of the *medulla* is similar to the tissues in the cortex except that the lymphocytes are not arranged in the form of nodules but form anastomosing *lymph cords*, and the trabeculae anastomose, frequently forming a meshwork.

Vessels entering a lymph node are called *afferent vessels*. These penetrate the capsule and empty into the *peripheral* or *marginal sinus*, a space lying between the capsule and the cortical nodules. From this sinus the lymph flows centrally past the nodules into the sinuses of the medulla and from here to the *efferent vessels* which leave the node. Lymph may pass through several nodes before it enters the main lymph vessels.

In passing through the lymph nodes, the lymph (1) receives lymphocytes, which are produced in the germinal centers of the nodes, and (2) is subjected to a filtering action in which particulate substances, such as bacteria, carbon particles, and vital dyes are removed from the lymph through the phagocytic action of leucocytes.

Lymph nodes tend to occur in groups in various regions of the body. In these regions, lymphatic vessels from the peripheral portions of the body converge. The lymph enters the nodes through afferent vessels, traverses the nodes, and leaves through efferent vessels which carry the lymph onward to other nodes or to larger lymphatic vessels. For this reason, the lymph nodes are referred to as *regional nodes*.

LYMPH NODES OF THE HEAD, FACE, AND NECK. In the *head and face* are several groups of lymph nodes, each consisting of varying numbers of nodes. Their names indicate the general position of the groups: occipital, posterior auricular, anterior auricular, parotid, facial, deep facial, lingual, and retropharyngeal. In the *neck* are the submaxillary, submental, superficial cervical, anterior cervical, and deep cervical groups. The *deep cervical group* contains large nodes which form a chain along the carotid artery alongside the pharynx, trachea, and esophagus. Efferent lymph vessels from this group unite to form the *jugular trunks*, which empty into the main lymph ducts.

LYMPH NODES OF THE UPPER EXTREMITY. These are concentrated mainly in the *axillary* group, which is located in the region of the armpit. This group includes 20 to 30 large nodes through which passes lymph from the afferent vessels of the arm, the thoracic wall, and the mammary gland. Efferent vessels lead to the *subclavian trunks*, which empty into the main lymph ducts.

LYMPH NODES OF THE LOWER EXTREMITY. These are concentrated mainly in the *inguinal group*. This group includes 12 to 20 large nodes which receive afferent vessels from the lower limbs, external genitalia, buttocks, and lower portion of the abdominal wall. Efferent vessels lead to the external iliac nodes.

LYMPH NODES OF THE ABDOMEN AND PELVIS. There are two groups of lymph nodes in the abdominal and pelvic regions: (1) the parietal and (2) the visceral.

1. The *parietal groups*, which lie beneath the peritoneum close to the aorta, include: (*a*) *External iliac nodes*, numbering 8 to 10, lying

along the external iliac artery. They receive vessels from the inguinal nodes, the lower portion of the abdominal wall, the inner portion of the thigh, and the reproductive and excretory organs. (*b*) *Hypogastric* (*internal*) *iliac nodes*, lying along the hypogastric vessels. They receive vessels from the pelvic organs, the perineum, the external genitalia, the buttocks, and the posterior portion of the thigh. (*c*) *Common iliac nodes*, four to six nodes which lie along the common iliac artery. They receive vessels from the hypogastric and external iliac

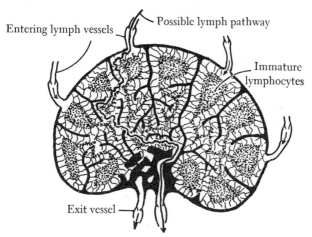

Fig. 10-17. Lymph node, with vessels. (Reprinted with permission of the University of Chicago Press from Carlson and Johnson, *The Machinery of the Body*, 4th, 1953.)

nodes. (*d*) *Epigastric nodes*, lying along the inferior epigastric vessels. (*e*) *Iliac circumflex nodes*, a small group lying along the deep iliac circumflex vessels. (*f*) *Lumbar nodes*, a large group of nodes lying in a chain-like position along the lower portions of the aorta and the inferior vena cava. They include three paired groups; the *lateral aortic*, *preaortic*, and *retroaortic nodes*. These receive afferent vessels from the abdominal and pelvic viscera, from the lower lymph nodes, and from the abdominal wall. Their afferent vessels empty into the *intestinal* and *lumber trunks*, which empty into the *cisterna chyli*.

2. The *visceral groups* lie along the arteries supplying the visceral organs. They include: (*a*) *Inferior gastric nodes*, which lie along the greater curvature of the stomach in the pyloric region. (*b*) *Hepatic nodes*, which lie along the hepatic and gastric arteries. They drain the liver, gallbladder, and portions of the stomach, duodenum, and pancreas. The hepatic nodes empty into the preaortic nodes. (*c*) *Pancreaticolienal nodes*, a group lying along the splenic artery on the superior surface of the pancreas. They drain the stomach, spleen, and

pancreas, and empty into the preaortic nodes. (*d*) *Superior mesenteric nodes*, from 100 to 150 in number, consisting of three groups: *mesenteric, ileocolic,* and *mesocolic nodes.* The afferents drain the jejunum, ileum, cecum, and vermiform process, and the ascending and transverse colon. The efferents lead to the preaortic nodes. (*e*) *Inferior mesenteric nodes,* groups of nodes which lie along the branches of the inferior mesenteric artery. Their afferents drain the lower portions of the alimentary canal; their efferents lead to the *preaortic nodes.*

The afferent lymph vessels of the mesenteric nodes have their origin in the alimentary canal and play an important role in the absorption of food. Large quantities of fats are absorbed by the lymph; consequently, the contents of the lymph vessels, called *chyle,* have a milk-like appearance, and the course of these vessels can be followed readily, especially after a meal that is rich in fats. The mesenteric nodes constitute the largest group of lymph nodes in the body. Their efferents lead to the preaortic nodes and through them to the *intestinal trunks,* which empty into the *cisterna chyli* at the lower end of the thoracic duct.

LYMPH NODES OF THE THORAX. The lymph nodes of the thorax, like those of the abdomen and pelvis, consist of (1) parietal and (2) visceral groups.

1. The *parietal groups,* lying along the inner surface of the thoracic wall, include: (*a*) *Sternal nodes,* lying in the intercostal spaces near the sternum. They receive afferent vessels from the mammary glands and the anterior abdominal wall. Efferent vessels empty into the *bronchomediastinal trunk,* which may open either directly into the blood stream at the junction of the internal jugular and subclavian veins or into the main lymphatic ducts. (*b*) *Intercostal nodes,* lying in the intercostal spaces just lateral to the vertebral column. They receive afferent vessels from the posterior and lateral portions of the thorax. The efferents from the lower nodes lead into a vessel which empties into the *cisterna chyli;* those from the upper nodes empty into the *main lymphatic ducts.* (*c*) *Diaphragmatic nodes,* lying on the superior surface of the diaphragm. They receive afferents from the diaphragm and the upper abdominal organs. Efferents pass to the *sternal* or *mediastinal nodes.*

2. The *visceral groups,* lying close to the thoracic viscera, include: (*a*) *Mediastinal nodes,* consisting of two groups: the anterior and the posterior. They drain the thymus, pericardium, esophagus, and diaphragm, and the upper surface of the liver. Some efferent vessels lead to the *bronchiomediastinal trunks,* others to the *thoracic duct* and to the *tracheobronchial nodes.* (*b*) *Tracheobronchial nodes,* consisting of four groups: tracheal, bronchial, bronchiopulmonary, and pulmo-

nary. They lie alongside the trachea and the bronchi and receive afferents from these structures as well as from the lungs and the heart. Their efferent vessels may lead to the *brochiomediastinal trunks,* which join the main lymphatic vessels, or they may open directly into the junction of the internal jugular and subclavian veins.

LYMPHATIC ORGANS

Lymphatic organs are those structures which are composed principally of *lymphoid (lymphatic) tissue.* They include the *lymph nodes* (previously described), *spleen, tonsils,* and *thymus gland.*

Lymphatic Tissue. Lymphoid or lymphatic tissue is not one of the primary tissues of the body but is rather a specialized form of connective tissue consisting of a supporting framework or *stroma* made up of a network of *reticular fibers* and *reticular cells.* The fibers when treated by silver impregnation methods stain selectively and hence are called *argyrophil fibers.* The cells of the stroma include *primitive reticular cells* and *phagocytic reticular cells* (macrophages). The former comprise a syncytial network in which the reticular fibers are embedded; the latter have the ability to engulf foreign particles and store vital dyes.

In the meshes of the reticulum forming the stroma are large numbers of *free cells* which consist largely of lymphocytes of varying sizes.

In some parts of the body, as in the respiratory and digestive tracts, the lymphatic tissue is not sharply delimited from the surrounding connective tissue. Such tissue is called *diffuse lymphatic tissue.* Generally, the tissue forms a more or less spherical mass of densely packed lymphocytes which constitutes a *lymph nodule,* the structural unit of lymphatic tissue. The nodules either exist as solitary or individual nodules, as in the digestive tract, or they are aggregated into groups which may be (*a*) nonencapsulated, as in Peyer's patches of the intestine, (*b*) partially encapsulated, as in the tonsil, or (*c*) encapsulated, as in the lymph nodes, spleen, or thymus.

Lymph Nodes. The structure and function of lymph nodes have been discussed on page 265.

The Spleen. The spleen is the largest lymphatic organ of the body. It is an elongated, dark red, ovoid body located beneath the diaphragm on the left side of the body, inferior and posterior to the stomach. It averages about 12 cm. in length, 8 cm. in width, and 4 cm. in thickness, and about 200 gm. in weight. Both the size and the weight are extremely variable.

SURFACES AND ATTACHMENT OF THE SPLEEN. The spleen exhibits four surfaces: basal, phrenic, renal, and gastric. The gastric surface, which adjoins the stomach, contains the *hilus,* through which blood vessels enter and leave. The spleen is invested by a layer of peritoneum which is continuous with the abdominal peritoneum at the hilus, its only point of attachment. The spleen moves freely with movements of the surrounding viscera.

SPLENIC PULP. The spaces between the trabeculae and connective tissue septa are filled with splenic pulp, a soft sponge-like substance consisting of lymphatic tissue. Strands of this tissue form the *pulp cords*. Pulp infiltrated with red blood cells constitutes the *red pulp* of the spleen; the *white pulp* consists of the more compact lymphatic tissue. At some points the white pulp is concentrated about arteries, forming spherical structures called *Malpighian bodies* or *splenic corpuscles*. These are similar to the nodules of lymph nodes, except that they contain within their substance a blood vessel, the *central artery*. In adults they may lack germinal centers.

BLOOD VESSELS IN THE SPLEEN. Blood enters the spleen at the hilus through branches of the *splenic artery*, branches of which follow the trabeculae as *trabecular arteries*. Branches of these enter the pulp, and along their course nodules of white pulp are found, in which is located the central artery. Finally, the arteries divide into a number of straight branches, forming a brush-like *penicillus*. Blood then enters the *venous sinuses*, which form an anastomosing plexus throughout the red pulp. The sinuses are lined with cells belonging to the reticulo-endothelial system which show marked phagocytic activity. From the sinuses, blood passes successively through *pulp veins*, *trabecular veins*, and *splenic veins*, which emerge from the hilus.

The nature of the terminal connections between arteries and veins in the spleen has not been definitely established. Some investigators hold that the terminal arteries open into the intercellular spaces of the red pulp ("open circulation"); others believe that the capillaries open into the venous sinuses ("closed circulation").

FUNCTIONS OF THE SPLEEN. The spleen performs several functions, all of them concerned with the blood.

1. *Blood Formation*. In fetal life and for a short time after birth, the spleen forms all types of blood cells. In the adult, it produces only lymphocytes and monocytes (mononuclear leucocytes).

2. *Blood Storage*. The presence of an elastic tissue framework and smooth muscle cells enables the spleen to undergo marked and rapid changes in volume. Splenic contractions which occur under nervous or hormonal stimulation expel erythrocytes and increase the number of circulating red blood cells. The size of the spleen is much reduced during exercise and following hemorrhage or oxygen lack.

3. *Filtration*. Foreign substances such as bacteria and worn-out red blood cells, both whole and fragmented, are destroyed and removed from the circulation by the action of the phagocytic cells of the spleen.

4. *Iron Storage.* Iron is recovered from broken-down hemoglobin and temporarily stored to be subsequently used in the formation of new hemoglobin.

5. *Bilirubin Production.* Bilirubin, one of the bile pigments, is formed from hemoglobin freed from red blood cells broken down by the reticulo-endothelial cells of the spleen.

6. *Antibody Formation and Immunogenic Action.* The spleen is a source of antibodies and plays an important role in the resistance of the body to bacterial and parasitic infections.

The spleen is not essential to life, for its functions, upon its removal, are taken over by other organs of the reticuloendothelial system, especially the bone marrow. One effect of removal is greater susceptibility to infectious diseases. Enlargement of the spleen occurs in a number of pathologic conditions, such as malaria, certain forms of anemia, and leukemia.

The Tonsils. These structures are masses of lymphoid tissue located in the walls of the pharynx. There are three pairs: *palatine tonsils*, in the oropharynx between the glossopalatine and pharyngopalatine arches; *pharyngeal tonsils*, in the median dorsal wall of the nasopharynx between the openings of the Eustachian tubes; and *lingual tonsils*, on the dorsum and sides of the posterior portion of the tongue.

STRUCTURE OF THE TONSILS. Each tonsil is a dense mass of lymphoid tissue lying in the connective tissue under the mucosa. Its free surface is covered by stratified squamous epithelium which is continuous with that of the pharynx. At many points on the surface there are deep indentations, or *crypts*, lined with stratified squamous epithelium. Bordering each crypt is a layer of lymphoid tissue in which are present numerous *nodules* of compact tissue which resemble in structure those of the lymph nodes.

Surrounding the tonsil on the basal side is a *capsule* of connective tissue from which fibers extend as *septa* separating the crypts, with their lymphoid tissue, from each other. The epithelium of the crypts is frequently infiltrated by masses of lymphocytes. Mucous glands of the pharynx are numerous about tonsils, and occasionally their ducts open into the crypts. Tonsils lack afferent lymphatic vessels, but lymph capillaries are present which constitute the beginnings of efferent lymph vessels leaving the tonsils.

FUNCTION OF THE TONSILS. The only known function of the tonsils is the formation of lymphocytes. This occurs in the germinal centers of the nodules. It has been thought that the tonsillar tissue, being strategically placed, serves to protect the body against invading microorganisms, but this has not been adequately demonstrated. Indeed, the reverse seems to be the case. The tonsillar crypts often provide lodging places for invading organisms, and their imperfect epithelium consti-

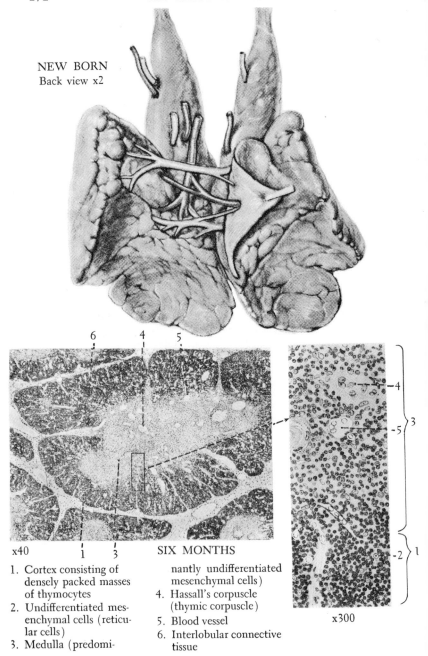

NEW BORN
Back view x2

x40

SIX MONTHS

x300

1. Cortex consisting of densely packed masses of thymocytes
2. Undifferentiated mesenchymal cells (reticular cells)
3. Medulla (predominantly undifferentiated mesenchymal cells)
4. Hassall's corpuscle (thymic corpuscle)
5. Blood vessel
6. Interlobular connective tissue

Fig. 10-18. Thymus. (From *Atlas of Human Anatomy*, Barnes & Noble, Inc., 1956.)

tutes a portal of entry inviting local or general infections. This has given rise to the "focal infection" theory which many believe has been overstressed, resulting in unnecessary tonsilectomies. Hypertrophy of the tonsils, however, is common in childhood and may necessitate their removal. Hypertrophy of the pharyngeal tonsils is commonly referred to as "adenoids." Adenoid tissue may obstruct the nasal passageways (and thus give rise to mouth breathing) or the Eustachian tubes (and thus cause ear disorders).

The Thymus. The thymus is a lymphoid organ located in the mediastinal cavity just anterior to and above the heart. Following birth, it grows rapidly until the second year; thereafter, growth is slow until the age of puberty, when it begins to undergo involution. In this process it decreases in size, the thymic tissue being replaced by adipose and connective tissue.

STRUCTURE OF THE THYMUS. The thymus consists of two flattened symmetrical lobes closely applied to each other, each of which is enclosed in a capsule. From the connective tissue of the capsule, trabeculae divide each lobe into many lobules, each consisting of a cortex and a medulla.

The *cortex* is composed of dense lymphoid tissue containing many cells (*thymocytes*) packed in a reticular framework. These cells resemble small lymphocytes in structure. The *medulla* also contains thymocytes, but they are less densely packed. The medulla has, in addition, ovoid bodies called *thymic corpuscles* (*Hassall's corpuscles*), each of which consists of concentrically arranged cells enclosing a clear hyalinized area of degenerated cells. These bodies are characteristic of the thymus. The thymus lacks germinal centers. There are no lymph sinuses or afferent lymph vessels.

FUNCTIONS OF THE THYMUS. The only known function of the thymus is the production of lymphocytes. It has been assigned an endocrine function, but the experimental evidence of this is inconclusive. There are, however, interrelationships between the thymus and certain endocrine glands, especially the gonads, adrenals, and thyroid. If the gonads are removed, involution of the thymus is delayed; if the thyroid is removed, thymic involution is accelerated. Removal of the adrenals delays involution and may even bring on some thymic regeneration. The removal of the thymus produces no significant effects.

11: THE PHYSIOLOGY OF CIRCULATION

Transportation of the principal body fluids from one part of the body to another is the main function of the circulatory system. These fluids are the media through which gases, hormones, and a vast number of chemical substances (including nutrient material and metabolites) are carried through the body.

BLOOD PRESSURE

Blood, which is contained within a closed series of tubes, flows (*circulates*) because of inequalities of pressure in different parts of the circulatory system. The pressure which blood exerts within the blood vessels is called the *blood pressure*. This pressure depends mainly upon: (1) the work of the heart, (2) peripheral resistance, (3) elasticity of the arterial walls, and (4) blood volume and viscosity.

Blood pressure is highest in the elastic arteries which are nearest to the heart; it is lower in the muscular arteries which are nearer to the periphery. As the blood passes successively through the smaller arteries, arterioles, capillaries, venules, and larger veins, its pressure becomes lower and lower until, in the vena cava, it is zero or slightly less (a "negative" pressure). This variation in blood pressure is the *pressure gradient*.

THE WORK OF THE HEART

The heart is a muscular pump which, by rhythmic contractions, keeps the blood circulating throughout the pulmonary and systemic circulatory vessels.

Properties of Cardiac Muscle. Cardiac muscle, like skeletal muscle, is striated, but the striations are less pronounced. The fibers lack a sarcolemma, and they possess branches by which the protoplasm of adjacent cells forms a continuous mass. Consequently, the heart muscle is a *syncytium*, that is, a large, multinucleated mass of protoplasm acting as a unit instead of being a composite of cells each of which contracts individually.

Cardiac muscle responds to the usual types of stimuli, namely: thermal, electrical, chemical, and mechanical. It possesses properties characteristic of all muscle tissue: *irritability*, *conductivity*, *extensibility*, and *elasticity*. In addition, it possesses *automaticity* and *rhythmicity*.

AUTOMATICITY. This inherent property of cardiac muscle is not only characteristic of the heart as a whole; it can be exhibited in a small portion cut from the organ. The heart of a cold-blooded animal can be removed from the body and, if kept moist by physiological salt solution, will continue to contract spontaneously (and rhythmically) for a considerable time. In the embryo the heart begins to contract even before nerve connections are established. Heart cells grown in tissue culture exhibit automatic rhythmical contractions.

RHYTHMICITY. Heart beats occur regularly, rhythmically. If a beating heart is stimulated artificially by a series of electric shocks, the rhythm may be altered (slowed down, speeded up, or made irregular), but the muscle will not go into a state of sustained contraction, as does skeletal muscle. Neither summation nor tetanus occurs in cardiac muscle.

Systole and *Diastole*. The ability of the heart to function as a pump depends on alternate contraction and relaxation. The contraction phase is known as *systole*, the relaxation phase as *diastole*. When the terms diastole and systole are used alone, they apply to the ventricle. They may, however, be specified, as: atrial systole, ventricular systole, atrial diastole, and ventricular diastole.

Electrolyte Balance. The rhythmic contraction and relaxation of the heart are dependent upon maintenance of a proper balance of calcium, sodium, and potassium ions in the blood and tissue fluids. The effects of electrolyte imbalance are: (1) *Calcium excess.* The heart stops in systole (a condition known as *calcium rigor*). (2) *Sodium excess.* The heart becomes progressively weaker, and finally stops in diastole. (3) *Potassium excess.* The heart becomes weaker, finally stopping in diastole (*potassium inhibition*).

REFRACTORY PERIOD. Cardiac muscle, if stimulated while contracting, will not respond to the stimulus. This period during which cardiac muscle is not amenable to stimulation is called the *absolute refractory period*. During relaxation, stimulation produces a response, but the reaction is below normal; consequently, this is called the *relative refractory period*. Stimulation of heart muscle can produce its full effects only when the period of relaxation is complete. Contraction results in loss of excitability (irritability), which can be restored only during the period of relaxation.

The refractory period for cardiac muscle has a duration about 66 times that of skeletal muscle. In a heart that is beating at a normal rate (70 times per minute) the refractory period lasts 0.3 second.

EXTRASYSTOLE (PREMATURE BEAT). If, when the heart is beating normally, a stimulus is applied during or at the end of a diastole, a response (contraction) will occur before the next regular contraction is due. This is called *extrasystole* or *premature beat*. Such a premature

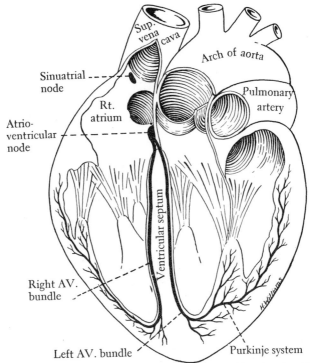

Fig. 11-1. Impulse conducting system of heart. (Reprinted with permission of C. V. Mosby Company and the author from Francis, *Introduction to Human Anatomy*, 2nd ed., 1954.)

beat is followed by a much longer diastole than is usual, an interval known as *compensatory pause*. Because the systole is usually weak and unnoticed, it seems as though the heart has "missed a beat." Extrasystoles may occur in the normal heart as the result of some abnormal stimulus, and are observed in certain pathologic conditions.

THE ALL-OR-NONE LAW. This principle holds true for a single striated muscle fiber or a single nerve fiber, but not for muscles consisting of numerous individual fibers. In the heart, it applies to the organ *as a whole*, for cardiac muscle consists of branching fibers that are all interconnected. Accordingly, if the heart contracts at all, it contracts to its fullest extent. But this does not necessarily mean that all its contractions are of equal strength. Several factors (among them fatigue, effects of drugs, and degree of stretch) may alter the extent to which the heart muscle is capable of responding. It does mean that under a given set of conditions, an increase in the strength of a stimulus will fail to increase the force of contraction.

The Origin of the Heart Beat. The impulse-conducting system of the heart consists of atypical muscle fibers (the Purkinje fibers) and includes the following:

SINUATRIAL NODE. The S–A node is located in the wall of the right atrium near the entrance of the superior vena cava. From this node, fibers extend throughout the walls of the atria.

ATRIOVENTRICULAR NODE. The A–V node is located in the lower part of the interatrial septum. From this node arises the atrioventricular bundle (bundle of His) which passes downward in the interventricular septum. After descending a short distance, this bundle divides into two trunks which branch repeatedly, sending fibers throughout the myocardium of the two ventricles.

The impulse that initiates the heart beat arises in the *sinuatrial node,* which as a consequence is called the *pacemaker* of the heart. Heating or cooling of this node speeds up the heart beat or slows it down, respectively. From the S–A node an *excitation wave* spreads throughout the musculature of the atria and to the atrioventricular node. The atria contract; at the same instant, the impulse is conducted through the A–V node and the *bundle of His* and its branches to the ventricles, and the ventricles contract. The delay in passage of the impulse through the A–V node gives the atria time to complete their systole before the ventricular systole begins. As a result, the two atria contract slightly ahead of the ventricles.

An interruption in the passage of the excitation wave through the conductile tissue of the A–V node is called *heart block.* Its consequence is lack of coordinated activity between the parts of the heart, the atria beating normally while the ventricles fail to beat in their normal sequence. When the interruption is in one of the branches leading from the A–V node, the condition is called *partial block* or *intraventricular block;* this is seen in infections (e.g., rheumatic fever) and other pathologic conditions.

The Cardiac Cycle. The cardiac cycle includes the complete sequence of events occurring during a single heart beat. The cycle in the human being, when the heart is beating at the normal rate of 70 times per minute, has a duration of 0.86 second. It is shorter when the heart beat rate is faster, longer when it is slower.

A number of methods have been employed to establish the events of the cardiac cycle:

1. Gross observations of changes occurring in the heart.
2. Successive photographs or motion pictures of an exposed heart.
3. Graphic records obtained by (*a*) measuring and recording pressure changes within the cardiac chambers, (*b*) recording volume changes by means of a *cardiometer,* (*c*) recording the movements of threads that have been attached to the walls of the atria and the ven-

tricles, (d) recording electrical variations by means of an *electrocardiograph*, and (e) recording sound vibrations transmitted from the heart to the chest wall with a *phonocardiograph*.

The time consumed in each of the phases of a single heart beat when the rate is approximately 70 beats per minute has been demonstrated to be:

Atrial systole	0.1 sec.	} 0.862 sec.
Atrial diastole	0.762 sec.	
Ventricular systole	0.379 sec.	} 0.862 sec.
Ventricular diastole	0.483 sec.	

It is seen, then, that both the atrial and the ventricular diastolic times are longer than the systolic. This allows a short interval for rest, *the only rest period available to the heart*, which never stops beating (except for these very short intervals) from the time when contractions begin in the embryo (at about the fourth week of development) until death. In the human being who has passed his or her seventieth year, the heart has produced *more than two and one-half billion beats*. The basic factors involved in death are, of course, the cessation of heart beat and consequent stoppage of circulation.

The Action of Cardiac Valves. The cardiac valves and their locations are: (1) *right atrioventricular* or *tricuspid valve*, between the right atrium and right ventricle; (2) *left atrioventricular, bicuspid*, or *mitral valve*, between the left atrium and ventricle; (3) *pulmonary semilunar valves*, at the orifice of the pulmonary artery from the right ventricle; and (4) *aortic semilunar valves*, at the orifice of the aorta from the left ventricle.

The *events of the cardiac cycle* (and the action of the valves that accompany them) are as follows:

While blood is entering the two atria, both atrioventricular valves are closed. The pressure in the atria rises until it exceeds the pressure in the relaxed ventricles, whereupon the atrioventricular valves open and blood flows to the ventricles; the valve leaflets float freely in the blood stream. Then atrial systole occurs, forcing *all* blood out of the atria into the ventricles. The ventricles begin their systolic contraction. As pressure rises in the ventricles, the force of the blood against the atrioventricular valves causes their closure. Ventricular systole continues until intraventricular pressure forces the blood past the semilunar valves, causing them to open. Thus the ventricle is emptied of blood, which enters the pulmonary artery and the aorta. Ventricular diastole begins, and the intraventricular pressure drops rapidly. As soon as it is below the pressure in the pulmonary artery and the aorta, whose elastic walls have been distended, the blood tends to flow back

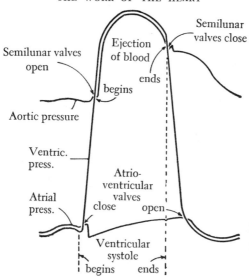

Fig. 11-2. Pressure changes and valve action showing sequence in which the heart valves open and close in single cardiac cycle as pressure in ventricles rises in systole and falls in diastole. (Reprinted with permission of the University of Chicago Press from Carlson and Johnson, *The Machinery of the Body*, 4th ed., 1953.)

into the ventricles. Back flow, however, is prevented by closure of the semilunar valves. Meanwhile, the atria are filling with blood and the ventricular diastole is being concluded. The cardiac cycle is now complete, and a new cycle is about to commence.

The primary function of the valves is to keep the blood flowing *in one direction*.

Heart Sounds. Through a stethoscope applied to the chest, two sounds produced by a beating heart can be heard distinctly. These, occurring close together, are described as "lubb-dupp"—the "lubb" being softer, longer, and lower in pitch. The first sound is caused by closure of the atrioventricular valves and contraction of the ventricular muscle; the second, by closure of the pulmonary and aortic semilunar valves. In some individuals, a third sound can be heard immediately after the second. It is thought to be due to vibrations of the ventricular wall resulting from the sudden entrance of blood from the atria.

Diseased or Malformed Valves. Sometimes, as a result of abnormal embryonic development or inflammatory conditions (e.g., rheumatic fever, septicemia), the valve leaflets become deformed or partially destroyed. When this has occurred, the cusps do not close properly, and blood leaks past them. This back flow is referred to as *regurgitation*, and a valve so affected is said to be *incompetent* or *insufficient*. This condition gives rise to alterations in the heart sounds; instead of being clear and distinct, they are abnormal sounds, or *murmurs*. The occurrence of a faint murmur, however, does not necessarily mean that a valvular lesion exists, for a murmur may occur in the absence of any organic disease. As a murmur is the result of the turbulence of blood flow within the heart, conditions which increase the velocity of blood flow (e.g., hyperthyroidism) or a condition in which the viscosity of the blood is reduced (e.g., anemia) may give rise to a murmur.

Another condition is the abnormal narrowing of an orifice, called *stenosis*. It may occur at any of the openings of the heart and is the result of abnormal development or of disease which causes the valves to lose their flexibility and become stiff and rough. The flow of blood through the narrowed opening is impeded, resulting in greatly increased velocity. Stenosed valves are usually also incompetent.

Effects of Valvular Disorders. Two of the most common effects of valvular disorders are (1) interference with venous return and (2) hypertrophy of the heart.

INTERFERENCE WITH VENOUS RETURN. Regurgitation of blood into the atria interferes with venous return of blood from the venae cavae and pulmonary veins into these chambers. This causes stagnation of blood in the capillaries (*passive congestion*).

HYPERTROPHY OF THE HEART. Incompetent valves reduce cardiac output; consequently, the heart must perform more work to maintain adequate blood flow. To accomplish this, the cardiac muscle fibers become longer and thicker, the walls of the heart become thicker, and the chambers grow larger. This brings about increased size and bulk (*hypertrophy* or enlargement of the heart). The foregoing adjustments are referred to as *cardiac compensation*. They enable an individual to live in spite of severe valvular deficiency, but *the reserve power of the heart is reduced* and activities must be kept at a minimum.

Cardiac Reserve. The ability of the heart to perform work above the basal requirements of the body is known as its *reserve power* or *cardiac reserve*. Under normal conditions, the heart has a reserve that is adequate to meet any demands to which it may be subjected; that is, it cannot be "strained" by overactivity. Even the most strenuous physical activity will not injure a normal healthy heart. It may hypertrophy (enlarge), but, within normal limits, no ill effects will ensue.

There are great individual differences in the reserve power of the heart. In the case of diseased hearts or those that possess valvular lesions or impaired circulation, the reserve power may be so low that the heart may be unable to maintain circulation adequate to meet the needs of the body. Then signs of heart failure occur, namely, breathlessness, cyanosis, edema (especially in the lower extremities), a tendency to fainting, and the occurrence of chest pains (angina pectoris).

Cardiac Output. The amount of blood leaving a ventricle at each beat is called the *stroke volume*. It is normally about 60 cc. for the average heart. The amount of blood discharged from the heart in one minute constitutes the *minute volume* or *cardiac output*. It averages 4 to 5 liters. Cardiac output depends on the *rate* and *force* of the heart beat.

RATE OF HEART BEAT. The rate of the heart beat is usually ascertained by feeling the pulse. The *pulse rate* is extremely variable, owing to many factors. Some of these are:

1. *Sex.* The rate is faster in women than in men (women, 72 to 80 per minute; men, 64 to 72 per minute).

2. *Age.* The rate is faster at birth, decreasing progressively to old age. The averages are: at birth, 140; at 1 year, 120; at 10 years, 90; for adults, 70.

3. *Body position.* The rate is faster in an erect than in a reclining or sitting position.

4. *Physical training.* As a rule, athletes have a slower resting pulse rate than do untrained persons.

5. *Miscellaneous factors.* The pulse rate is increased by the following *normal* conditions—muscular activity, high altitudes, activity of the digestive tract, and normal emotional excitement; and by the following *abnormal* conditions—high body temperature (fever), hemorrhage, surgical shock, cardiac disease and disorder, hyperthyroidism, and exaggerated emotional states.

FORCE OF HEART BEAT. Although the heart follows the all-or-none law, the force of its contractions varies according to the needs of the body. It is thus capable of *graded* contractions, which may be weak or strong. In skeletal muscle, as an increase in load increases the force of the contraction, similarly, in cardiac muscle, an increase in the stretch of the muscle, up to a certain point, increases the force of the contraction. This is known as *Starling's law of the heart*.

The volume of blood entering the ventricles during diastole is the primary factor in the stretch of heart muscle. During exercise, venous return is greatly increased, and as a result the heart beats more vigorously. Following hemorrhage or shock, when the volume of blood in circulation is lessened, venous return is reduced and heart contractions are feeble.

Nutrition of the Heart. For nutrition of the organ itself, the heart receives its blood supply through two *coronary arteries*. These arteries ramify to all parts of the heart, supplying cardiac muscle. In excessive activity, they are capable of dilating in order that an adequate supply of oxygen and food materials may be maintained. Any interference with blood supply lessens the efficiency of the heart and reduces cardiac reserve.

The *energy material* for the heart is thought to be lactic acid rather than glycogen, as in the case of skeletal muscle. Cardiac muscle is incapable of contracting an oxygen debt. The release of energy in the heart is aerobic, in contrast to the anerobic process that takes place in skeletal muscle. This accounts for the serious effects of oxygen-deprivation even for a short period of time.

REGULATION OF THE HEART BEAT

The rate and force of the heart beat are regulated by (1) nerve impulses, (2) chemical substances in the blood stream, and (3) physical factors, such as temperature and pressure within the heart and the great blood vessels.

Nervous Regulation of the Heart Beat. The rate and force of the heart beat are regulated by impulses transmitted over the afferent and efferent fibers of the cardiac nerves, operating through the cardiac center located in the medulla oblongata.

CARDIAC NERVES. Nerves which supply the heart tissue are known as cardiac nerves. Although, as previously stated, the heart beat is an automatic action originating within the heart itself, nervous impulses discharged from centers in the brain are capable of altering the heart rate in response to various bodily conditions. This is accomplished reflexly. Cardiac nerves are of two types: afferent and efferent.

Afferent Nerves. These nerves carry sensory impulses from the heart to the central nervous system. Pain impulses thus conducted are of clinical significance, for they are indicative of coronary disturbances or other pathologic conditions. Afferent fibers enter the spinal cord through dorsal roots of spinal nerves by way of sympathetic ganglia. Their cell bodies lie in the dorsal root ganglia.

Afferent fibers also carry impulses from receptor cells lying in the base of the aorta. These cells are sensitive to pressure, which serves as a stimulus for reflex control of blood pressure. Such fibers are called *depressor fibers*; as blood pressure rises, they reflexly slow down the heart rate. Receptors are also present in the large veins and in the right atrium. Distention of these structures by increased venous return initiates impulses which reflexly increase the heart rate. These fibers are called *pressor fibers*. Both pressor and depressor fibers pass through the vagus trunks to the reflex centers of the medulla.

Efferent Nerves. The heart receives nerve impulses through two sets of efferent fibers, both of which belong to the autonomic nervous system. These are the *right* and *left vagus nerves* (of the parasympathetic division) and the *accelerator nerves* (of the sympathetic division).

Efferent fibers of the *vagus* (10th cranial nerve) are preganglionic fibers ending in a small ganglion in the wall of the heart. Here they synapse with postganglionic neurons the fibers of which are distributed to the S–A node, the A–V node, and the bundle of His. Impulses carried by these fibers are *inhibitory;* that is, they slow down or stop the beat of the heart. The fibers of the right vagus are distributed principally to the S–A node; its impulses affect the rate of the heart more than do impulses of the left vagus, which are distributed principally to the A–V node. Nevertheless, both nodes receive fibers from both vagus nerves.

Efferent fibers of the *accelerator nerves* consist of preganglionic and postganglionic fibers. The former are axons of neurons located in the gray matter of the first five thoracic segments of the spinal cord. They synapse with neurons whose cell bodies lie in the ganglia of the sympathetic trunk (the upper thoracic ganglia, stellate ganglia, consisting of the first thoracic and inferior cervical ganglia, and the middle and superior cervical ganglia). Axons of these neurons (postganglionic fibers) pass to the heart, some ending near the S–A and A–V nodes, others in the wall of the ventricle. Impulses over the accelerator nerves *increase* the rate of contraction of both the atria and the ventricles; the *force* of their contractions is also increased. For this reason, these nerves are also called *augmentor nerves.*

The vagus nerves bring about their inhibitory effects through the liberation at their endings of a chemical substance, *acetylcholine.* Similarly, the accelerator effects of impulses over the accelerator nerves are due to the release of a chemical substance, *sympathin,* at their peripheral ends.

Tonic Action of Cardiac Nerves. Both the vagus and the accelerator nerves exhibit *tone;* that is, they exert a continuous effect on the organ innervated, the heart. Nerve impulses from centers in the brain are continuously being discharged over the vagus, exerting their restraining action to slow down the heart rate. Simultaneously, and also continuously, the heart is receiving impulses over the accelerator nerves which tend to speed up its rate. When inhibitory impulses (vagus) are blocked, as by the administration of atropine, the heart rate increases markedly. When the influence of the accelerator nerves is removed, as by excision of the sympathetic ganglia, the heart rate decreases.

Stimulation of the vagus may cause a decrease in rate of beat, or it may decrease the force without decreasing the rate, or it may stop the beat. When the heart has ceased beating as a result of vagal stimulation, it may resume beating temporarily even though the stimulus is still being applied. This is known as *vagal escape* or *escape from vagal inhibition.*

THE CARDIAC CENTER. Nervous control of the heart resides primarily in the *cardiac center,* which is located in the medulla in the floor of the fourth ventricle. From a portion of this center, the *cardio-inhibitory center,* impulses are discharged through the vagus nerves to the heart; from another portion, the *cardio-accelerator center*, impulses travel down the spinal cord to the upper thoracic region, then by way of spinal nerves and sympathetic ganglia through accelerator nerves to the heart.

CARDIAC REFLEXES. Stimulation of sensory nerves in almost any part of the body may reflexly bring about a slowing of the heart: a blow to the abdomen; manipulation of internal organs, as in an operation; inflammation of the middle ear; application of cold water to the surface of the body; inhalation of an irritant gas; or pressure on the eyeball (*oculomotor reflex*). Stimuli that give rise to exaggerated emotional states, however, in general tend to speed up the heart rate reflexly (a loud sound, a sudden flash of light).

Pressoreceptors. Changes in blood pressure also reflexly affect the rate of heart beat, which is inversely proportional to the arterial blood pressure. This principle is known as *Marey's law.* If the blood pressure rises, the heart rate is reflexly slowed; if it falls, the rate is reflexly increased. These effects are brought about through stimulation of *pressoreceptors* located in the arch of the aorta, the base of the heart, and the carotid sinus. Afferent fibers from these receptors pass through the vagus nerves, and the *sinus nerve* (a branch of the glossopharyngeal, the 9th cranial nerve). They conduct impulses to the cardio-inhibitory center which bring about the reflex slowing of the heart.

Bainbridge Reflex. This term refers to the acceleration of heart rate as a result of distention of the venae cavae and the right atrium by blood. The rise in venous pressure stimulates afferent vagal endings, and the heart is reflexly speeded up. Note that this is in contrast to the distention of the aorta and carotid sinus with consequent reflex slowing of the heart rate. This reflex, in part, accounts for the increase of heart rate during muscular exercise. The milking action of skeletal muscles and the action of respiratory muscles increase the volume of blood entering the venae cavae and the right atrium. This serves as a stimulus for accelerated heart action, which speeds the flow of blood through the heart to the lungs and to body tissues.

Chemical Factors in Regulation of the Heart Beat. Chemical substances in the blood play an important role in the control of the heart beat. (The significance of calcium, sodium, and potassium ions in this regard was described on page 275.)

CO_2 AND OXYGEN TENSION. Carbon dioxide tension and oxygen tension have marked effects on the heart rate.

Carbon Dioxide Tension. This affects the heart in several ways. A *slight* excess stimulates the vasoconstrictor center of the brain, bringing about construction of the blood vessels. Blood pressure rises and the heart is reflexly slowed as a result of stimulation of pressoreceptors of the aorta and the carotid sinus. Overventilation, with consequent lessened CO_2 tension in the blood brings about the opposite effect, that is, increase in the heart rate. A *great* excess of CO_2 decreases the tone of the cardio-inhibitory center and decreases impulse conduction in the atrioventricular bundle, with resulting slowing of the heart. Excessive increase of hydrogen ions, as occurs in acidosis, results in heart block.

Oxygen Tension. Low oxygen tension stimulates the heart rate to increase, but if it is continued and *oxygen want* becomes severe, marked irregularities in heart action occur. The rate becomes slower, and the heart fails. Interference in oxygen supply, as occurs in coronary thrombosis, may damage the heart tissue and lead to heart failure.

EFFECT OF HORMONES ON THE HEART. Cardiac action is affected by hormones. *Epinephrine* (from the medulla of the adrenal gland), when experimentally applied to isolated mammalian hearts, increases both the rate and the amplitude of heart contractions. Injected into the body, it raises blood pressure, which reflexly slows the heart. *Thyroxin*, a thyroid secretion which speeds metabolism, increases the rate of the beat.

DRUGS. Many drugs, especially alkaloids, affect heart action. Some produce their effects principally through their action on acetylcholine, which is produced at the vagus endings. *Atropine* increases the rate by neutralizing the action of acetylcholine. *Muscarine*, a poisonous substance found in mushrooms, accentuates vagus action, slowing down the heart or bringing it to a complete halt.

Pilocarpine, physostigmine (*eserine*), *choline*, and *acetylcholine* all have an effect similar to that of muscarine (inhibitory). Physostigmine acts by inhibiting the action of cholinesterase, the enzyme which destroys acetylcholine. It prolongs any inhibition initiated by vagal stimulation.

Nicotine at first slows the heart by stimulating the vagal ganglion cells of the heart. Later, however, paralysis of these cells results in acceleration of heart action.

Digitalis, a drug widely used in the treatment of cardiac ailments, has a steadying and slowing influence on the heart. It depresses conduction in the atrioventricular bundle, causing a slowing of ventricular activity. It should be noted that excessive dosage, however, may cause heart block.

Physical Factors in Regulation of the Heart Beat. In cold-blooded animals, the rate of heart beat is dependent on body temperature; it decreases as this temperature is lowered, increases as it is raised. In warm-blooded animals, the body temperature remains constant under normal conditions, but slight rises in this temperature, as in strenuous exercise or in fever, increases the heart rate.

PERIPHERAL RESISTANCE

With each contraction of the heart, blood is forced into the aorta and its larger branches, the elastic arteries. From these last, the muscular arteries distribute the blood to the various organs; smaller branches, the arterioles, distribute blood to the capillaries of the specific tissues. The arteries and arterioles contain in their walls smooth muscle fibers so arranged that upon their contraction, the lumen of the blood vessel is constricted. Through such changes in the caliber (diameter) of the blood vessels supplying the tissues, the volume of blood supplied to the tissues is controlled.

In the tissues, the capillaries play an important role in peripheral resistance. The total cross-section area of the capillaries (the *capillary bed*) in a tissue is much greater than the cross-section area of the vessel or vessels supplying that tissue. This increased capillary bed results in a reduced rate of blood flow; consequently, blood flows very slowly through the capillaries. This is the principal factor in the marked drop in pressure in the capillaries shown in tables of pressure gradients. But the extremely small caliber of the capillaries, which resists the flow of the viscous blood, acts to increase the resistance and to counteract the drop in pressure due to the increased capillary bed.

The caliber of the arteries and arterioles is under both nervous and chemical control. Nervous impulses from reflex centers in the brain may constrict or dilate the vessels. Chemical substances may alter the size of blood vessels either by acting directly on the vessels or by stimulating sensory receptors and thus initiating reflex control.

Physical factors such as temperature also influence the size of blood vessels.

Nervous Control of Blood Vessels. The smaller arteries and arterioles possess a thick layer of smooth muscle fibers arranged in a circular fashion which is under nervous control. Contraction and relaxation of the fibers of this layer determine the diameter of the vessels. The muscles are supplied by two sets of nerve fibers: *vasoconstrictors*, which bring about contraction of the muscles, and *vasodilators*, which bring about relaxation of the muscles. Through coordinated reflex mechanisms, supplemented by the action of chemical substances in the blood, the diameters of the vessels are so regulated as to bring about the proper distribution of the blood to the various tissues in response to their physiologic needs.

VASOCONSTRICTOR NERVES. These belong to the sympathetic division of the autonomic nervous system. The nerve fibers arise from cell bodies which lie in the gray matter of the spinal cord. They pass through spinal nerves and white rami to sympathetic ganglia, through which the impulses are relayed to the various parts of the body. Fibers to the head and neck pass from the cervical ganglia to the carotid and other arteries, sending branches to the smaller arterioles in those regions. Fibers to the visceral organs of the abdomen pass through the *greater, lesser,* and *least splanchnic nerves.* Fibers to the blood vessels of the body wall and limbs pass from sympathetic ganglia through the gray rami to the spinal nerves, which distribute them to the smooth muscles of the blood vessels.

A *vasoconstrictor center* (*vasomotor center*) lies in the medulla oblongata. Stimulation of this center brings about a contraction of smooth muscle in the walls of blood vessels. Vasoconstriction of the arteries, especially the arterioles, is marked, bringing about a rise in blood pressure. The action of this vasoconstrictor center is *tonic*; that is, it is constantly sending out impulses to the blood vessels, keeping them in a continual state of moderate contraction. If this center is destroyed, or if the spinal cord is severed in the cervical region, the stream of impulses is stopped, and arterial tone is abolished. This brings about passive vasodilation with reduced peripheral resistance, and the blood pressure is greatly reduced. After a time, however, arterial tone begins to be re-established and blood pressure may rise, which indicates that there must be secondary reflex centers in the spinal cord capable of inducing vasoconstriction.

Although it is tonic, the vasoconstrictor center *does not act automatically*. Its action depends on the continual reception of impulses from receptor organs. Voluntary control cannot be exercised over it, for its action is entirely reflex in nature. But the reflexes mediated through it may involve conscious states.

Inhibition of the vasoconstrictor center reduces the outflow of impulses, and vasodilation occurs as a result of the reduced arterial tone. This is called *passive vasodilation* in contrast to *active vasodilation* which is brought about by impulses carried by the vasodilator nerves. Cutting or sectioning of nerves carrying the vasoconstrictor fibers results in vasodilation and a fall of blood pressure to the parts involved.

VASODILATOR NERVES. These nerves are much less widely distributed to various part of the body than are the vasoconstrictors. Some of the fibers belong to the *sympathetic division* of the autonomic nervous system; these are distributed to the blood vessels of the muscles and the viscera. Others belong to the *parasympathetic division*; these are distributed through the cranial nerves, especially the chorda tympani branch of the facial nerve, which supplies the blood vessels of the tongue and the salivary glands, and the nerves of the lumbosacral plexus, which supply blood vessels to the bladder, rectum, and external genitalia. Experimental evidence seems to indicate the existence of a third type of vasodilator fibers which pass from the spinal cord via the *posterior roots of spinal nerves* and supply arteries in the skin of the limbs. When these fibers are stimulated, vasodilation results. There are two views on the nature of these fibers: one, that they are efferent fibers contained in the posterior root; the other, that they are fibers of sensory neurons capable of carrying vasodilator impulses peripherally. If the latter be the case, the impulses must pass in a direction opposite to that of sensory impulses. For this reason they are called *antidromic impulses*. On the basis of this view, these nerve fibers would serve a double function, namely, carrying (1) *afferent* impulses from the sense organs centrally and (2) *efferent* impulses peripherally from the spinal cord to the smooth muscles of blood vessels. An understanding of their function awaits further experimental work.

Impulses carried by vasodilator nerves, then, bring about dilatation of blood vessels with an accompanying increase in the flow of blood to a tissue.

A *vasodilator center* is thought to occupy an area of the medulla oblongata, lying close to the vasoconstrictor center. The existence of such a center has, however, been questioned, since some vasodilator reflexes (for example, those involving the erection of the penis) have their centers in the lower portion of the spinal cord.

Vascular Reflexes. Changes in the caliber of blood vessels are entirely of a reflex nature. Afferent impulses pass to reflex centers in the spinal cord or the brain, where connections are made and impulses are discharged along efferent nerves (vasoconstrictors or vasodilators) to blood vessels. The blood flow to an organ or tissue then increases or decreases and the blood pressure rises or falls, depending on which center is involved.

Afferent nerve fibers carrying impulses that result in vasoconstriction are *pressor fibers*; those resulting in vasodilation are *depressor fibers*. A reflex rise in blood pressure is a *pressor reflex*; a reflex fall, a *depressor reflex*.

PRESSOR REFLEXES. Pressor nerve fibers are widely distributed in all regions of the body; probably all spinal and cranial nerves contain pressor fibers carrying afferent impulses from the skin. Various types of stimuli can bring about vasoconstriction; cold air or cold water striking the skin causes constriction of blood vessels in the skin in parts quite remote from the area stimulated, as well as in the mucous membranes of the respiratory tract (nose, pharynx, trachea). Almost any strong stimulus to the skin may induce vasoconstriction with accompanying rise in blood pressure; stimulation of pain receptors also produces this effect.

DEPRESSOR REFLEXES. Reflex dilatation of blood vessels is accomplished in two ways: (1) by inhibiting the action of the vasoconstrictor center, thus reducing its tonic state; and (2) by stimulating the vasodilator center. There are relatively few regions of the body where blood vessels have been shown to possess true vasodilator nerves. Two such regions are the genital organs (penis and clitoris) and the salivary glands. There is also evidence that vasodilator fibers may go to the blood vessels of the mucous membranes of the mouth, pharynx, nose, and skin of the face.

Two important sets of afferent depressor fibers are those originating in (1) the aorta and base of the heart and (2) the carotid sinus, a slightly dilated area at the junction of the external and internal carotid arteries. Their endings are called *pressoreceptors* because they respond to a pressure or stretch stimulus. The normal stimulus is blood pressure. When the blood pressure rises (as after an increase in heart rate) the increased flow of blood through these structures stretches their walls, stimulating the pressoreceptor endings. Impulses are initiated which ascend to the vasomotor centers, and efferent impulses are discharged through the vasodilator fibers or vasoconstrictor impulses are reduced. Vasodilation takes place, and blood pressure is reduced.

The *carotid sinus* can be stimulated by applying pressure to the skin lying over it. Reflex slowing of the heart and vasodilation, with reduced blood pressure, result. In some individuals the sinus is hypersensitive, responding to even light pressure applied in the vicinity of the sinus; a tight collar or other undue pressure on the neck may induce a fall in blood pressure accompanied by dizziness or fainting, or both.

Blood Flow through Capillaries. It was originally thought that all the capillaries connecting arterioles with venules were simple endothelial tubes, but it has been found that some of the vessels extending beyond the terminal arteriole in the capillary plexus contain smooth muscle fibers in their walls. These vessels which extend from arterioles to venules are called *metarterioles*, and from these vessels the true capillaries are given off. The latter, after following a short course, re-enter the metarteriole near its venous end. The metarteriole forms a more or less direct channel, called a *thoroughfare channel*, through which blood can pass into the venules.

At the point of exit of a capillary from the metarteriole, are present some fibers of smooth muscle which form a *precapillary sphincter*. This sphincter, by contracting or dilating, controls the flow of blood through the capillary. When a tissue is in a resting state, the precapillary sphincters are constricted so that the blood is confined to the thoroughfare channel; when the tissue becomes active, the sphincters dilate and the capillaries open up, increasing the flow of blood to the tissue involved.

The smooth muscle cells of the metarterioles and precapillary sphincters are responsive to nervous control, for stimulation of sympathetic nerves induces their constriction. However, local capillary responses are due principally to humoral factors, that is, chemical substances resulting from metabolic activities in the tissues or the presence of chemical substances in the blood. Histamine, a substance released from injured tissues, is a powerful capillary dilator, acting on the metarterioles and capillary sphincters; hormones such as epinephrine and pituitrin have a constricting effect. Metabolites (CO_2 and other substances) which lower the pH have a dilating effect.

The fact that capillaries are capable of independent activity is shown by the various reactions of the skin to different types of stimulation. If a blunt instrument is drawn gently across the skin, a well-defined white line appears after an interval of several seconds. This is known as the "*white reaction*" and is due to contraction of the capillaries in response to the stimulus. No nervous factors are involved. If the blunt instrument is drawn more forcibly across the skin, a distinct red line (instead of a white line) is seen. This result of localized capillary dilatation is known as the "*red reaction.*" If a stronger stimulus is applied, about the red line for some distance a red area appears. This area, designated *erythema* or *flare*, is due to arteriolar dilatation and is dependent upon local nervous factors (the axon reflex). In normal individuals, if an intense stimulus (such as the lash of a whip) is applied, an elevated area, called a *wheal* or *welt*, develops in the injured area. In sensitive individuals, this response may occur from a slight stimulus. A wheal is due to the escape of fluid from the capillaries into the tissue spaces; it is a localized edema resulting from increased permeability of the capillary walls.

These three reactions to injury (the red reaction, flare, and wheal) comprise the "triple response," which can be induced by various types of skin injury such as scratching, burning, freezing, or applying injurious chemical agents. It is thought to be brought about by the release of histamine or a substance smiliar to it (a postulated H-substance) from injured cells. The responses of tissue to inflammation (redness, heat, swelling) can be accounted for in this way

Influence of Higher Brain Centers on Blood Vessels. The vasomotor centers, especially the vasoconstrictor center, are highly responsive to conditions that involve the higher brain centers. Various emotions are registered by changes in the size of blood vessels. Blushing from embarrassment or shame, and turning pale from fright are common reactions. The former is brought about by dilatation, the latter by constriction of the vessels of the face and neck. Anger may bring about either constriction or dilation of blood vessels; which it will be depends on the personality make-up or life experiences of the individual.

Chemical Control of Blood Vessels. Among the chemical substances that have an effect on the size of blood vessels and, through them either increase or decrease the blood pressure, the more important are the following:

CARBON DIOXIDE. This compound is thought to be the normal stimulus for the tonic action of the vasoconstrictor center. The lowering of CO_2 tension, as in voluntary deep breathing, brings about vasodilation of blood vessels in the visceral organs, with resultant lessened cerebral circulation. This accounts for the feeling of dizziness.

In the tissues, carbon dioxide and lactic acid, normal products of cell metabolism, bring about dilation of arterioles and capillaries.

EPINEPHRINE. When epinephrine is injected into the blood stream, a marked constriction of abdominal and cutaneous arterioles occurs, and this is accompanied by a rise in blood pressure. Applied locally, too, epinephrine constricts the arterioles.

EPHEDRINE. Effects are similar to those of epinephrine but they are less pronounced. It is widely used in the treatment of colds and hay fever, being applied as a spray or in "drops" to the nasal mucosa. Its constriction of the blood vessels lessens nasal congestion.

HISTAMINE. This substance, produced in many tissues, is believed to be especially liberated from injured and dying tissues. It causes extreme dilation of arterioles and capillaries, with consequent stagnation of blood in the tissues, accompanied by a marked fall in blood pressure. Histamine is regarded as the principal causative factor in surgical or wound shock.

ALCOHOL. Alcohol dilates the blood vessels, especially those of the skin. It has a depressant effect on the vasoconstrictor center.

TOBACCO. Smoking increases the heart rate and brings about constriction of peripheral vessels. Blood pressure is greatly increased.

ELASTICITY OF THE ARTERIES

The elasticity of the arteries is the primary factor responsible for the maintenance of blood pressure between the contractions of the ventricles (diastolic pressure) and for the steady continuous flow of blood through the capillaries. Normally, the arteries are always overfilled with blood and their walls are slightly stretched. At each contraction of the ventricles, a quantity of blood is discharged into the aorta and its branches, further distending their walls. At the cessation of the contraction phase (systole), the stretched walls, by virtue of the elastic tissue contained within them, recoil. This exerts pressure on the blood, forcing it onward in the arteries during the interval between the ventricular contractions. As a result, the blood flow through the capillaries is steady and continuous, rather than in spurts as would be the case if the arteries possessed rigid instead of elastic walls. The elasticity of the arterial walls prevents the blood pressure from falling to excessively low levels between the beats of the heart.

BLOOD VOLUME AND VISCOSITY

In addition to its response to nervous and chemical influences, blood pressure is affected by the volume of the blood and its viscosity.

Blood Volume. Under normal conditions, blood volume is fairly constant. If, however, there is a significant reduction in the volume of the blood in circulation, the pressure will fall. This may occur as a result of severe *hemorrhage* or in conditions of *shock*. In the latter instance, although the blood is still within the body, the plasma is lost from the circulation to the tissues, and there is stagnation of blood in the greatly dilated capillaries. Changes in *osmotic pressure* may also alter the volume of blood in circulation from time to time.

Blood Viscosity. The pressure required to force any fluid through a narrow tube varies with the viscosity of the fluid, a greater pressure being required to propel a viscous or "thick" fluid. The relative high viscosity of the blood (five to six times that of water) is due to the presence of blood proteins and corpuscles within the plasma. Conditions which alter the viscosity affect the ease of flow and consequently affect blood pressure. Alterations in blood proteins or their loss, as in kidney disease, or a reduction in the number of red blood cells, as in anemia or following a hemorrhage, result in reduced viscosity accompanied by a fall in blood pressure. Conversely, an increase in the number of blood cells, as in polycythemia or leukemia, or a decrease in the fluid portion of the blood (anhydremia) increases the viscosity of the blood and brings about an increase in blood pressure.

VENOUS CIRCULATION

Blood pressure, which is high in the aorta and the larger arteries, drops significantly in the capillaries and is gradually reduced until it approaches zero in the large veins. This is due principally to the fact that when a person is standing, the blood in the lower portion of the body must rise against the force of gravity in the large veins. Under ordinary conditions, the force of the heart beat is not strong enough to maintain adequate venous return to the heart without the aid of certain supplementary factors, the more important of which are:

Suction force of the atrium, when it is expanding following contraction.

Respiratory movements, which bring about changes of pressure within the thorax. Increase in intrathoracic pressure during inspiration acts on the venae cavae, exerting an aspirating effect on the veins of the abdomen. In addition, increased intra-abdominal pressure caused by downward movement of the diaphragm forces blood in the abdominal veins upward.

Contraction of skeletal muscles, especially those of the limbs, during muscular activity acts to compress the veins and to exert a massaging action on them. The presence of valves that prevent a "back flow" enables this pressure to propel the blood onward toward the heart. Contraction of the abdominal muscles tends to force the blood in the abdominal veins upward.

Movements in the visceral organs, such as peristaltic action of the intestines and vasoconstriction in the splanchnic area, favor venous return.

Fainting (*syncope*) may result from inadequate venous return. Shock or a strong emotional reaction may induce dilatation of splanchnic veins, with reduced blood return to the heart, and subsequent loss of consciousness may occur. Standing still for a prolonged period of time (as when a soldier stands at attention) may result in fainting, owing to lack of muscular activity. Tenseness of antagonistic muscles may also impede circulation. The alternate contraction and relaxation of limb muscles produce a "milking" effect on the blood vessels lying between them, which favors the flow of blood to the tissues and venous return to the heart.

PRACTICAL CONSIDERATIONS

Velocity of Blood Flow. Blood flows very rapidly in the aorta and the large arteries (about 40 cm. per second). Its velocity decreases in

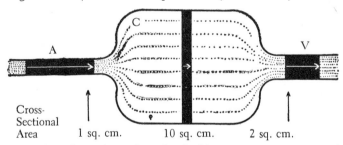

Fig. 11-3. Blood flow velocity. Lengths of white arrows represent rates of flow (10 cm. per sec. in A, 1 cm. per sec. in C, and 5 cm. per sec. in V). (Reprinted with permission of the University of Chicago Press from Carlson and Johnson, *The Machinery of the Body,* 4th ed., 1953.)

the smaller arteries and arterioles, and in the capillaries its flow is very slow (about 0.5 mm. per second). This is due to (1) the extremely narrow caliber of the lumen of the capillaries and the added resistance they offer to the flow of blood, a viscous substance; and (2) the great increase in the cross-section area of the *capillary bed,* which is estimated to be 800 times that of the aorta.

When the blood has passed through the capillaries and has entered the smaller veins, the velocity picks up somewhat, and it increases progressively as the blood passes through the larger veins toward the heart. But the flow in the venae cavae is never so rapid as that in the aorta.

The Pulse. When the finger is placed over an artery lying near the surface of the body, a beat or pulsation is felt. This is due to the alternate expansion and contraction of the arterial walls owing to the beat of the heart. When the blood is forcibly ejected from the heart into the aorta, its impact on the elastic walls of the aorta sets up a pressure wave which travels along the arteries. This is known as the *arterial pulse*, or simply the *pulse*. It is not due to the passage of blood, for the pulse wave travels much faster than does the flow of blood. The velocity of the pulse wave averages about 7 meters per second; that of the blood ranges from 10 to 50 cm. per second. It takes about 3 seconds for the blood discharged from the heart to reach the wrist (where the pulse is commonly felt); but the pulse wave originating in the aorta traverses the same distance in about 0.1 second.

The speed of the pulse wave varies with age. In children it averages 5 meters per second. As age increases and the arteries lose more and more of their elasticity, the speed increases until in old age it may reach 8 to 10 meters per second; in atherosclerosis the velocity of the pulse wave may be even higher.

WHERE THE PULSE IS FELT. All arteries exhibit a pulse, but the pulse is most readily felt at points where an artery lies near the surface, especially when it is located over a bone. Following are the places where the pulse is most readily distinguished: *radial artery* (at the wrist), *temporal artery* (temporal region of the skull), *facial artery* (where it crosses the mandible), *carotid artery* (side of the neck), *brachial artery* (inner side of the biceps muscle), *femoral artery* (where it crosses the pelvic bone), *popliteal artery* (posterior surface of the knee), and *dorsalis pedis artery* (at the instep).

RECORDING OF THE PULSE. A graphic record of the pulse wave can be obtained with a *sphygmograph*, a recording device connected with a *sphygmomanometer*, which is attached to the wrist. The *sphygmogram* is the record itself, showing the tracing of the pulse wave. A normal tracing shows an abrupt upstroke, called the *anacrotic limb*, and a more gradual downstroke, the *catacrotic limb*. The latter normally reveals a secondary elevation, known as the *dicrotic wave* or *notch*. This is due to a slight back flow of blood which occurs at the time of the beginning of ventricular diastole. This back flow is stopped by closure of the aortic semilunar valves; consequently, variations in elevation of this notch are indicative of irregular action of the valves, or *valvular dysfunction*. Other variations in the pulse wave are characteristic of certain pathologic conditions.

No pulse occurs in the capillaries or the smaller veins, but in the large veins a distinct pulse can be detected. The latter is due primarily to pressure exerted on blood in the veins by the auricular (atrial) systole and by the protrusion of the atrioventricular valves into the atria during ventricular systole.

Blood Pressure. This is the pressure that is exerted by the blood against the walls of the vessels within which it is contained. Blood pressure varies in different parts of the system, being highest in the aorta, lower in the arteries, and progressively lower in the capillaries and veins. The higher pressure in the arteries can be noted when an artery is cut, for the blood flows out forcibly and in spurts. On the other hand, from a cut vein the flow is continuous and steady.

KINDS OF BLOOD PRESSURE. The term "blood pressure" when unqualified refers to *arterial pressure* (that is, pressure in the large arteries), which is usually determined by taking the pressure of the blood in the left brachial artery. Pressure of blood in the veins is called *venous pressure*; that in the capillaries, *capillary pressure*.

Blood pressure is highest in the arteries at the time of contraction of the ventricles (*ventricular systole*); this is known as *systolic pressure*. Pressure during ventricular diastole is known as *diastolic pressure*. The latter is due principally to the force exerted by the elastic rebound of the arterial walls.

RANGES OF BLOOD PRESSURE. Blood pressure is usually expressed as a fraction; for example, 120/80, which is read "one-twenty over eighty." The first of these figures is the systolic pressure, the second the diastolic. They record the mark on the scale of the sphygmomanometer that is reached by the column of mercury, which responds to the force of the pressure. For the young adult in good health, the average blood pressure in different parts of the circulatory system is:

> *Brachial Artery*
> systolic   110–120 mm. Hg
> diastolic   65– 80 mm. Hg
> *Capillaries*   20– 30 mm. Hg
> *Veins*   0– 20 mm. Hg (in veins near the heart)

Pulse pressure is the difference between systolic and diastolic pressure.

Mean blood pressure is the average of systolic and diastolic values. For an adult in good health, this is about 100 mm. Hg.

METHODS OF DETERMINING BLOOD PRESSURE. Two methods are used to determine blood pressure: the direct method, used principally on experimental animals; and the indirect method, which is used clinically on humans.

Direct Method. A glass or metal tube called a *cannula* is inserted into an artery, and the cannulated vessel is connected to a *manometer*,

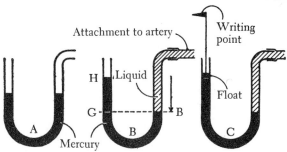

Fig. 11-4. Mercury manometer. (A) Condition with both arms of U-tube open to the air. (B) Condition with one arm of manometer attached to artery by rubber tubing. (C) Manometer equipped with float and writing point to transcribe blood-pressure record. (Reprinted with permission of the University of Chicago Press from Carlson and Johnson, *The Machinery of the Body*, 4th ed., 1953.)

a U-shaped tube filled with water or mercury. The manometer is usually equipped with a recording apparatus (*kymograph*) so that a permanent record will be obtained.

Indirect Method. The apparatus used in the indirect method is called a *sphygmomanometer*. The principle underlying the method involves the balancing of pressure within the artery with an external pressure which is exerted by air contained within a cuff applied externally around the arm. Actually, what is measured is the air pressure in the cuff. The manometer may be of either the mercury or the aneroid type. ("Aneroid" means "without fluid"—in place of the mercury, there is a delicate metal spring that is sensitive to changes in pressure).

The steps in determining blood pressure in man, through this indirect method, are:

1. The cuff or armlet is wrapped securely about the arm *above* the elbow.

2. Air is pumped into the cuff by means of a rubber bulb until the pressure in the cuff is sufficient to stop the flow of blood in the *radial artery*. The radial pulse disappears at this point. The amount of pressure within the cuff is exhibited on the scale of the sphygmomanometer.

3. The observer then places a stethoscope over the brachial artery just *below* the elbow and gradually releases the air from within the cuff. When the air pressure falls to a point that permits the blood to flow and fill the artery below the cuff, faint tapping sounds will be heard in the stethoscope. These correspond with the heart beat. At the appearance of the first sound, the pressure is read on the scale; this is the *systolic pressure*.

4. As the air in the cuff is further released, the sounds become progressively louder, then disappear. Just before they disappear, they

change in quality from very loud to very soft. At this point the manometer reading is again taken; this is the *diastolic pressure.*

The foregoing method is called the *auscultatory method.* It is the method most generally employed. In the *palpatory method* (*palpation*), the flow of blood in the radial artery is determined by digital pressure on that artery at the wrist. It is desirable to check auscultatory readings with palpatory readings.

FACTORS INFLUENCING BLOOD PRESSURE. Several factors, aside from the structure and functioning of the heart and the circulatory system, influence the blood pressure. They are: age, muscular activity, sleep, emotional states, sex, weight, and pathologic conditions.

Age. The average systolic pressures at different ages are as follows:

	mm. Hg
At birth	40
At end of 12th month	80
At age 12	100
At age 15	110
At age 20	120
At age 40	125
At age 65	134
After age 65	tendency to rise more rapidly

(Blood pressure above 160 mm. Hg indicates hypertension.)

Muscular Activity. Blood pressure rises with increased muscular activity. The increase may be 60 to 80 mm. Hg above normal. After cessation of activity, normal pressure is resumed.

Sleep. Systolic pressure falls during quiet sleep, owing to prone position and reduced body activities. It rises slowly just before awakening. In disturbed sleep (e.g., during nightmares) systolic pressure may become very high.

Emotional States. Excitement, fright, anger, worry, and other extreme emotional states usually bring about a rise in systolic pressure. Grief, feelings of hopelessness and deprivation, and depression tend to lower the blood pressure.

Sex. Blood pressure averages 8 to 10 mm. lower in women than in men. For women, this is applicable up to the time of menopause, when the pressure begins to rise. At age 60, blood pressure in women usually equals, and may even exceed slightly, the average of men.

Weight. An increase in body weight after age 60 is usually accompanied by a rise in blood pressure.

Pathologic Conditions. In arteriosclerosis and certain diseases of the kidneys, liver, and heart, blood pressure may become elevated. In certain other diseases of the heart and under conditions of shock, blood pressure may be below normal.

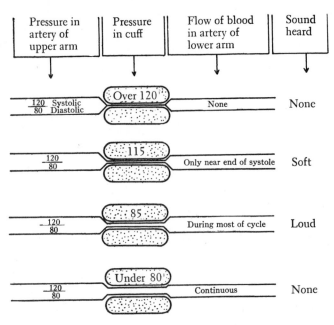

Pressure in artery of upper arm	Pressure in cuff	Flow of blood in artery of lower arm	Sound heard
120 Systolic / 80 Diastolic	Over 120	None	None
120 / 80	115	Only near end of systole	Soft
120 / 80	85	During most of cycle	Loud
120 / 80	Under 80	Continuous	None

Fig. 11-5. Blood pressure determination. Pressures in millimeters of mercury.

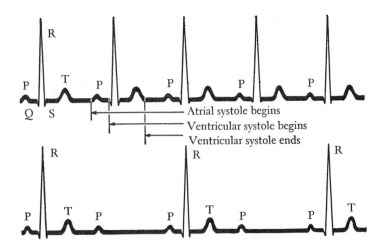

Fig. 11-6. A normal electrocardiogram. The P wave corresponds to atrial contraction; the QRS and T waves correspond to ventricular contraction.
(Figs. 11-5 and 11-6 reprinted with permission of the University of Chicago Press from Carlson and Johnson, *The Machinery of the Body*, 4th ed., 1953.)

Recording the Heart Beat. The *electrocardiograph* is used to record changes in electrical potential originating from the action of a beating heart. It is, in effect, a very sensitive galvanometer. The record obtained from it is called an *electrocardiogram* (sometimes *ECG*). Deflections of the tracings on this record are produced in response to the passage of the heart current through the galvanometer. A normal electrocardiogram tracing is shown in the accompanying figure. Irregularities of heart action revealed in the electrocardiogram are of value in the diagnosis of certain heart disorders, especially disturbances in impulse conduction and changes in the integrity of heart muscle.

DISEASES AND DISORDERS OF THE HEART AND CIRCULATORY SYSTEM

Angina Pectoris. Severe thoracic pain which tends to radiate from the region of the heart to the shoulder and down the left arm. It is accompanied by a feeling of suffocation and syncope. It is due to an inadequate supply of blood to the myocardium of the heart, generally the result of coronary spasm or thrombosis. Attacks are frequently precipitated by muscular activity or excitement.

Aneurysm. A dilatation of an arterial wall, forming a sac which fills with blood. It is due to a weakening of the artery wall, usually the result of injury or inflammatory changes. Aneurysms may occur in any artery, but they are most common in the aorta because of the high blood pressure there. Aortic aneurysms are commonly brought on by syphilitic infections.

Arteriosclerosis. "Hardening" of the arteries. A condition in which there are thickening and loss of elasticity of the layers of the artery wall, especially the tunica intima, associated with degenerative changes in the middle coat. Arteriosclerosis is common in advanced age.

Atherosclerosis. A type of arteriosclerosis in which fatty deposits develop within and beneath the intima. Degenerative changes occur in the elastic and muscular tissue, accompanied by hyperplasia of the tissue and resulting in reduction or obliteration of the lumen of the vessel.

Bradycardia. Abnormally slow rate of heart beat.

Coronary Occlusion. Obstruction of or interference with the flow of blood through an artery owing to either narrowing of the lumen of the vessels from arteriosclerosis or presence of a thrombus or embolus. The deprivation of oxygen and accumulation of metabolic substances stimulate the pain endings of afferent nerves, giving rise to agonizing chest pains (*angina pectoris*). Attacks are usually precipitated by muscular exertion or emotional excitement. The pain may be referred to the left shoulder and arm. Relief may be obtained by inhalation of amyl nitrate, which dilates the coronary arteries.

Fibrillation (Delirium Cordis). A condition in which the heart beats with such rapidity (400 to 600 per minute) that the beats are not distinguishable one from the other. It may involve the atria (*auricular fibrillation*) or the ventricles (*ventricular fibrillation*). Auricular fibrillation usually occurs in association with other cardiac disorders (e.g., *mitral stenosis*). Ventricular fibrillation may be induced by lack of oxygen (as in *coronary occlusion*), mechanical injury to the chest wall, strong electric shock, chloroform or cyclopropane anesthesia, or the effects of certain drugs.

Flutter (Auricular Flutter). A condition in which the atria beat at an excessively fast rate (250 or more beats per minute). There is functional impairment in impulse conduction which causes the ventricles to beat much slower, usually at a ratio of 2 or 3 to 1 atrial beat.

Heart Block. Interference with the passage of impulses in the conductile tissue at the atrioventricular node. It is usually the result of degenerative conditions. Heart block may be *partial*, resulting in "missed" beats; or it may be *complete*, with complete functional dissociation between the atria and the ventricles.

Hypertension (High Blood Pressure). A persistent elevation in blood pressure above that which is normal for a given age level. It is due primarily to a spasm of the muscles of the arteries, but may also be brought on by arteriosclerosis. A systolic pressure of 160 mm. Hg or higher constitutes hypertension. Blood pressure has been known to reach 280 mm. Hg, and even higher in rare instances. Some of the effects of hypertension are: cardiac hypertrophy, with eventual cardiac failure; further hardening of the arteries (arteriosclerosis); possible rupture of blood vessels, especially in the brain (cerebral hemorrhage, "apoplexy"); and kidney dysfunction due to degenerative changes in renal vessels. There are two types of arterial hypertension: *primary* or *essential*, in which the hypertension is not preceded by kidney disorder or other pathologic condition; and *renal* hypertension, which accompanies Bright's disease (*nephritis*) and is initiated by renal damage or malfunctioning.

Hypotension (Low Blood Pressure). A condition in which the blood pressure is persistently below that which is normal for a given age level. In an adult, systolic pressure below 90 mm. Hg is regarded as indicative of hypotension. But low blood pressure, in the absence of other unfavorable findings, is not regarded as necessarily indicating a pathologic condition; indeed, it distinctly favors longevity.

Phlebitis. Inflammation of a vein, usually accompanied by formation of pus. It frequently leads to the formation of a thrombus within a vein (thrombophlebitis) which may break loose and result in the distribution of infective emboli to other parts of the body. Phlebitis occurs most commonly in the veins of the lower extremities, often following long confinement in bed, abdominal operations, or childbirth.

Phlegmasia alba dolens ("Milk Leg"). Acute edema that begins in the ankle and ascends or begins in the groin and descends, resulting from obstruction of venous return. It usually occurs as a consequence of septic infection following childbirth or surgical operation.

Tachycardia. Excessive rapidity of heart beat. In paroxysmal tachycardia the heart begins suddenly to beat at an abnormally high rate, as fast as 150 or more beats per minute. The causes are numerous and varied.

Varicocele. Dilation of the veins of the spermatic plexus, occurring most frequently on the left side.

Varicose Veins. Swollen, knotted, and tortuous veins, most commonly seen in the lower extremities. They are brought on by weakening of the walls of the veins or interference with venous return. Blood tends to stagnate in the vessels, and valves become incompetent. Varicosities are more common in women than in men. Obesity seems to be a predisposing factor. They frequently develop during pregnancy.